KU-732-677

916

Presented to Gilmour

By Mummy and Daddy

To mark his first year of

Perfect Attendance at School.

8th July, 1948.

Mr. Daniell begged leave to present Rebecca

See page 11

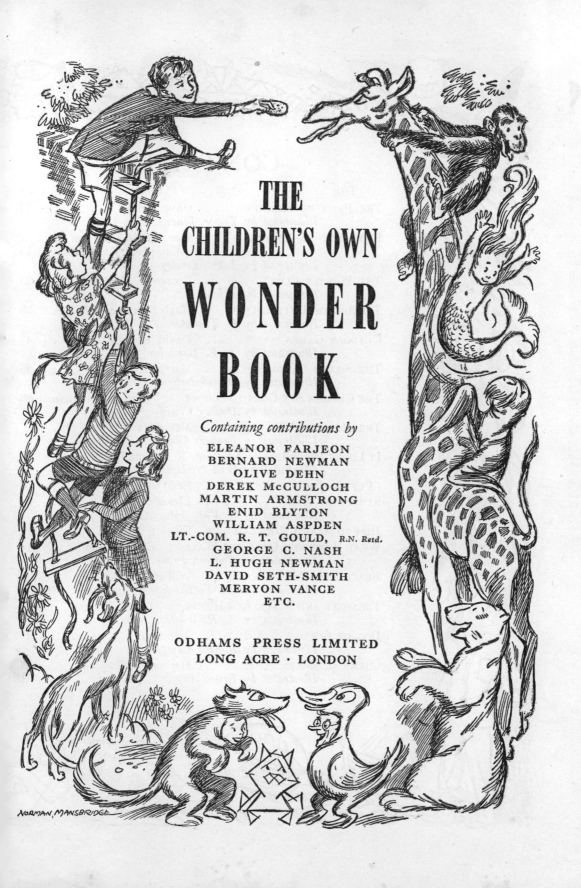

THE CHILDREN'S OWN WONDER BOOK

Containing contributions by

ELEANOR FARJEON
BERNARD NEWMAN
OLIVE DEHN
DEREK McCULLOCH
MARTIN ARMSTRONG
ENID BLYTON
WILLIAM ASPDEN
LT.-COM. R. T. GOULD, R.N. Retd.
GEORGE C. NASH
L. HUGH NEWMAN
DAVID SETH-SMITH
MERYON VANCE
ETC.

ODHAMS PRESS LIMITED
LONG ACRE · LONDON

NORMAN MANSBRIDGE

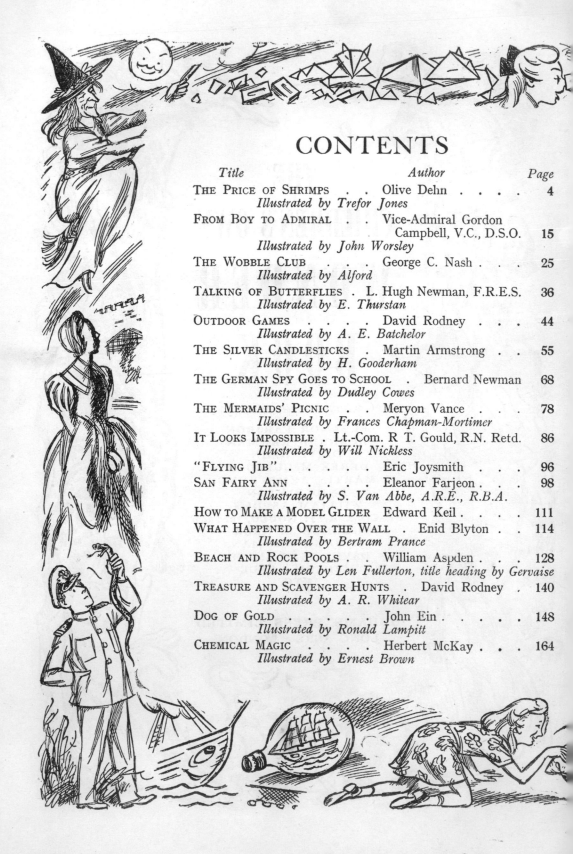

CONTENTS

NORMAN MANSBRIDGE

THE PRICE

Have you ever heard of the Witch of the North who sails about the Atlantic Ocean in an egg-shell? No, you never have! Did you ever meet the Witch of the South who lives in a Giant Convolvulus on the very tip of the Lizard at Land's End? No, you never did! Would you be clever enough to spy out the Witch of the East, who swims in and out of Yarmouth harbour with the tides, and sleeps in a different bloater barrel each night? No, surely, you never would! Then there only remains the Witch of the West who sits all day and all night in a Cave of Quicksand beneath the Dee Estuary. What do you know about her? Nothing! You don't believe in witches? Well, I have just spent a whole summer on the Dee Estuary, and I can tell you a tale:—

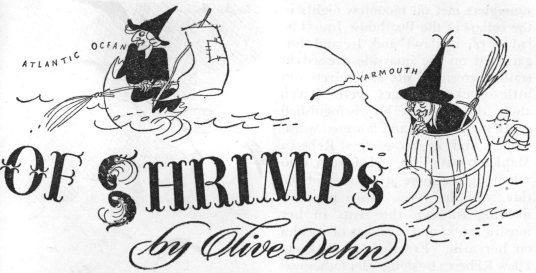

OF SHRIMPS
by Olive Dehn

Long, long ago, when Birkenhead was a cottage and Liverpool consisted of two shops and a church, the ships going to and from Ireland sailed up the River Dee to other ports whose names have long been forgotten. There were no docks then at Liverpool, and none at Birkenhead. Those were the days when ships docked at Neston and Dawpool, at West Kirby and Parkgate —especially at Parkgate. For Parkgate was a gay and fashionable town, with rows of brightly painted houses, fields full of wild flowers, and a great wide sea-wall covered with thrift and torn salmon nets, where one might sit and look across to Wales and the Welsh mountains, and watch the sea come stealing in, serpentwise, down the furrows of the sand. Those were the days when the coaches rattled through Parkgate at nine miles an hour, and

For Parkgate was a gay and fashionable town

smugglers met on moonless nights in the cellars of the Boathouse Inn. The ladies of England and Ireland forgathered on the quayside dressed in trailing gowns of silk and velvet, and little donkey-carriages were driven along the sea-front by distinguished gentlemen in wigs and flowered waistcoats. And in those days Rebecca Mapletop was a little girl of seven, who ran along the shore at the turn of the tide, with her pink calico petticoat showing through the rents in her muslin frock, and a basket of cockles on her arm. Everyone in Parkgate knew Rebecca by sight. Her father was William Mapletop, the fisherman, who lived in a thatched cottage at the sea's edge. He had twelve children, and Rebecca was his seventh child. The old wives of Parkgate told Mr. Mapletop to take particular care of Rebecca on her seventh birthday. They said that seven was a magic number, and the seventh birthday of a seventh child would be an anxious time. But Mr. Mapletop did not care much about his children; he had too many. He was really only interested in flat fish. Mrs. Mapletop was an invalid and crippled with rheumatism, for the cottage was built so very near the edge of the sea that she always let the high tide wash the kitchen floor for her. She thought it would save time—and she needed time to look after twelve children—but the damp got into her bones, and in the end she couldn't look after her children at all. So Rebecca ran wild with the rest, and earned a few pennies selling cockles to the rich visitors.

And on her seventh birthday she ran out over the sands, as usual, with her father's cockle basket on her arm. It was a wild, stormy day in October.

The sea-birds wheeled above her head crying, " Go back ! Go back !"

Wales was blotted out in mist and the sea-birds wheeled above her head crying, "Go back! Go back!" But Rebecca ran on and on searching in the ribs of sand for cockles.

Now, all this time the Witch of the West was sitting in her Cave of Quicksand, pickling shrimps and biding her time.

When Rebecca's feet ran over the sands on that fatal birthday, the echoes of her footsteps stole down to the Witch, and she sent her pet cormorant to see if Rebecca Mapletop was really coming her way at last. The cormorant came back in the twinkling of an eye and said, "Yes, she was."

Then the Witch took a great paint-brush and painted the sky black as ink. She took an egg-whisk made from the bones of sharks and whipped the tops of the waves with it, until the foam rose mountains high. Next she passed her hands over the walls of her cave so that they burst apart, quaking like jelly-fishes, and engulfed the feet of Rebecca Mapletop and drew her down, down to the very bottom of the Dee Estuary with her father's cockle basket still on her arm.

"Now, you Seventh Child," said the Witch, "you can come and work for me. I need someone to shell me my shrimps. I do not see as well as I used."

"No, ma'am," whispered Rebecca, so frightened, she could barely speak.

"Well, and do not stand there staring like a lost sole," shouted the Witch. "Hurry up, miss! Get to work! Shell me some shrimps!"

"Sh-shrimps, ma'am?" said poor Rebecca.

"Do you not know what a shrimp is?" asked the exasperated Witch.

"No, ma'am," replied Rebecca.

"Good lack! What do they eat between meals at Parkgate?"

"Cockles," gasped Rebecca.

"Ha! Those filthy scallops!" cried the Witch. "Why, even my cormorant will not touch them. Well, my girl, before this day is out, I'll have you shell me a quart of shrimps, or go to your bed without supper. And talking of supper—can you cook?"

"Only bread and milk, ma'am."

"Miserable child!" cried the Witch, who had a hearty appetite. "No matter, there will be time enough to learn." And the witch passed her hands once more over the walls of her cave, so that they closed over Rebecca's head and the daylight knew her no more.

* * * * *

Rebecca was sadly missed in Parkgate. The ladies of England and Ireland wept a little, and several of the distinguished gentlemen tried to find out where she had gone. It was feared she had wandered too far out across the treacherous sands and had been caught in the storm and drowned. Yet no trace of her was ever found; neither the cockle basket, nor a salt-stained ribbon from her dark curls was ever thrown up by the sea. She became something of a legend, something of a warning to the people of the town. And it was no uncommon thing to hear her name upon the lips of visiting mammas: "Keep by me, Charlotte! Have you not heard what happened to that poor Rebecca Mapletop?"

And what had really happened to Rebecca? She was now the servant and companion of the Witch of the West. She had learnt to shell and pickle shrimps according to the Witch's recipe, and an excellent recipe she found it. She swept out the cave with a broom made of shrimps' whiskers, and dusted it with a coral feather-duster.

It was her duty, also, to cook the witch's meals, to dress her, put her to bed, help her in and out of her mussel rocking-chair, and to comb her hair carefully once a month with a sword-fish's snout.

For seven years she waited on the Witch of the West hand and foot, and the Witch grew fat and was not ungrateful.

Rebecca did not grow fat, but she grew tall and by the time she was fourteen her muslin frock and pink calico petticoat were so worn and short that it was pitiful to see them. She asked the Witch if she might go home and borrow a dress from one of her sisters, but the Witch said no, certainly not. So Rebecca went about looking more and more untidy and uncared for.

One day the Witch heard her singing as she sat, sorting shrimps, in a corner of the cave : —

"Oh, wherefore should I lift my
    hand?
And wherefore should I comb my
    hair?
I'll see no more the green grass
    land,
The buttercup and daisy fair."

"Stop moping!" said the Witch sharply. "I do not keep you here to mope. If you must sing, let it be a merry song."

So Rebecca tried again : —

"When I did live in Parkgate town,
I lived in goodly company.
My sister had a green gauze gown
And I, myself, wore organdie."

"Enough, Rebecca! How vain you are becoming. What is the use of putting on airs when you live in a quicksand? Get me my breakfast, girl. Come along! Be sharp!"

"How will you take your whale-bones this morning, ma'am?" inquired Rebecca obediently.

"Devilled!" replied the Witch, morosely.

"Remember, June,
    When cuckoo crazy goes
    And stammers out of tune;
    And Robin's waistcoat pales beside
        the rose,
    Remember, June...."

sang Rebecca wistfully, over the frying-pan.

"What ails you this morning, Rebecca?" cried the Witch.

"I want to go home, ma'am."

"What for?" asked the Witch.

"To fetch a new gown, ma'am."

The Witch looked closely at Rebecca. There was no doubt about it, her frock was disgracefully old and tight.

"As you please," said the Witch at last. "You may go, but for one day only. I shall be on the quayside at twelve o'clock tonight. I shall call you as the clock strikes midnight, and if you do not answer"—the Witch's voice took on a blood-curdling note— "Woe betide you—that is all I say, WOE BETIDE YOU."

"And if anything should happen to you—if you should forget to call me, what then?" asked Rebecca.

"Forget!" said the Witch. "ME? Don't be impertinent. Well, if I did forget, you would be free. The spell would be broken, that goes without saying. But it is a foolish question," said the Witch of the West, "because I never forget — NEVER!"   "No

She swept out the cave with a broom made of shrimps' whiskers

ma'am," said Rebecca sadly. "By the way," said the Witch. "Would you care to take a pot of shrimps home to your poor mother?"

So Rebecca Mapletop came back to Parkgate, after seven years. And all she had to show for it was a pot of shrimps under one arm, and a pink calico petticoat shrunk well above the knees. And the first thing her father said to her was, "Where is my cockle basket?" But her mother was overjoyed to see her. Her rheumatism was so bad that she could not leave her bed, and they had to bring Rebecca to her bedside, where she told her adventures, sitting on a little stool, with her mother's quilt wrapped round her to hide her short petticoats. Afterwards, she handed round the shrimps and they each tried a few. They had never tasted anything so delicious. "You say you

So Rebecca Mapletop came back to Parkgate, after seven years

know the recipe, my love?" said Mrs. Mapletop, smacking her lips. Rebecca said she knew it only too well.

"Why then, our fortunes are made at last!" cried Mr. Mapletop. "Becky shall pickle some more and sell them instantly in the market place."

"But not in that petticoat, I beg you, William," said Mrs. Mapletop feebly from her pillows.

"You forget, Ma," said Rebecca sadly. "The Witch is to call for me on the quayside at twelve tonight."

"She has no right to take you! You shall stay with us! Be brave Becky, and we will find a way out!" cried the Mapletops, rallying round their sister.

At that very moment, there was a loud knocking at the door and the whole family became silent as though their tongues had been cut off with an invisible knife. They all felt certain that the Witch had come to claim Rebecca before her time!

But no, it was only Mr. Daniell, the landlord of the Boathouse Inn, who came to see Mr. Mapletop, a great friend of his, about supplying one or two of his guests with salmon. A gown was hastily found for Rebecca, and she was sent for to tell her story. When she had finished, Mr. Daniell stroked his chin and looked thoughtful. Rebecca was told to offer Mr. Daniell some shrimps. After tasting a few, Mr. Daniell spoke earnestly to Rebecca. In no circumstances must she go back to live with the Witch again.

"It would be tragic—yes, tragic," said Mr. Daniell, "if Parkgate were to be deprived of such a delicacy as these shrimps. It would also be a pity," he added, "if Parkgate were to lose Rebecca." Of course he should have

said this first, but he was not a gallant man. He then told Mr. Mapletop that he had, staying at the Boathouse Inn, an extraordinarily clever gentleman, a Dr. Jonathan Swift, the Dean of St. Patrick's, who was on his way from Ireland to London. This Dean Swift wrote books and pamphlets, and was very well spoken of by the gentry. He —Mr. Daniell—was of the opinion that this Dean Swift was one of the cleverest men in England. If anyone could help Rebecca, this Dean Swift would be the man to ask.

Would Rebecca care to walk along to the Boathouse Inn with Mr. Daniell and see this Dean Swift?

Rebecca, looking very pretty in a sprigged muslin dress belonging to her eldest sister, and with a green sash and a chip-straw bonnet tied with white ribbons, said she was much obliged to Mr. Daniell for the trouble he was taking, and she would walk along with pleasure.

And so, a few minutes later, she was being ushered into a long, dark room, with a raftered ceiling, where three gentlemen in splendid wigs and black silk knee-breeches, were sitting by the fireside drinking wine and singing softly amongst themselves. Mr. Daniell coughed to attract their attention.

"Would you have a settled head
    You must early go to bed.
  I tell you, and I tell't again,
    You must be in bed at ten,"
sang the three merry gentlemen. Mr. Daniell coughed again and begged leave to present Rebecca. The gentlemen bowed. Mr. Daniell bowed. "She has a remarkable story, gentlemen," said Mr. Daniell. Rebecca curtsied. The gentlemen bowed again. Rebecca

was formally presented to Dr. Swift. Dr. Swift then formally presented his friend, Mr. Addison, and his friend, Mr. Steele. It all took quite a long time, and Rebecca felt the moments were slipping away. What could these elegant gentlemen do for her? They would only laugh at her story. But there she was wrong. After eating the last of her shrimps and proclaiming them altogether admirable the gentlemen consulted together and appeared to hit upon a plan, but not without some chuckling. Rebecca heard Mr. Steele ask some question about the moon, to which Mr. Addison replied, "Yes, yes, Dick. 'Tis a full moon, I do assure you." Dr. Swift then left the room and returned in a few minutes with a large parcel.

"At what hour precisely do you expect this old beldame to appear on the quayside, Miss Mapletop?" he asked kindly.

"Midnight, sir," answered Rebecca.

"Then place this parcel on the quayside at a little before twelve," said the dean. "If anything will detain her, *this* will do so."

Then the three gentlemen burst out laughing once more, but Rebecca thanked them and slipped away with a light heart. And on her way home, she sat down on the sea-wall and peeped inside the parcel, but she was none the wiser.

As Mr. Addison had foretold, the moon rose round and full and shone with a bright magical light upon the parcel, as it lay so innocently upon the empty quay-side. Oh, how still and quiet was Parkgate harbour that night, almost as though it knew it breathed its last. The fishing boats had all gone out with the tide. There was not a soul stirring. Only the moon seemed alive as she dropped her silver diamonds, one by one, into the glassy sea.

Then, suddenly, the harbour quivered as though a hand had shaken the water from side to side. The Witch, in a new pair of octopus boots and a hat decorated with inverted winkles, appeared over the edge of the jetty. At once, the whole quayside came to life. Rats waved from every crack and crevice; cockroaches, with horns entwined, advanced, bowing and scraping; cats rose, spitting in all directions; a passing owl shrieked with joy, and goats halloo-ed from the meadows.

Pleased with her reception, the Witch looked about her and straightway noticed the parcel. She had, like most people, a passion for undoing parcels, so very soon she glided across and undid this one. And inside she found a book. Now the Witch was very fond of reading, although the books that drifted down into her cave were few and far between. She took in one or two Sea Reviews, *John Dory's Weekly* and *The Sprattler*, and she grabbed an occasional letter or sodden pamphlet as it floated by, but that was all. And so she seized this particular book with great enjoyment, sat down with it upon a pile of fishing nets and began to turn the pages by the light of the moon. It was then a quarter to midnight. The Witch turned a page and read: "The travels of Lemuel Gulliver into several remote regions of the world. . . . Lemuel Gulliver gives some account of himself and family . . . he is shipwrecked and swims for his life . . . he gets safe on shore and comes to the country of

*Pleased with her reception, the witch, looking about her,
straightway noticed the parcel and glided across towards it*

Lilliput. . . ." The Witch was entranced. She read on and on. The church clock struck midnight. What did the Witch care for church clocks? She was deep, deep in *Gulliver's Travels*. And, in the fisherman's cottage, by the edge of the sea, Rebecca Mapletop turned with a sigh to her little truckle-bed and slept sweetly with her head upon her arm.

Lemuel Gulliver had arrived in Brobdingnag, when the Witch heard her cormorant calling, " Come, come, come!" over the water. She jumped with a yell to her octopus boots and saw, by the moon, that it was nearly three in the morning. Rebecca Mapletop was lost to her for ever. " Highcockolorum!" screamed the Witch.

She was deep, deep in Gulliver's Travels

"A plague on all books!" and she hurled poor Lemuel Gulliver into the sea. Mad with rage, she seized her pet cormorant and wrung its neck. Then she jumped astride her broomstick of shrimps' whiskers and shrieked and howled and yelled and screamed up and down the sands of Dee for seven days and seven nights like one possessed. If a sea-bird came near her, she choked it; if she saw a boat, she sank it. She brewed and baked such storms in her cauldron that the meadows were flooded from Chester to Hoylake, and when at last her fury had abated, it was found that the Dee had silted up and it was no longer possible for ships going to and from Ireland to dock at Neston and Dawpool, at West Kirby and Parkgate. And so, they had to build a new coaching road from Warrington to Liverpool. And Liverpool woke up and established a very superior line of packet-boats from Liverpool to Dublin. And from that time onwards, there was no more travelling between England and Ireland from the banks of the River Dee.

And no more lovely ladies and distinguished gentlemen came to Parkgate, so that the town grew smaller and smaller until it became what it is today, a single line of wind-swept houses, staring over a sea-wall against which no sea will ever break again. But Rebecca Mapletop grew up and married and lived to be an old, old lady. And her recipe for potted shrimps was passed on to her children and grandchildren, and is used in Parkgate to this very day. And most people say there are no shrimps in England like those of Parkgate. But what a heavy price to pay for a pot of shrimps!

FROM BOY TO ADMIRAL

By Vice-Admiral Gordon Campbell, V.C., D.S.O.

We were mustered in oilskins on the lee-side of the deck

THERE used to be an old saying that the fool of the family was always sent to sea! Well, I came from a family of sixteen and two of us were sent to sea. Luckily, I wanted to go, and never had any other ambition in my life. I soon got to love the sea, and I never regret having joined the Sea Service.

We were caught young—I was only fourteen when I joined my first ship, H.M.S. *Britannia*, as a cadet. By the time I was sixteen, I was at sea as a midshipman on board what was at that time considered to be a very big ship —10,000 tons — although nowadays they talk in terms of 40,000 tons.

I joined my ship, the *Prince George*, at Portsmouth under the eyes of Nelson's flagship, the *Victory*. Soon after joining we sailed for Spain, North Africa and through the Mediterranean.

What an experience for a boy! We were quickly knocked into shape, but strange to say the strongest memory of the *Prince George* which stays in my mind was our first Sunday at sea when we were going through the Bay of Biscay in a gale. The waves and spray were coming over the deck, yet we were mustered with the sailors on the lee-side, in oilskins, while the padre

We crashed on the rocks and nearly turned right over

in his surplice conducted a stand-up service and we sang the hymn "Eternal Father Strong to Save." A good beginning, and one that has often stood me in good stead.

Life as a midshipman was all one could wish for—practical work on deck, lessons, games and opportunities to handle boats, either steam, sail or oars. One learnt how to try to command and earn the respect of the men. On Sundays we used to wear little round jackets, crowded with brass buttons, called by us "bum freezers," and a dirk or small sword at our side.

I wonder how many youngsters were first attracted (or perhaps their mothers were), by the uniform.

All this time we were being trained to defend our Empire, to relieve distress at sea or the ravages on land of famine, fire or earthquake; to stop slave traffic, to protect our life-lines or trade routes, and at all times to uphold the honour of our country. For, you see, the Naval Discipline Act lays it down that it is "on the Navy under the Good Providence of God that the wealth, strength and safety of the Empire doth chiefly depend."

We all know, especially those with experience of two or even more wars, that war in itself becomes more cruel every day, yet as no one has yet invented a way to prevent it, one must therefore be prepared for it. Indeed, candidly, as a young officer, I often longed for a scrap because, I suppose, I considered it my duty.

I did not have to wait long before my first thrill, and I remember then, as now, one liked the idea of doing something of an adventurous nature. It is born in a Britisher's blood. But perhaps I am going too fast. From the Mediterranean I came home for a " football " knee to be operated on, and then was sent off to Esquimalt in British Columbia by the Canadian Pacific Railway, which was not the up-to-date express it is now. At that time, even Vancouver had not been fully explored.

I had not been long in my new ship, *Flora*, a cruiser, when we were sent up to the inland waters between Vancouver and the mainland. One morning, when I was midshipman of the watch, we ran into a dense fog. We were looking for a buoy with a white cage on top of it. The look-out reported it, and the captain altered course to what he thought was the proper channel. However, the white cage flew away! It was a seagull and we crashed on to the rocks, and nearly turned right over. We were there for a week. There was no wireless in those days with which to call for help, but luckily we had gone ashore by a forest, and the sailors sawed down big trees and wedged them under the ship's bottom, which at low water was practically high and dry. Then we gutted the ship of everything to make

her lighter and were eventually towed off on the rollers, like a small boat being launched on Margate sands.

One amusing incident was the captain's breakfast egg. It was at breakfast time that we had our crash, and the whole stern went under water, including the captain's cabin. When eventually the ship was pumped out, there was the captain's breakfast nicely laid, as it had been a week before, and the egg in its egg cup undamaged— but I don't think he ate it! The excitement of the wreck was followed by three months in dock, then more cruising, this time to Mexico and Chile.

While there we had our first war thrill. " Prepare for war " was the signal throughout the ship.

It is old history now, but there was a " slip up " with Russia and we were ordered to fill up with coal, which we did on a Sunday, and go across to Vladivostok.

How excited we midshipmen were! Anyhow, even in those days, big wars were avoided if possible—but as a youngster I was disappointed, and I imagine even the older officers felt the same when war was " off!"

I make no apologies for my feelings because if one reads of the great deeds of the Navy in the past, one naturally wants to be ready to follow in our great sailors' footsteps. It all came to nothing, however, and we just rolled back to England. I say " rolled " because we were a light cruiser and they used to roll so that one sometimes wondered whether one was looking at the sea or the sky.

I reached my mother's home in the middle of a Christmas party, and, being a gallant midshipman and seeing mistletoe about, I kissed the prettiest and youngest girl in the room. She became my wife when I reached the exalted rank of lieutenant.

I was soon sent to another ship in the Mediterranean, and later to the famous Greenwich College, where Nelson's body lay in state after Trafalgar. I had to work there studying all kinds of highbrow subjects. These were not in my line, but I scraped through with one mark to spare!

I became a sub-lieutenant, and was thrilled when I was appointed first

I kissed the prettiest and youngest girl in the room

lieutenant of a destroyer—that is to say, second in command, and having about sixty men to look after. We were what the Navy calls a " happy ship." There were just four officers, and my captain and I possessed twin bull terrier pups. Mine was called Nelson, and he became an " able seaman " (without pay) and lived to serve in the First World War. He had the keenest sense of humour of any dog I have met. For example, when I had him with me in Plymouth one day, and had about two and a half miles to walk to our ship, I would have liked to have taken a tram, but as dogs were not allowed in trams I knew I had to walk. I looked round for Nelson, and to my amazement and amusement I saw a tram flying past with Nelson in the stern waving his tail at me!

Once he jumped into a stationary cab, the driver of which he knew, and having calmly taken his seat, he waited till he was driven home to where we lived; and even then, he would not get out until I came to the door and paid the cab driver the fare.

When the First World War came and I was given command of a destroyer which had to crash about in the Channel, I gave him a shore appointment to look after my wife.

Life in a small destroyer in any war is one that keeps you busy. You have to keep your eyes open, for the enemy may be sighted at any time. What a change it was from the two and a half years I had spent in the flagship of the China squadron seeing China, Japan, Singapore and many of the places we read about nowadays. This was followed by over two years as lieutenant of a boys' training ship. They were a

*I saw a tram flying past
with Nelson in the stern*

splendid lot of lads—about 1600 of
them, but how naughty and even
cheeky some of them could be! I had
the job of looking after the boys who
could not pass their examinations.
This was done in the dog watches, so
called because they are " cur-tailed "
—that is to say, two-hour watches
instead of four—4 p.m. to 6 p.m. and
6 p.m. to 8 p.m.

I remember one boy in particular,
with whom I spent the evenings of
three months, trying to teach him to
swim. During that period, it was the
custom for boys to have their leave
stopped; that meant they must stay on
board until they passed their tests.
Eventually, my young charge passed
the test and the next day, a Sunday,
when he was at last allowed ashore
again, I happened to pass him when I
was walking along by the sea with my
wife. He stared at me, but did not
salute. I sent for him the next day and
said, " Don't you know, my boy, you
are to salute your officers whether in
plain clothes or uniform?" " Yes, sir."
" Why didn't you salute me last
night?" " Please, sir, I didn't recognize you." " You must have done," I
said sternly. " I'm sick tired of your
face, and I should have thought you
were sick tired of mine." " No, sir, I

didn't recognize you because you were
smiling, and I have never seen you
smile before!" was the reply.

So the world goes round, and we get
back to the First World War of
1914-1918. When you younger ones
go to school no doubt you will read of
the Napoleonic Wars and the First and
Second World Wars. It will not take

you very long at school to learn about them, *but* if you want to read about them more fully, there is a fund of information at your disposal.

For myself, the First World War led me in the beginning into destroyers, till I tried to make my engines go too fast when I thought I had sighted an enemy vessel and my old ship finally broke down.

What I was chasing was not an enemy ship but a channel steamer specially altered for war conditions. I then turned my hand to what were called Q ships or mystery ships. This was a great adventure. Ordinary merchant ships looking outwardly as such were inwardly veritable men of war. We had guns on board, but they were hidden so that no submarines could see them. The crew manning these guns were concealed, too. Every endeavour was made to deceive the German sub-

The ship would apparently

marines, which at that time, and as they have since done, were trying to terrorize and if necessary kill the persons on board merchant ships, which were supposed to be safe from attack.

Our job in the mystery or Q ships was to return blow for blow. We had not the scientific instruments which are now available for locating U-boats, such as asdics and so on. It was a question of wits against wits and it was an exciting game. We had to encourage the submarines to come to the surface, so that our concealed guns could be unmasked and sink them by gunfire. To do this we eventually decided to let them torpedo us. This was a great experience and almost as bad as the whizzes and bangs of an air attack. But

be " abandoned "

the difference was that our crews had to carry out all kinds of camouflage in order to get the submarine to surface after her attack. The ship would apparently be " abandoned " and the only men left on board would be at the concealed guns or in the engine or wireless rooms. It was often a long wait before the U-boat captain had confidence to come alongside the innocent looking steamer, usually with the idea of searching for any secret log books or papers on board, and perhaps to get extra supplies. When he did surface we invariably got him. It was a long and trying game, for the submarines at sea were not so many as in the Second World War, nor, as already mentioned, were the scientific developments so great.

I will tell you one more incident in my connection with this form of warfare, just as I have related my first impression of the *Prince George*. I happened to be in command of a ship called the *Dunraven*. She had been battered about, we had casualties, and were torpedoed; her magazine exploded and her end was coming nearer and nearer. Eventually, in the middle of the night, in the Bay of Biscay, not far from the very spot where we held that stormy church service in the *Prince George*, she started to sink.

The remaining men, twenty in all, fell in on the forecastle deck. It was pitch dark, the gale and waves were roaring. A boat came over from a destroyer to take the crew off. The order was given : " Only four men to get into the boat," otherwise it would have capsized, and it was also unlikely that it would be able to return. Not a man moved, until the senior hand said to the captain: "Sir, will you please mention four men by name as no one wants to leave before the others!" The captain was obliged to mention four men by name, and they went off in the small boat. The remainder got on to the tipped-up end of the ship and jumped one by one into the darkness on to the deck of a destroyer although, again, not one man jumped until called on to do so by name. Discipline and unselfishness were maintained to the end.

My service in Q ships had given me rapid promotion, and at the age of thirty-one I found myself the youngest captain in the Navy and went in command of a light cruiser. This was a different type of warfare, and rather dull during the period I had to patrol off the south coast of Eire, but soon I was transferred to Grimsby. I brought the ship down channel and when off Yarmouth we met a steamer going in the opposite direction. We should have hit each other had we not altered course to avoid collision. It was lucky we did so as a mine was between us a few yards away.

I soon found myself in charge of the anti-submarine flotilla in the Irish Sea, with headquarters in a cruiser at Holyhead. The anti-submarine measures consisted of destroyers, warships, airships, motor launches, U.S.A. chasers, yachts, trawlers and so on. I think we did succeed in absolutely destroying the submarines; so successfully did we keep them under water that only two ships were sunk during the six months we were there. We had many exciting chases and false alarms.

On one occasion a submarine was reported to be in my area. He had

come in at the north of the Irish Sea and, as I anticipated, had gone down towards Dublin. I had a destroyer waiting there for him so that when he surfaced one morning the destroyer went for him full speed and dropped two depth charges. These had no effect. It must be realized that once a submarine has submerged it can often move off in safety east, west, north or south. Days went by and there was no

news of this submarine, nor were any ships attacked. I had the feeling, however, that he must still be off Dublin, so the following day I had two destroyers sent there. Sure enough, he popped up in the same place at the same time. The destroyers made a concerted attack and dropped six depth charges. Again without suc-

We steamed round in circles and dropped sixty depth charges

cess. Without further delay I sent three destroyers to lie off Dublin at daylight, and on the third day he popped up again in exactly the same place, at the same time; the destroyers dropped twelve depth charges. By this time I had begun to feel it a personal insult that this U-boat fellow popped up day after day in the same place as if to show off what he could do without being sunk. As I had some sixty depth charges on my decks I decided to make a present of them to him, so I slipped from my moorings at Holyhead and steamed across the Irish Sea at full speed. When I had reached the appropriate place I said to my sailors, "This fellow is still down there somewhere—just you tickle him up." We steamed round in circles and dropped sixty depth charges. That evidently settled him and he went back to Germany that night. I learned afterwards that the crew had become fed up because each time they appeared on the surface somebody dropped depth charges, and the thing came to a climax when some fellow dropped sixty just as they were having breakfast!

At the end of the war, I took command of a 10,000 ton cruiser with cadets from the Royal Naval College, Dartmouth, on board, and we went to the West Indies. I had one very trying experience after leaving Madeira when, in mid-ocean with nothing in sight, I stopped the ship and gave permission for the crew and the cadets to bathe. Some hundred dived into the water, the men from the forecastle, the cadets from the quarter-deck, while I looked on from the bridge. Suddenly someone shouted " Shark ! " and something like a panic started. Of course, I immediately ordered the boats to be lowered and lifelines and lifebelts away overboard, but to my horror some of the men started to swim away from the ship instead of towards her. I had visions of losing scores of men, though in the end everyone got on board safely. There was no shark! What happened was that one of the swimmers thought the ship looked very small and far away and became frightened; then he shouted "Help!" Someone else thought he cried "shark," and started all the trouble.

I was with the cadets a year and a half, then I went back to my old training ship, H.M.S. *Impregnable*, as the captain. My original service as her lieutenant came in very useful, and when the boys tried to bluff me they found that I knew more about the routine than they thought.

I seemed fated to be ashore for a time, and my next appointment was in South Africa, where I was captain of the dockyard. It was in Africa that I got the biggest fright of my life. One day I was walking over the hills in thick scrub by myself when I suddenly felt something cold by my knee inside my trousers. Had anyone else been in sight, I would probably have called out for help but as there was no one about I pulled up my trouser leg and seized what was a small snake by its head. It shot away probably as scared as I was. I hurried down the hill and went to the nearest doctor as I was not sure whether I had been bitten or not. The doctor told me that from my description, it was probably a puff-adder, and had it bitten me I would not have been alive to tell the tale. When I reached the club, I looked at a book about snakes and it said that the safest place for a snake to be was up one's trouser leg, as it cannot get its head reared back to strike. However, after that experience, I always went about in thick grass with my trousers tucked into my socks!

On returning from South Africa, I was soon at sea again in command of the great battle cruiser *Tiger*, which had so distinguished herself in the 1914-1918 engagements in the North Sea. She still bore the scars of battle. It was a sad day when the Admiralty told me that I had to leave her and my naval career for a time. The moral of this tale is that if you want to see life and enjoy it, join the Navy.

I pulled up my trouser leg and seized a small snake

P.S.—The only thing Admiral Campbell has *not* told you is that he won the Victoria Cross for his courageous work in Q ships.—*Editor*.

THE WOBBLE CLUB
By George C. Nash

"LOOK!" said Hatch Pyke to his sister Dimmy. "The shop door with the funny name—it's open." "So it is," said Dimmy, "the Wobble Shop and I've never known it open before."

Hatch and Dimmy Pyke were wandering round the town and had reached the point when they didn't know what to do with themselves next.

They stopped and examined the open shop door most carefully. Clouds of dust were billowing from the inside where someone was sweeping the floor, and there were sounds of much puffing and much grunting. As they stood looking and listening a large floor brush suddenly hurtled out across the pavement. The grunting and puffing stopped, and almost immediately there appeared from the dusty interior —rather like a shiny balloon coming out of a dark rain cloud—a bald head.

A moment later the children were looking into the twinkling blue eyes of a rather little man who was dressed in a pair of dark green velvet trousers and a red shirt. There was something about his face that made Hatch think of one of Snow White's dwarfs, but Dimmy thought he looked like a picture she'd once seen of Puck.

"Beg pardon," said the little man rubbing his rounded chin and lifting his wire spectacles from the bridge of his nose to the tip, "But that wretched brush *will* keep flying out of my hands."

"Mr. Wobble?" asked Dimmy.

"Course I'm Mr. Wobble," the little man replied. "Poor old Alfred Wobble, and doing my usual one day a year dusting."

"One day a year?" said Hatch.

"Yes," said Mr. Wobble. "One day a year."

"Then what do you do on the other three hundred and sixty-four days of the year?"

Mr. Wobble looked up at the sky and down at the pavement. "Well, let's see," he said uncertainly. "I wake up in the morning, have breakfast, stroke the cat, get ordered out of the *kitchen* by my wife, have lunch, have forty winks, stroke the cat again, get ordered out of the *house* by my wife, walk round and round the town doing nothing...." "Walk round and round the town doing nothing?" interrupted Hatch. "Why, that's just what we do."

Mr. Wobble smiled and his heart began to warm towards his new friends. "Pretty kettle of fish, aren't we?" he eventually said. "And all, as it were, in the same boat."

"What on earth do you sell in your shop?" Dimmy suddenly said.

"Nothing," sighed Mr. Wobble.

"Nothing?" said Hatch.

"Nothing!" said Mr. Wobble.

"Then how does it pay?" Dimmy asked.

"It doesn't," came the reply.

"Then why...?"

"It was left to me seven years ago by my Uncle Alec," explained Mr. Wobble. "The building and everything in it—Uncle Alec used to do quite well with it—selling and hiring out things to theatres and concert parties."

"What sort of things?" asked Hatch.

"Oh, dresses and wigs for actors and actresses; furniture for the stage. Indeed, as he once said himself, he could supply everything for a panto-mime, from a giant's boot to a fairy-queen's wand."

"And you don't hire out anything any more?" interrupted Hatch.

"I don't have to," said Mr. Wobble. "I retired from business six years ago. Made my money in biscuits."

"Biscuits?" echoed Dimmy.

"And that's why you come dusting your shop one day a year," asked Hatch, "just to see that everything's in order?"

Mr. Wobble nodded his head.

"Could I see the giant's boot?" said Dimmy, "I've never seen a giant's boot."

"By all means," said Mr. Wobble, and bowed the children politely into his shop.

It was a quaint building into which they went. Mr. Wobble owned it all from street level to attic—four floors —and in each room on the first three there was an astonishing collection of stuff. But as Mr. Wobble didn't know where anything was, the giant's boot took a lot of finding, and in their search for it they passed through nearly every room in the house.

On the ground floor Hatch and Dimmy saw nothing but furniture and furnishings—umbrella stands, a piano, cuckoo clocks, dining-room tables, coal scuttles and a rocking chair. The second floor contained such odds and ends as tin baths, frying pans, tiger-skin rugs, native spears and mouse traps, while the third was given up to dresses for every period and occasion from Roman toga to airman's flying suit, and from ballet dress to head-master's cap and gown. It was here too that the giant's boot was found, with a Cinderella glass slipper sticking through one of the eyelet holes.

"Well, of all the lovely places I've ever been in," said Dimmy to Hatch as they turned to go downstairs again.

"But there's another floor still," said Mr. Wobble, who was beginning to enjoy himself.

"Another floor still?" said Hatch. "But what more could there be?"

Wondering greatly, they mounted the last flight of stairs, opened a door and walked on to a huge floor space which covered the entire top of the house.

"Well, children?" said Mr. Wobble, "And what do you think of those?"

Hatch and Dimmy gulped and their eyes grew big, for here, there and almost everywhere, were all sorts of pantomime animals specially made for a human being to dress up. Some were of brown cloth with a plaster moulded head, others were made of fur. A few seemed to be nothing but feathers, while one was of imitation fish scales. In nearly every case the ears moved (except the fish!), the eyes winked and the mouth opened and shut. There was even a crocodile and a pantomime horse.

With a whoop of joy Dimmy dashed forward and thrust her arms and legs into the four feet of Dick Whittington's cat, while Hatch almost as quickly turned himself into Red Riding Hood's wolf. He began to growl and

Hatch and Dimmy gulped, and their eyes grew big . . .

bark, Dimmy to miaow, and a moment later they were chasing each other round the attic floor.

Mr. Wobble looked on delightedly, until suddenly—and because, as he afterwards admitted, " he couldn't resist it "—he too dashed forward and got himself into the " feathers " of the Goose That Laid the Golden Egg, immediately joining in the fun. But after a very short time Mr. Wobble got so out of breath, and they were all so overcome with laughter that the three of them collapsed on the floor.

" Isn't that marvellous?" said Hatch, as they extricated paws from wings and tails from webbed feet.

" Marvellous!" said Dimmy.

" And I've just had a marvellous idea," gasped Mr. Wobble.

And there and then, still out of breath, he told them what it was.

" Just seeing you enjoying yourselves like that," he began, " has given me an idea of what to do with this shop of mine. It is to open the place as a sort of club where children can come to amuse themselves. I have heaps of furniture and things like that to make it all comfortable." Mr. Wobble stopped and beamed—the children beamed back at him. " And I'd help run it," went on Mr. Wobble, " for having something to do like that would be grand. I'd be the happiest man on earth."

" You don't really mean it?" said Dimmy.

" Of course I mean it," said Mr. Wobble.

" Then we'll call it the Wobble Club," said Hatch. And in a very short time the Wobble Club it was.

Hatch, Dimmy and Mr. Wobble worked very hard in the Wobble Club for over a week. Dusting, washing, shifting, carrying, dragging, hammering, sawing, until gradually there began to appear some sort of order in the rooms.

Downstairs there was a place for hats and coats, a reading room and, what Dimmy insisted on, " a Mess Room " —not a place to eat in like the army, but a place where you could make a real MESS. Varnish chairs, and play sea lions with plenty of water to splash, and what Mr. Wobble specially wanted —a place where he could do a bit of experimental cooking—the making of a roly-poly being one of his life's ambitions, an ambition which up to now his wife had always thwarted.

The second floor consisted of a picnic room, a toy room and a make-and-mend room, and on the third there was a museum and two exercise rooms for boxing, ping-pong, bagatelle and other games.

The attic, where they had found the animal dresses, was cleared of everything for concerts, plays, cinema shows and dances.

It was just when they had finished their first complete inspection of the altered rooms that Mr. Wobble said:

" You know, Dimmy and Hatch, there's two things we haven't got yet —money and club members."

" Yes, I've been thinking about that too," said Dimmy.

" The club members will be easy," said Hatch, " they'll come from near and far and they'll bring in the money themselves—they'll have to pay an annual subscription and so on. . . ."

" But we want quite a bit of cash right now to get started," said Mr. Wobble. " There's those parallel bars for the exercise room—and a wireless set." "Not forgetting a cinema," put in Hatch.

"You agree of course we must make the club self-supporting, that's a matter of pride, isn't it?" Mr. Wobble said. "Just like a golf or tennis club."

"Of course," both children agreed. Suddenly Hatch had a bright idea. "I've got it!" he said. "Those

seem that they decided to try it out immediately, and without a single further thought of what they were going to do or how it was to be done, Dimmy and Hatch and Mr. Wobble again became the cat, wolf and goose they had been when they played around in the attic. After a brief exchange of ideas on where they should

As they ran they shouted at the top of their voices, "Come and see our show everyone! Children especially!"

animal dresses that we found in the attic; we'll put them on and go around the town acting to people and doing shows, tumbling and gagging, and then passing round the hat when we've finished. And as we go we can tell everyone what we want the money for and get the children to come along to the club, and that will kill two birds with one stone."

So apt and happy did this scheme

go, they rushed out along the street, heading for the nearest busy thoroughfare. Dimmy's tail was held straight up in a business-like way, Hatch had his ears erect and his teeth showing, while Mr. Wobble was all feathers and wings and looked rather like a feather duster. As they ran they shouted out at the top of their voices, "Come and see our show everyone! Children especially; Good value for your money. Come on! Breath-taking announcement when we've finished."

The immediate result surprised even Mr. Wobble, for first one and then another fell in around them, shoppers and shop-keepers, business men and labourers, boys and girls, until so big a crowd had collected that Hatch, Dimmy and Mr. Wobble could make no further progress, and they were hedged in on every side.

They looked very odd and rather woebegone as they stood there not quite knowing what to do next.

The crowd looked on without saying anything, but eventually a baker's boy shouted out, " Come on the zoo, I'll buy it, what's it all about?" That did it. Mr. Wobble blurted out, " You just watch me, I'll show you!"

Mr. Wobble had intended to be very ungooselike and turn some somersaults, but he hadn't got properly started before a policeman forced his way through the crowd and caught hold of his beak.

" Hoi, my beauty," he said, " you can't do that here!"

" Why not?" said Mr. Wobble, shaking his beak clear. " We aren't doing any harm."

" Harm," said the policeman, " of course you are. You're stopping all the traffic. Look—three trams in the High Street and two in the Cornmarket can't get by."

" Goodness," said Mr. Wobble, looking round, " so we are."

" What's the game, anyway?" continued the policeman.

Hatch blurted out—" It's to raise money for the Wobble Club."

" *Wobble* Club?" said the policeman, in an angry, incredulous voice.

" Yes, Wobble Club," said Dimmy.

" You just come along with me," said the policeman. " I'll Wobble Club you."

It was difficult to get the crowd to go away. Some were in favour of letting them do their show in spite of the traffic, but others demanded they be arrested.

At first Mr. Wobble found it difficult to persuade the policeman not to take them off to the police station. But once Mr. Wobble was able to undo the zip fastener which did up his goose's neck, and he could get his head out, it was all right, for the policeman then recognized Mr. Wobble and Mr. Wobble recognized the policeman.

" Why we used to play bowls together," said Mr. Wobble.

" So we did," said the policeman, and then began talking about the time when Mr. Wobble made biscuits.

Seeing there wasn't going to be any more fun the crowd gradually dropped away and Mr. Wobble, Dimmy, Hatch and the policeman walked off to the Wobble Club.

" Well, I'm surprised at you, Mr. Wobble," said the policeman, taking a chair in the new reading room and removing his helmet. " A Goose trying to cook his own goose, if I may say so!"

" Surprised at myself," said Mr. Wobble—" no fool like an old fool—never thought of the consequences, only thought of the Wobble Club."

" This Wobble Club you're talking about," said the policeman. " What exactly *is* it?"

Enthusiastically Mr. Wobble told him all about it, Hatch and Dimmy helping when he got out of breath.

So the next day Mr. Wobble, Hatch and Dimmy called on the Mayor, and the visit was most successful

The policeman listened intently, and at the end of half an hour said— "Why, it's a great idea, Mr. Wobble —only thing is you've gone about getting the money for it in the wrong way."

"But how then *are* we to get the money?" asked Dimmy.

"Why not have a talk to the Mayor?" said the policeman. "He's always very helpful, you'll find, in things like that."

"The *Mayor*?" said Mr. Wobble.

"Yes," said the policeman. "Why not?"

So the next day Mr. Wobble, Hatch and Dimmy called on the Mayor and the visit was most successful, for after listening carefully to the whole plan he offered to help them

organize a concert and so raise money in that way.

Mr. Wobble thought this was an excellent idea, and Dimmy chipped in, saying: " Couldn't we also do our Wolf, Goose and Cat show and get some more money that way?"

Mr. Wobble scratched his chin and remembered how the policeman had caught hold of his beak. But Hatch said, " Yes, why not—and even better why not have a show with all sorts of turns besides ours, and all done by children?"

" Oh yes, do let's," said Dimmy, " Mr. Wobble's got heaps of dresses for the actors and all sorts of other things as well."

" Done!" said the Mayor. " Then if you three stage a Grand Variety Con-

The children began to work very

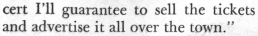

cert I'll guarantee to sell the tickets and advertise it all over the town."

"And we could have it in the Wobble Club Concert Room," said Dimmy.

"Exactly," said the Mayor, "in that attic place you were telling me about."

"Wonderful!" said Mr. Wobble. "This *is* a day."

The Wobble Club Grand Variety Concert was eventually billed for four weeks ahead, and in the meantime the local talent—all children—was engaged, and began to work hard rehearsing their turns.

There were jugglers and singers and mouth organ players. There was a fat boy who could make animal noises, a thin girl who was an expert ventriloquist, clowns, three Boy Scout buglers

hard, rehearsing all their turns

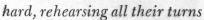

Heralded by a stirring set of calls from the buglers, Mr. Wobble, Hatch and Dimmy waddled forward in their costumes and bowed to the audience

and a first class accordion band to keep the whole show together.

Everyone helped during those four weeks. Parents came with scissors, tape measures and needles and thread to alter and cut down Mr. Wobble's theatrical dresses; other parents came and did carpentry and electrical work, while some painted scenery.

A great deal was done by Hatch, Dimmy and Mr. Wobble. Indeed the latter worked so hard he had three blisters on his right hand, a bruise on his left knee and a scratch on the back of his neck.

On the night of nights the Wobble concert hall was so crowded that extra seats had to be provided, and many of the audience had to stand. Excitement was intense from start to finish, and each turn as it came and went received much applause and cheering, and there were many encores.

Just before the curtain was rung down the Mayor himself came on to the stage and made a speech. He explained all about the Wobble Club, and that already seventy-six children had joined and had paid their subscriptions while others were waiting to join, and this in spite of the fact that it wasn't being officially opened until to-morrow. He also said that thanks to the concert just ending, he now had a large sum of money to hand over to the three people who were responsible for the idea of starting the Wobble Club.

At this, there was a great deal of applause and clapping, followed by considerable commotion back stage, where—heralded by a stirring set of calls from the buglers—Mr. Wobble waddled forward to the footlights, all dressed up in his original part of the Goose That Laid the Golden Egg. At his heels walked Hatch and Dimmy, and as before they were again Red Riding Hood's wolf and Dick Whittington's cat. When the bugle calls faded out they all bowed to the audience, the Mayor stood to one side, the accordion band struck up a waltz, and Hatch and Dimmy began a most exciting acrobatic dance, tumbling over and over, gambolling, romping, pulling each other's tails and even playing leap-frog. The Goose That Laid the Golden Egg meantime stood keeping time to the music by flapping his wings and, whenever things got very thrilling, doing a lot of excited quacking.

The turn ended in thunderous applause, and when it had died away Mr. Wobble waddled up to the Mayor, who handed him the money that had been collected and Mr. Wobble took it from him in his beak and tucked it safely away under his wing. He then popped out his little bald head from his feathers and made a speech, thanking everybody very warmly (especially the Mayor) for their support. He added that this was quite the proudest moment of his life, and if it hadn't been for Hatch and Dimmy there never would have been a Wobble Club at all.

Just as he said this Hatch and Dimmy " jumped out of their skins " and they in turn bowed all round.

There then followed more applause and clapping and so, with everyone singing *For They are Jolly Good Fellows* and the Mayor bowing to Mr. Wobble and Mr. Wobble bowing to Hatch and Dimmy the band struck up *God Save the King*. Thus that exciting day ended and the success of the Wobble Club was assured.

TALKING OF BUTTERFLIES

By L. Hugh Newman, F.R.E.S.

ONE of the best things about the dark winter evenings is that you can sit in front of a pleasant fire and not feel that you're being at all lazy, but relax and think of all the happy times you've had during the past year—and other years, too, for that matter.

That is one of the things about the study of butterflies which is such fun. You spend a glorious day in the country in search of a special butterfly. Perhaps you capture one, or photograph one, or maybe only just catch a glimpse of one. But whichever it is, that particular butterfly becomes a talisman, a sort of magic token, which, the moment you see it again or even think about it, has the power of recalling to your mind all those joyous hours you spent when searching for it, perhaps years and years before.

You can start butterfly hunting quite early in the year; and if you look carefully, you'll find them in many quaint places. There is a narrow pathway along the sunny sheltered side of a wood in Kent, which has earned the name of Peacock Walk, as every warm spring day, you always see there two or three Peacock butterflies. They regard it as their very own territory, and should a Green-veined White or a Speckled Wood or an early Orange-tip butterfly appear on the scene, these Peacocks hustle the intruders away without any ceremony.

One Christmas holiday two Tortoiseshell butterflies were found sleeping away the winter in a very curious place. A party of young people went for an all day hike in the country. Very soon they had left the town behind and were out in the fields, the hoar-frost crackling under their feet and their breath making trails of vapour in the air like planes high up in the sky. Then somebody noticed a scarecrow propped up against a hedge, banished from the fields for the winter, presumably.

This scarecrow was a very fine old gentleman with a battered top hat stuck on top of his head, and he looked very dignified in a frock coat, green with age, covering his thin straw body, and with his face carved out of a large, round turnip. Someone said he had a friend who had once found a nest of young field mice in the pocket of a scarecrow during harvest season, and although it was not the time of year for anything like that, they thought they might find something interesting in it—perhaps an old bird's nest—and so strolled over to have a closer look at the scarecrow. Have you guessed already what they found? Lifting up the flap they saw two Tortoiseshell butterflies clinging to the torn lining, side by side, and of course fast asleep! They had been there for at least three

There were two Tortoiseshell butterflies clinging to the torn lining

months and probably would not wake up again until about Easter.

Another butterfly that appears very early in the spring is the little ragged Comma butterfly, the wild gipsy of the woods. Like the Peacock and the Tortoiseshell she sleeps all through the winter, perhaps in the roof of a gipsy caravan! After all, Peacocks and Tortoiseshells both come into our homes. No doubt you have seen one fluttering frantically against a bedroom window on the first warm sunny day in late February or early March. It has been a quiet visitor in your room the whole winter, probably without your knowing it! The most usual haunt of the Comma butterfly is the dark hollow of a dead or dying tree, where this ragged little gipsy will be rudely awakened in the spring by the woodpeckers seeking a nesting site. Curiously enough, Peacock butterflies in the wild, not the tame garden variety, often choose a rabbit hole in which to sleep!

You may wonder how this was found out? Well, the writer was out with a farmer ferreting for rabbits one cold November afternoon some years ago, on the downs in Kent, at a spot simply pitted with rabbit burrows. A ferret had been down quite a long time and they had almost given up hope of turning out any rabbits, and had come to the conclusion that the warren must have been deserted. They were peering down into a hole when suddenly there was a flutter of wings and a Peacock nearly hit them in the face. It circled round and round their heads, looking very bewildered and lost, and then fluttered down to earth again and disappeared into another rabbit hole farther down the hill. You will agree that this Peacock butterfly was very wise, for when you come to think of it, a butterfly could hardly find a more sheltered place in which to spend the winter than in Brer Rabbit's home.

One autumn a Brimstone butterfly was actually seen looking for hibernating quarters. It was in an old-world garden in the little village of Bexley. All one morning this brilliant yellow butter-coloured insect fluttered around the garden as though looking for something. Then it settled on a thick clump of ivy covering an old tree-stump, and suddenly disappeared. By carefully parting the ivy, he could be seen clinging to the underside of a leaf, already drowsy for his winter's sleep.

Well, he remained there all the winter, and was quite all right.

The Brimstone butterfly has been wonderfully equipped by Nature with a very long tongue. If he wakes up on

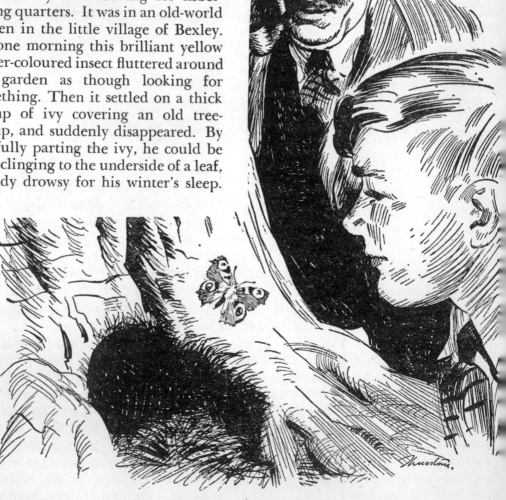

They were peering down into the rabbit hole when suddenly there was a flutter of wings, and a Peacock butterfly nearly hit them in the face

a mild winter's day and feels thirsty, all he need do is to unroll his tongue and curl it over the edge of the leaf under which he is sheltering, and draw in a few beads of dew, or drops of rain if it has been raining. And all this can be accomplished without moving an inch, or disturbing the bedclothes, so to speak!

When the south wind loosens its breath in the spring, warning creatures to awaken from their winter sleep, the hibernating butterflies begin to crawl from their winter hiding places. You know now where Peacocks, Tortoiseshells, Comma butterflies and Brimstones have been hiding, but what about some of the other kinds of butterflies we always see in the spring and early summer? In country lanes the Orange-tip will have emerged from the chrysalis where he spent the winter, and you can watch him dally among the wild flowers. But the pretty flicker of white and orange suddenly vanishes when he alights on a head of wild parsley. You see, he closes his wings when he settles, and the mottled green and white undersides blend perfectly with the colour scheme of this tall wayside plant. By the way, in case you do not know, it is only the male in the Brimstone and the Orange-tip that has brilliantly coloured wings. The female Brimstone is not yellow at all; her wings look more like the bits of old parchment you may see in museums. Again, the female Orange-tip hasn't any gaudy tips; she is just plain white, and you might even mistake her for a common Cabbage White butterfly unless you know the secret of her patterned underwings.

Summer heralds the appearance of the Fritillaries, that large family of

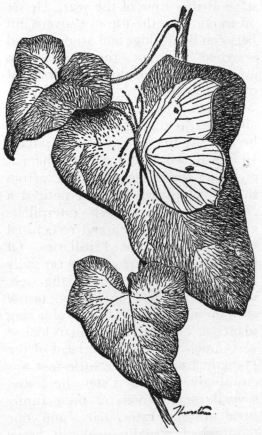

If the Brimstone butterfly feels thirsty, he curls his tongue round the edge of the leaf, to draw in a few beads of dew

elegant speckled brown butterflies, noted for their size and swift flight. You can see them playing hide and seek between the tree-trunks, and in and out of the sunlit patches in woodland ridings. One of the Fritillaries can only be found in the Isle of Wight. Even on this island, it only occurs in a few scattered places along the coast, and so you can imagine it is somewhat rare. The name of this butterfly is the Glanville Fritillary, and on his first half holiday from school on the island, the author decided to make a hunt for them. It was early May and he knew that they would be in the caterpillar

stage at that time of the year. He set off to climb to the top of Culver Cliff between Bembridge and Sandown, and searched amongst the short grass growing along the cliff edge for a nest of the caterpillars.

He had worked his way right down almost to the edge of the shingle before he saw the first brood of caterpillars. In fact, he wouldn't have seen them at all if they had not wandered away from their food plant. He first noticed a couple of spiny black caterpillars crawling over a stone and recognized them as Glanville Fritillaries. Of course he started to look very carefully after this, and soon found the web, with the rest of the colony, neatly woven amongst the leaves of a big plantain. The black caterpillars looked very much like the flowerhead of the plantain itself, and the little nest was cunningly hidden. Later, he found several more broods of these funny little stumpy caterpillars, and one family had actually made its home round a plantain growing in the shingle. At high tide all the caterpillars would presumably have to get under the shelter of their web, which really made a very nice little tent, otherwise they would get very wet from the spray. Before school term finished he got so used to finding these caterpillars that wherever he went he looked for them, and even found a brood on the football field. He told the headmaster of his discovery, and was very proud when he saw it specially featured in the school magazine, with the heading, " Rare Butterfly Found On The Playing Fields." In case you

He searched along the side of the cliff, looking for a nest of the Glanville Fritillary caterpillars

ever go to the Isle of Wight for a holiday in June or July and want to look for this butterfly, it is a medium-sized golden-brown butterfly chequered in nigger brown, with a much lighter underside banded in cream and white.

Summer hasn't arrived properly until you see the first Meadow Brown, rather in the same way that the cuckoo announces spring. If you are walking by the side of a field of long grass just before haymaking time these large Browns will fly up in dozens, but not until you almost tread on them. They are the laziest butterflies! Really, the whole family ought to be called Ringlets instead of Browns, as nearly all of them have dark, white centred eye spots on their wings which look like tiny rings.

Once in July the author went specially to Scotland to find the Small Mountain Ringlet, as this was the only Brown butterfly he had not seen alive, and he was determined to find it. But it was very difficult. He stayed at a pleasant little hotel in a sheltered valley, and set out early the first morning to climb to the top of the mountain where he had been told these butterflies were supposed to be seen. It was a long, weary climb, and very hot in the sunshine, but then, when he was about three-quarters of the way up he seemed to walk straight into the clouds and everything was covered in a thick white mist. Although he stayed up there quite a long time in the hope that the sun would come out again, he did not dare wander about searching for the butter-

If you walk beside long grass just before haymaking time, these large Meadow Browns will fly up in dozens

By lunch time he was eating his sand-
wiches in the sunshine, with Mountain
Ringlets flying all around him

flies in case he should lose the pathway.
Of course he did not see a single
butterfly, let alone a Mountain
Ringlet.

That evening he talked it over with
the hotel proprietor, who warned him
that he would have to be very patient,
as so often the top of this mountain
was hidden in clouds. And then one
morning he awakened to find that the
whole valley was misty and grey, and
it at once gave him an idea. In

Switzerland it is often beautifully
sunny in the mountain resorts while
the valleys are hidden below the
clouds, and so he thought he would
climb this Scottish mountain path once
again, just on the chance that it would
be sunny above. He was right, and by
lunch time was eating his sandwiches in
the warm sunshine with Mountain
Ringlets flying all around him. And
then a very curious thing happened.
A tiny cloud passed across the face of
the sun and almost in a flash all the
butterflies were gone. It made him
laugh, because it reminded him so
much of the way rabbits bolt down
their holes at any sign of danger.
Obviously these butterflies thought
the bad weather was going to return
and hurried for shelter deep down

amongst the grass and heather. But as soon as the sun came out again they were flying as merrily as before.

Perhaps the prettiest of all the butterflies to watch are the Hairstreaks, but you need a pair of good binoculars to see their antics clearly. The Green Hairstreak is the commonest and most easy to find, and this is the best way to set about it. Walk along the sunny side of a lane in May, just about the time the hawthorn bushes are coming into flower, and tap the bushes with a long stick as you pass by. The undersides of their wings are the same green as the leaves of the hawthorn, and so they usually choose a twig of this bush to settle upon. All at once one or two will flip out looking like bits of leaf rising in the air, but instead of falling like leaves, they will loop the loop, twist and turn, and weave a hundred patterns in the sky, all in a minute!

If you watch carefully you will notice that each butterfly returns to the same leaf upon which it was sitting when you disturbed it.

And then there are the Blues. All day long they dance from flower to flower in the meadows and on the chalk hillsides, but when evening comes they get tired and settle down on the grass stems.

You may come upon them in little groups on a late summer evening just as the sun is slipping behind the horizon, dozens of them clinging to the grass stems, one above the other, like people who live in flats in a town. They look just like tiny living jewels with their scintillating blue wings wide open to catch the last rays of the sun. And then, as the light fades, they slowly close their wings over their backs, and all their beauty is hidden until the sun brings them to life again on the morrow.

Perhaps you will be more interested in butterflies than you were before. If so, treat them gently and do not catch them unless you are a real collector, and unless you have learned something about these wonderful creations of Nature. It is a pity to catch these beautiful wild creatures just for fun.

You may come upon the Blues, on a late summer evening, clinging to the grass stems, one above the other

OUTDOOR GAMES

By David Rodney

FOX AND GEESE

MARK out two bases in chalk about twenty feet apart. One player is chosen to be the fox and stands between these bases. The other players are the geese and half of them stand in one base and the rest in the other base.

The geese try to run from one base to the other without being caught by the fox, who chases them as soon as they come out of their base. Once they have come out of their base they must continue across to the other base and are not allowed to run back to the one from which they started.

Any geese caught by the fox must help him to catch the other geese, so that it soon becomes very difficult for the remaining geese to get across without being caught.

SUNDAY, MONDAY

Up to seven players can play this ball game. Each player takes the name of a day of the week and " Sunday " begins by throwing the ball up against a wall. As he throws it he calls out the name of a weekday.

The player whose name is called has to catch the ball before it falls to the ground, and if he succeeds he then throws the ball up again and names another day. If he misses it, however, he must quickly pick it up and try to hit one of the other players, who have in the meantime run as far away as possible. They must stop running as soon as he has picked up the ball, and they must stand still while he throws it.

If he hits one of them, that player loses a life, but if he misses, then it is he who must lose a life. The game then continues as before, and he throws up the ball to the wall again, calling out another day.

Each player has three lives, and is out when he has lost all three.

SNATCH THE HANDKERCHIEF

The players are divided into two teams, which stand facing each other twenty yards apart. A handkerchief is placed on the ground in the centre of the space between the teams. The members of the teams are numbered from one onwards, so that there are two players, one from each team, with the same number.

To start the game, a number is called out and immediately the two members of the teams bearing that number rush forward to snatch the handkerchief. The first one to pick it up must then run back to his team with the handkerchief, without being caught by the other player. If he succeeds, his team scores a point, but if he is caught by the player from the other team, then that team scores

the point. The team with the highest number of points at the end of the game is, of course, the winning one.

FOLLOW MY LEADER

Choose a good leader for this game. He is allowed to go anywhere he likes and perform any actions he likes with his arms and legs. For instance, he can skip, or run, or hop, circle his arms above his head, and so on. He must remember not to do " stunts " that are too difficult for some of the followers to try, particularly if some of the players are younger ones.

The others, of course, have to copy him and follow him wherever he goes.

EGG CAP

Here is a game for boys. Put a row of caps against a wall, each one touching the next, and draw a line about five yards away from the caps.

Now stand behind the line, and try to throw a ball into one of the caps. If you succeed, the owner of the cap must run quickly to pick up the ball, while you and the other players run away as far as possible. As soon as he has picked up the ball, the others must

Follow my Leader

stop running and stand still while he tries to hit one of them with the ball by throwing it from where he has picked it up. If he hits one of them, a stone is placed in the cap of the player he has hit, who is the next to throw the ball at the caps. If he misses, he must have the stone in his cap and throw the ball again.

If any player misses all the caps when throwing he has an " egg " in his cap. Three of these in a cap mean that the owner is out of the game.

TOM TIDDLER'S GROUND

Tom Tiddler has a large base with boundaries marked out with chalk. The other players walk into his territory saying, " I'm on Tom Tiddler's ground, picking up gold and silver."

As soon as they set foot on his ground, Tom Tiddler chases them and tries to catch them before they can escape over his boundaries. If he succeeds in catching one, that player has to become the new Tom Tiddler.

I SPY

A base or " Home " is chosen and then half the players go off and hide, the others giving them two or three minutes. Then they start to look for those in hiding, spreading out and proceeding separately. Each of the seekers moves forward very cautiously and as soon as he spots a hider he calls out " I spy Tom Jones behind the oak tree," or wherever he may be hiding.

If this is correctly called out, the one in hiding must come out and chase the seeker, and if the latter is caught before reaching " Home " he is out of the game.

If the person in hiding is seen in the open, the cry is given " Home for ——!" calling his or her name. It is a good plan to leave one seeker at " Home " to spot those in hiding who may come out into the open and try to cut off some of the seekers. He can then shout the warning to the seekers, so that they can get " Home " without being caught.

When all the seekers are " Home " or caught it is their turn to hide.

STEPS

One of the players stands with his face to a wall or fence, and the rest of the players stand behind a line chalked about twenty yards away from him. While he is facing the wall they creep up silently and cautiously. Suddenly he turns round and they all stand quite still. Any one who is caught moving has to go back to the starting line and begin again.

The game continues, the players advancing step by step and the player at the wall trying all sorts of tricks to catch them out. For instance, he may turn round and then do so again immediately after turning back, thus often catching the players as they begin to move. The first player to get

I Spy

up to him and touch him without being seen takes his place at the wall.

A LETTER TO MY LOVE

All the players except one stand in a circle with hands joined. The one left outside the circle takes out his handkerchief and walks round the circle saying, " I sent a letter to my love and on the way I dropped it. Someone must have picked it up and put it in his pocket."

Then he touches each one he passes on the shoulder with the handkerchief, saying " It isn't you." Suddenly, after he has been saying " It isn't you " several times, he drops the handkerchief on the shoulder of one and says " It *is* you." Then he starts to run round the circle.

The one left with the handkerchief seizes it quickly and runs round the circle in the opposite direction. Whichever reaches the gap first, joins the circle, and the other has to go round with the handkerchief as before.

TWOS AND THREES

The players pair off and the couples stand in a ring facing the centre, one standing in front of the other, except for one couple. One of these is the catcher and he chases the other and tries to catch him.

The one who is being pursued runs off and dodges until he has an opportunity to run in front of one of the couples in the circle. As soon as he stands in front of this couple the one at the back must run off quickly before being caught by the pursuer, and he in his turn stands in front of one of the other couples as soon as he gets the chance.

If any one is caught, of course,

he will become the catcher and pursue the one who has caught him.

JUMPING THE ROPE

One player stands in the centre of a ring of players with a length of rope, to the end of which is attached a bean bag or something similar. He swings the rope round until it reaches the players' ankles so that they have to jump each time it goes round the circle. If any one fails to clear the rope, he is out, and the one in the centre starts to swing the rope again.

FEET OFF THE GROUND

In this form of " He," as soon as any one has his feet off the ground he is safe, but as soon as he stands on the ground again he is liable to be caught.

SHADOW HE

This is a game for a sunny day when the players' shadows are clearly marked on the ground. It is played like ordinary " He," except that the catcher has to step on one of the shadows instead of touching another player. As soon as he does this, the one whose shadow is stepped on becomes " He."

CHAIN TAG

Every one knows how to play " He " or " Tag," of course, in which one player has to chase the others until he catches one of them.

Chain Tag is a slightly different way of playing this. One of the players is chosen to be " He " as usual, but when he catches one of the others, that player has to join hands with him and they chase the rest together.

As other players are caught they must join the chain, and so on until

Feet off the Ground

the last one is caught. The chain must not be broken and if any break off, the rest must wait until they have joined on again.

The last one to be caught is " He " next time.

TOUCH WOOD

This is another form of " He " or " Tag," the difference being that immediately any one touches wood he is safe and cannot be caught. When he stops touching wood he can be chased and, if caught, becomes " He."

HOT RICE

An old tennis racket and a ball are needed for this game. One player takes the racket and another the ball. The latter stands about five yards away and tries to hit the legs or feet of the other player, who defends himself with the racket. The ball must strike *below* the knee to count as a hit.

The player with the racket hits the ball away as far as possible, since he is not allowed to move his feet, and all the other players are clustered round him ready to field the ball and throw it at him again. They also are not allowed to move, once they have picked up the ball. When the ball is picked up near the defending player he must be very skilful to ward it off.

If he is hit, he must immediately drop the racket on the ground. The player who hit him with the ball now rushes to pick up the racket, but directly he has done so, the other players try to hit him, in his turn, with the ball. If they succeed, he must again drop the bat in favour of the one who hit him, who then rushes to pick it up himself.

If any player sends up a catch when defending himself, the same rule applies as if he had been hit, and the catcher runs to try to pick up the bat.

THE FARMER WANTS A WIFE

First the farmer is chosen, and then the others form a circle round him, joining hands. They walk round in this circle, singing:

> The farmer wants a wife,
> The farmer wants a wife,
> Hey, ho, hey, ho,
> The farmer wants a wife.

When they have finished singing this verse, the farmer selects a wife from the circle, and she joins him in the centre. The others then continue:

> The wife wants a child,
> The wife wants a child,
> Hey, ho, hey, ho,
> The wife wants a child.

The wife then chooses a child to join the family in the centre and the next verse is sung:

> The child wants a nurse,
> The child wants a nurse,
> Hey, ho, hey, ho,
> The child wants a nurse.

After the child has chosen her nurse, the other players sing:

> The nurse wants a dog,
> The nurse wants a dog,
> Hey, ho, hey, ho,
> The nurse wants a dog.

Then the dog is chosen and the fun begins. The players break from their circle, singing:

> We all pat the dog,
> We all pat the dog,
> Hey, ho, hey, ho,
> We all pat the dog.

and as they do so they all crowd round the dog and try to pat him, while he tries to escape. His only consolation is that he knows he will be allowed to be the farmer in the next game.

BROKEN BOTTLES

The players stand in a circle, each one a few yards apart, and one of the players holds a tennis ball, or a ball of that size. He begins by throwing it to the player nearest to him, who

Broken Bottles

he must kneel on one knee and catch with one hand, and if he fails again must kneel on two knees. There he stays until he catches the ball with one hand. Each time he succeeds in catching the ball, he is allowed to go back to the stage before. He is only allowed to go back one stage at a time and if he drops the ball again, back he goes to his original position.

You will find that most of the circle will be bobbing up and down during the game, and only the very good catchers on their feet all the time.

SNAKE TAG

All the players form a chain by each putting his hands on the shoulders of the one in front. The front one now has to catch the one at the tail end, the front ones trying to help the catcher and the back ones trying to help the last one dodge. The unfortunate middle ones will find they can do very little but go where they are pulled and pushed.

The chain must not be broken, but if it does break, it must join up again before proceeding.

When the leader has caught the last one he goes to the end of the chain and in turn has to dodge a new catcher. The game goes on like this until every one has had a turn at catching and being caught.

PAPER CHASE

Two players are chosen to be the hares, or only one if there are not many players. The hares are armed with a satchel of small pieces of paper and they start off while the hounds stay behind and count one hundred, then they set off in pursuit of the hares.

The hares must leave a trail of paper

throws it in turn to the next, and so on round the circle. The ball must be thrown fairly, and " No ball " is called when a bad throw is made.

If any one drops the ball, he must pick it up and throw as usual, but the next time it is his turn to catch it, he must catch it with one hand only. If he succeeds in doing so, he can return to catching the ball with two hands as before. If he again drops it, however, which can be followed, but they may try all sorts of tricks, such as going up a lane and then coming back, so as to baffle the hounds. If they are able to get home without being caught, they are the winners, but if the hounds catch them the game is over and they return home with the hounds.

This game can be played with the hares using chalked arrows instead of laying a paper trail.

FLOWER-POT RACE

Each player has two small flower-pots. These are turned upside down and long pieces of string are threaded through the holes, with large knots at the bottom to prevent them from being pulled through the holes.

At the word " Go," the players stand on their flower-pots, one foot on each, and then they move the pots forward by the string, one at a time, each time balancing on the pot which is not being moved. In this way they walk forward to the finishing post. If any one falls off the flower-pots, he or she must go back to the starting line and begin again.

LEG AND EAR RACE

The players must hold the left leg with the right hand, and the right ear with the left hand, and at the signal must hop all the way to the finishing line without letting go either the ear or the leg. Any one who is unable to do so must go back to the starting line and begin again.

BEAN-BAG RACE

The players are divided into two teams, each of which lines up one behind the other and facing the front. The leader of each team has a bean-bag

and on the word " Go," he throws the bean-bag over his head to the next player, who has to catch it and throw it on in the same way to the next player, and so on along the line.

When it reaches the last player, the team all stand with legs wide apart and he crawls through their legs to the front of the team. There he throws the bean-bag over his head again to the former leader, and it travels up the line again, the last player crawling through the legs as before. This goes on until the original leader is once more back in his place in front of the team.

THREE-LEGGED RACE

In this race the players are divided into couples, and the inside feet of the two players are tied together, so that they only have three legs between them. In this way they must run the race, being careful to keep in step, or they will soon be left behind by their more expert rivals.

POTATO RACE

Place a row of about five potatoes for each player. The potatoes should be about two feet apart, the first one of each row being level with the others, so that the players all have the same distance to run. The starting line is drawn about ten yards from the nearest potatoes.

Each player is given a teaspoon, and at the word " Go," runs up to the first potato, picks it up with the spoon, and carries it back behind the starting line. Having done this, he runs back to pick up the second potato, and so on, until all the potatoes have been picked up and carried safely behind the line. If the potato rolls off the spoon on the

Bean-bag Race

way back, the player must pick it up again with the spoon and then continue the journey.

The players must not touch the potatoes with anything else but the spoon and they are not allowed to push them along the ground.

LEAP-FROG RACE

The players are divided into two teams, each with about eight members; everyone bends over to make a back, except the last two members of the teams. There should be enough room between each player to allow a proper landing. At the word "Go," the last player leap-frogs as quickly as he can over all the backs, and when he has finished, he calls out "Go" to the next player and immediately bends over to make a back himself. The next player does the same, and so on until all the players have had a turn at "leap-frogging," the winning team, of course, being the one to finish first.

WHEELBARROW RACE

This is a race for pairs, one of each pair being the wheelbarrow and the other the one who pushes it. The wheelbarrow puts his hands on the ground and his partner then lifts him by the ankles. At the word "Go," he walks forward on his hands. No other part of his body touches the ground, and his partner gives him whatever help he can by pushing him from the ankles. If any of the couples tumble over, they must go back to the starting line and begin all over again.

Wheelbarrow Race

THE SILVER CANDLESTICKS

By Martin Armstrong

IT was half past ten on a warm night in June. Diana and Ronnie had gone to bed at least two hours ago and were fast asleep. Cookie and Elsie had gone to bed too, leaving the kitchen deserted; but there were still four people in the drawing-room —Peckham, the dog, who lay curled up, nose to tail, at one end of the hearthrug; Mompty, the cat, who sat bolt upright at the other end, with eyes half-closed, thinking her own thoughts; and Mum and Dad, who sat reading in their chairs. At least, Mum was reading, but Dad was lying back with his mouth wide open and his eyes shut and his book on the floor beside his chair. He was snoring loudly. Mum glanced at him thoughtfully. " No," she said to herself, " you can't call that reading; in fact, he might just as well be in bed," and she began to wake him up.

" Dad!   Da-a-ad!"   she called. " Wake up, Dad!"

Dad wriggled, made a peculiar face and opened his eyes. " Yes? No! What's that?" he mumbled. " Oh! All right!   Coming!" And then his eyes settled on Mum. " What's the matter now, Mum?" he said.

" The matter is," said Mum, " that you must wake up. It's time to go to bed."

" Wake up?" replied Dad indignantly. " I haven't been to sleep."

" Haven't you?" said Mum. " Then why is your book lying on the floor, and why have you been snoring for the last twenty minutes?"

" Oh, very well!" said Dad. " Have it your own way. The truth is, I suppose, that *you're* feeling sleepy. All right, I'll come, if I can get myself out of this chair." He yawned loudly and then turned to Mompty and Peckham. " Now then, you two animals, wake up! It's bedtime. Now Peckham, uncurl yourself!"

Peckham opened one eye and groaned. " O bones," he grumbled, " why can't you leave a dog alone?"

Dad turned his attention to the cat. "As for you, Mompty, you ought to have been on duty in the garden an hour ago. Goodness knows what the mice will be doing to the vegetables."

Mompty glanced at him scornfully. "I know that, Dad, but if you don't open the door, what's a cat to do?"

"You can ask him to, can't you?" snapped Peckham.

"Ask him to?" said Mompty. "What's the good of that? He never understands a word I miaou."

Mum went to the door. "Well, I'm going upstairs, Dad. Don't forget to lock up the house."

"Now I ask you, is that likely?" said Dad indignantly. "I've locked up this house every night for twelve

At some unearthly hour or other, Peckham began to bark

years. Three hundred and sixty-five days in a year. . . . Call it three hundred and fifty. . . . Twelve fives, sixty; twelve threes, thirty-six, and six, forty-two. I've locked up this house, Mum, well over four thousand times. It's a wonder all the doors and windows aren't worn out. And you say 'Don't forget!' Now, Peckham, into the kitchen with you. Come on, Mompty, I'll open the back door for you." As he spoke, Dad staggered down the passage into the kitchen and then opened the back door. "Now," he said to Mompty, "there you are. Good night, and good sport."

"Thanks, Dad," said Mompty, as she slipped out, "and good night."

"Now Peckham," said Dad, "get into your basket. Good night."

"Same to you, Dad," said Peckham, as he curled himself up.

Dad plodded upstairs and in half an hour there wasn't a sound in the house except the quiet breathing of Mum, Diana, Ronnie, Cookie and Elsie, the less quiet snoring of Dad and Peckham and, from time to time, those strange night noises that are heard in every house—a wheeze from a loose floor-board in the passage, an occasional hiss or chuckle from the cistern as if it were enjoying some joke it had heard during the day, a subdued bump from a hot-water pipe, a dry creak from the wicker chair in the hall as if some invisible body had sat down in it. Then, at some unearthly hour or other, Peckham began to bark. He might have barked his head off, for all the good it would have done, if it hadn't been for Mum. She heard him and woke up. Not only that: she woke Dad. "Dad! Dad!" she said, digging him in the ribs. "Wake up!"

"Eh? What? Whadjersay?"

"I said 'wake up.'"

"What, again? What's the good of my going to sleep if you keep on saying 'wake up'?"

"Peckham's barking," said Mum.

"Well, let him bark."

"Certainly not. He'll wake the whole house. Besides, he must have a reason for barking."

"Well," said Dad, "we'll ask him the reason in the morning."

But Mum persevered. "I think you ought to go down and see, Dad; I really do."

Dad sighed. "I wish you'd think *you* ought to go down and see, Mum. However, I suppose I've got to go." Yawning and groaning, he got out of bed. "Heavens," he moaned, "I wish I were a woman."

After a good deal of groping he arrived in the kitchen. "Now then, Peckham," he said sharply, "what's all this about? There I was, having a well-earned sleep, in fact, bang in the middle of my beauty sleep, and you must needs wake Mum. What on earth's the matter with you?"

"Bow wow," said Peckham.

"Dinner?" said Dad. "Nonsense! You had a huge dinner in the middle of the day."

"Bow wow. Bow wow. Bow wow," replied Peckham.

"Want to go out?" said Dad. "At this time of night? Certainly not! You're not a cat, are you? Or a bat? Or an owl? No! Very well, shut up! Not another sound. You understand? Not another sound."

Peckham did understand (which was more than Dad had done) and there was not another sound, except the quiet sound of people sleeping and

"Now then, Peckham," Dad said sharply, "what's all this barking about?"

the house living its slow, regular life.

Next morning was Sunday and breakfast was comfortably late. When Dad came downstairs, he met the two animals in the hall. Having wished each other a hearty good morning, they all made for the dining-room door. As usual, Peckham barged in first, and as usual Mompty stood politely aside to let Dad pass and then followed him. They found Elsie putting breakfast on the table.

"Ah, good morning, Elsie," said Dad cheerfully.

"Good morning, sir," said Elsie, and then, after a moment's hesitation, she added: "If you please, sir, have you taken the candlesticks off the sideboard?"

"The candlesticks?" said Dad. "Certainly not, why do you ask?"

"Because they're not there, sir," said Elsie.

"No more they are," said Dad. "Animals, can you explain?"

Mompty and Peckham both replied in their own languages, which Dad always pretended to understand. "No suggestions?" he said. "Then

Good morning, young 'uns," said Dad. "Here's a conundrum for you!"

no doubt Mum will know. She probably carried them off to polish them."

"Well, I made sure you or the missus must have taken them," said Elsie, "when you came down early this morning."

"Early this morning?" said Dad. "What ever do you mean, Elsie? Have you ever known me come down early on a Sunday morning? The idea! What put it into your head?"

"The window, sir," said Elsie. "I found it open when I drew the curtains this morning."

"The window open?" said Dad, horrified. "How open?"

"Wide open, sir," said Elsie. "Pushed up as far as it would go."

At that moment Mum and the two children came into the room. Dad turned to them. "Hallo, Mum! Good morning, young 'uns! Here's a conundrum for you. Elsie found that window wide open this morning and the four silver candlesticks have

vanished from the sideboard. Now what's the answer? Did you take them away last night to polish them, Mum?"

"Of course I didn't," said Mum. "I don't polish silver candlesticks in the middle of the night."

"Then what about you kids?"

asked Dad. " Diana, is this a feeble attempt to make April fools of us?"

" No, Dad," said Diana. " Besides it isn't April Fool's Day."

" That's true," said Dad. " Then what about *you*, Ronnie? Have you melted them down to make tin soldiers?"

" No, Dad," said Ronnie. " I don't know how, worse luck, or I would."

Dad looked very serious. " Then it looks as if we'd had a burglar."

"A *burglar*?" said Diana, delighted. " You mean to say there's been a burglar in this house?"

" I *say*," shouted Ronnie, " what fun! A real, live burglar?"

" Well," said Dad, " real enough and live enough to carry off four heavy silver candlesticks."

"A burglar! I *say*!" Ronnie danced about with glee. " Tony Bright's father was in a railway-accident last week, but a burglar's better than that, isn't it, Di? Do you think he had a dark lantern, Dad?"

" And a mask?" said Diana. "And a . . . what's it called? . . . a jemmy? What *is* a jemmy, Dad?"

Dad hummed and hawed and looked rather embarrassed. "A jem-my, my child," he said at last, " is an instrument used by burglars."

" Yes, but what sort of an instru-ment?" asked Ronnie.

" Well," replied Dad, " haven't I just told you? An instrument used by burglars! Just as a piano is an instrument used by pianists. You can't expect me to describe the thing completely: it would take *hours*."

" The truth is, Ronnie," said Mum, " your father doesn't know exactly what a jemmy is, and I'm afraid he's trying to pretend he does."

" Then do *you* know, Mum?" asked Diana.

" No, my dear," said Mum, " I don't. And I'm not ashamed to say so. Well, burglar or no burglar, I'm going to have my breakfast, and if you children want any, you'd better sit down quickly."

As they went to their places, Dad had an idea. " One moment! I think I'll just ring up the police." He went over to the telephone and this is what the rest of the family heard, as they sat eating their breakfast:

" Hallo, Hal . . . lo! Can I have the police station, please? Yes, police station! P for past participle; O for mouth organ; L for oranges and lemons; I for I'm-in-a-hurry; C for Mompty, I mean cat, and E for enny-thing you like. Right! Thank you. Hallo! Oh, good morning, Sergeant. Mr. Jackson of The Laurels speaking. We seem to have had a burglary here. Our maid found the dining-room window wide open this morning and four silver candlesticks are missing from the sideboard. Good! Good! What time did you say? Right! Goodbye!" Dad left the telephone and went to his place. " He'll be round in ten minutes," he told them.

" Then get on with your breakfast, all of you," said Mum, " or we shan't be finished before he comes."

But before they had finished, there was a ring at the front-door bell and Elsie showed Sergeant Blower into the dining-room. He was a plumpish person with a pleasant red face, very much the same shape as the moon, and a dark little moustache. Dad jumped up politely from his chair. " Ah, good morning, Sergeant. Sorry to disturb you so early on a Sunday morning."

"The window was shut and fastened last night, I presoom?" said the Sergeant

"That's all right, sir," said Sergeant Blower. He bowed to Mum. "Good morning, Madam."

"Good morning, Sergeant," said Mum. "I'm afraid all this excitement about the burglar has made breakfast rather late. Would you like us to . . .?"

But the Sergeant held up his hand. "Don't you trouble about me, Madam. You go on with your breakfasts and I'll just put a few questions to Mr. Jackson." He took out a notebook from his pocket and turned to Dad. "Now, sir; this is the room, I take it, where the burglary occurred."

"That's right, Sergeant," replied Dad. "There's the sideboard, behind you, and that's the window in question. Our maid declares she found it wide open at the bottom when she drew the curtains this morning."

The Sergeant inspected the window. "And it was shut and fastened last night, I presoom?" he asked.

"Undoubtedly," said Dad. "I always go round myself, last thing at night, and lock the outer doors and shut and fasten all the ground-floor windows."

The Sergeant raised his eyebrows. "And you rec'lect shuttin' and farstenin' this perticklar window last night, sir?"

"Well . . . well . . . well, I won't say that, Sergeant," Dad replied. "The fact is, I do it automatically. I've done it, year in and year out, for the last twelve years. I don't suppose you remember taking off your boots last night, but there can't be the slightest doubt you did so!"

"And, if you recollect, Dad," Mum

remarked, " I specially reminded you last night." She turned to Sergeant Blower. " So it isn't very likely he'd forget, is it, Sergeant?"

" No, I should say not, Madam," said the Sergeant. " But had you any perticklar reason for remindin' 'im?"

" None whatever!" said Mum. " It's simply a bad habit of mine. I'm always reminding people to do the things they never forget."

The Sergeant turned to Dad. " It's curious this should 'ave 'appened last night, Mr. Jackson," he said, " because the constable on dooty tells me he inspected the front of this 'ouse, but omitted to go round to the back. Instead of doin' the job proper, he just tried the front door and then walked up the garden and out at the top. Now if 'e'd gone round to the *back* he might 'ave noticed that winder— might even 'ave 'ad the luck to catch the feller at the job. Well now, I'd like to 'ave a look outside, if you don't mind."

" By all means," said Dad. " I'll show you the way round. Come along."

As soon as Dad and the Sergeant had left the room, Diana and Ronnie jumped from their chairs. " Can I go with them, Mum?" asked Diana.

" And me too?" asked Ronnie.

" Well, you can come with me, children," said Mum. " We must keep out of Sergeant Blower's way. I expect he'll be on the lookout for footprints. Come along and shut the door after you. We don't want those two animals scratching about."

Diana and Ronnie jumped up from their chairs

And as soon as the door was closed, Mompty turned to Peckham. "Well," she said scornfully, "did you ever hear anything like it?"

"Like what?" said Peckham.

"All that talk about Dad having shut the window," said Mompty.

"Well," said Peckham, "didn't he shut the window?"

"Not he," said Mompty with a snigger. "When he let me out last night it was raining, so I wandered round the house, just on the chance, and bless me if that window wasn't wide open. So I jumped up, pushed through the curtain, and sheltered in here for an hour or so."

"Hm!" said Peckham doubtfully. "I didn't hear you."

"Of course you didn't," said Mompty. "I'm not one to stamp my feet and bang into things."

"But I heard the burglar all right," said Peckham, "and I smelt him too."

"Did you now?" replied Mompty. "Then why didn't you mention it at the time?"

"Mention it?" said Peckham. "I mentioned it till I was hoarse, but what's the good of mentioning things to human beings? You should have heard Dad. 'I heard a stranger in the dining-room,' I said. 'Dinner?' said Dad. 'Dinner at this time of night?' 'Dinner be blowed,' I said. 'Can't you hear what I say? There was a stranger in the dining-room when I first shouted to you. He's gone now, of course.' 'Want to go out?' says Dad. 'Certainly not!' Well, there you are. That's all that comes of mentioning things. I might as well mention them to the moon. Just jump on to the window-sill, Mompty, and see what they're doing outside."

When the door was closed, Mompty turned to Peckham

Mompty shook her head. "Better not! They'd see me. Ah, there they are, right up against the window. Listen; I can hear them talking."

Both the animals listened hard, and this is what they heard.

"Yes, Mr. Jackson, 'e's flattened out this flower-bed proper."

"He has indeed, Sergeant. He's smashed a couple of my best snapdragons, the clumsy beast."

"Hm, yes! Well, I'll just take one or two measurements. U . . . m! I'm not so good at bendin' down as what I used to be. Now, what's this? Fifteen hinches. Yes, and seven and an 'arf, as near as makes no matter. Now, where's me notebook and pencil? 'Ere we are. 'Two snapdragon plants flattened out in border, fifteen and seven and an 'arf inches respectively from 'ouse wall. Soil trampled considerable. Traces of mud on

Peckham, with his tail proudly raised, came scrambling

winder-sill.' Well, Mr. Jackson, I think I've got all the necessary hinformation. I'll be getting along now, and when I've somethin' to report, I'll let you know."

Sergeant Blower departed and life at The Laurels went on as usual, except that there were no candlesticks on the dining-room sideboard.

In the afternoon the whole family went out on to the lawn to play cricket; that is to say, Mum, Dad, Diana, Ronnie and Peckham played cricket, while Mompty, very proud and self-contained, sat at the foot of the cherry-tree watching the proceedings with half-closed eyes. She didn't attempt to hide her disgust. Diana was batting, Dad bowling, while Mum, Ronnie and Peckham were fielding. After ten minutes or so,

Dad decided it was time that Diana was bowled out, and so, with a deadly eye fixed on the wicket, he bowled her a tremendously fast ball, so fast that Diana didn't even see it coming. Before she knew where she was, it had hit her bat, knocked it out of her hands, and shot up high into the air. The fieldsmen watched it with every muscle braced. It sailed up in a long curve in the direction of Peckham, who stood with his head raised, eyes fixed on the ball, mouth open and tail stuck straight out behind. Down curved the ball. "Yours, Peckham! Yours!" everybody shouted, but Peckham took no notice. Then, just when it seemed too late, he gave a sudden jump and caught the ball in his mouth.

" Out! She's out, by Jove!" yelled

out of the bushes, dragging an old sack after him

Dad. "Well caught, Peckham! You couldn't have caught that, Ronnie."

"No, not in my mouth," said Ronnie. "But does it count out, Dad, if you catch it in your mouth?"

"Certainly," said Dad, "if you're a dog. If you don't believe me, look it up in the rules. Well, I must say, that dog ought to be playing for the county. Now, next in! Who is it? You, Ronnie."

Ronnie snatched the bat from Diana and ran to the wicket. "Give him a good hard one, Dad," shouted Diana, "like the one you gave me."

"Ready! Off you go, Dad!" called Ronnie. "As hard as you like."

Dad bowled another terrifically hard one and next moment there was a deafening smack and the ball went whizzing high over the lawn and over the flower-beds and plunged into the shrubs. "Well hit, Ronnie! Well hit!" cried Mum. "Why, it's a boundary. Fetch it, Peckham; good dog!"

Without a moment's hesitation Peckham was after it. "It's all very well to say 'Fetch it,'" remarked Dad, "but how on earth is he going to find it? Well, meanwhile I shall take a rest."

So saying, he flung himself full length on the grass and the others followed his example. Mompty, from where she sat under the cherry-tree, could hear Peckham rummaging about among the bushes. At last he came scrambling out. But he hadn't got the ball; he'd got something much bigger. With his head twisted on one side and his tail proudly raised he was dragging an old sack after him. Sometimes he trod on it and it pulled his legs out from under him, sometimes he turned round and towed it backwards. The others, lying flat on the lawn and staring up at the sky, hadn't noticed him; but Mompty had, and she sat watching him with a sneer on her face. "If only you could see what a fool you look," she remarked as he passed her.

"Grrr! Not such a fool as you," growled Peckham. "Why can't you join in games like any other decent animal?"

Then Diana caught sight of him. "I say," she shouted; "look at Peckham."

"What on earth has the dog got hold of?" asked Mum.

Dad sat up and stared. "Hi, Peckham! Fetch the ball! That's not the ball, you silly chump."

"But what is it?" said Ronnie. "Bring it here, Peckham. Bring it here, Peckham. Bring it here."

"No, Ronnie, no!" said Mum. "It's a filthy old sack."

"Wait a minute, though," said Dad. "It's got something in it. I can hear a rattling. Here, bring it here, Peckham. Good dog. That's right. Now, drop it. Diana, take it from him."

Diana took the sack from Peckham. "I say," she shouted, "What a weight! I think it must have bits of iron in it."

"Perhaps it's hidden treasure," remarked Ronnie.

Dad held out a hand. "Here, hand it over, Diana. Let's investigate." He got out his penknife, cut the string that was tied round the sack's mouth, and peered inside. "Well! Bless my

soul!" he said. "You're right, Ronnie; it's buried treasure and no mistake. There we are. One, two, three, *four*!"

As he spoke he took four heavy objects out of the sack and placed them on the lawn. "But, good heavens," exclaimed Mum, "it's the silver candlesticks. How on earth did they get there?"

"Burglar put 'em there, I suppose," said Dad.

"But why did he throw them into the bushes?" asked Diana.

"Well," replied Dad, "it looks to me as if he'd heard the policeman coming up the garden last night, just as he was making off with them, and chucked them into the bushes so as not to be caught red-handed. But what does it matter what the burglar did? The important thing is what that dog did. My dear Peckham, what can I say? How can we ever thank you? You're a dog in a thousand. Why, you're not only a first-class cricketer, but now you've also become a first-class detective."

Mompty turned up her nose. "Detective indeed! Rubbish! It was just a lucky accident. He wasn't looking for the candlesticks, he was looking for the ball."

"I know that," answered Peckham; "but why did I find the sack and not the ball? Tell me that."

"I've told you," Mompty snapped back. "You came on it by accident, and even when you did, you're not going to tell me you knew what was in it."

"Of course I did," said Peckham, "And I didn't find it by accident either. I had to have a jolly good hunt for it before I managed to find it."

" Well! Bless my soul! It's buried treasure and no mistake!"
cried Dad, as he pulled from the sack the four silver candlesticks

" Indeed?" replied Mompty loftily. " You'll be telling me next that you smelt the candlesticks inside it."

" So I did," said Peckham. " When I ran into the bushes I was sniffing for a cricket-ball. I admit that. But there wasn't a smell of cricket-ball. The whole place was full of a terrific smell of a burglar, the same as I smelt last night. So I followed that. It grew stronger and stronger, and at the place where it was strongest, there was the sack and there were the candlesticks. It's quite simple, Mompty, so long as you have two things."

" Really?" said Mompty coldly. "And what are *they*, pray?"

" A nose and brains," said Peckham; " especially brains. Do you hear that, my dear Mompty? *BRAINS*!"

THE GERMAN SPY GOES TO SCHOOL

By Bernard Newman

How would you like to be a spy? Before you answer, let me point out that your first job or assignment might not be very romantic. In fact, you would be sent to school!

In the spy thrillers or films, such a beginning is not necessary of course. In real life it is. You have seen the spy at work on the pictures. He is a master of disguises. He rushes into a room, disguised as a Chinaman. The police are after him, so he halts before a mirror. A few rapid passes with grease paint, some hurried shuffling with wigs and whiskers, and he goes out of the room disguised as a Russian, humming the Volga boat song and kicking the snow off his boots.

If you think you can get away with wigs and whiskers in the real thing, try them and see! The dangerous spy is no imitation of Conrad Veidt, but an ordinary man sitting behind a newspaper in a corner of a railway carriage —so ordinary that scarcely anybody would ever look at him twice. This is precisely why he is dangerous. One of the first lessons the spy must learn at his school is that he should always be ordinary.

It would be interesting, I think, to take you inside a German spy school. I once went to one myself, and some of my friends passed through such institutions quite recently, so I can give you a true picture. Let us consider the case of Hans Berger.

Hans had proved useful to the Berlin Gestapo by snooping around in his own district, reporting the opinions of his friends—even of his own family. Then it was discovered that he spoke fluent English—he had once been a steward on a famous transatlantic liner. Thus he was invited to " volunteer " for full-time secret service work.

He was instructed to report to a spy school. It did not look like one, as it was an ordinary country house about twenty miles outside Berlin. There a doctor gave him a thorough medical examination.

"Well, let's get a breath of air," said the doctor. "There are fine grounds here, and they are quite private, of course."

But as they walked across the park, Berger stopped short in horror. Three or four men were running across the grass, when a machine gun fired on them. They fell to the ground abruptly, and lay still.

The doctor pounced on Berger

again, to test his pulse and heart. The "dead" men got up and walked away. The whole episode was planned to test the spy-recruit's nerve.

Now Hans Berger began his serious training. He lost his name and became Number 57. He was warned not to mingle with the other students—lest there should be a traitor among them! Every day he attended a dozen lectures, each followed by a keen examination. A spy must have a sound technical background, otherwise he may not understand the information he gathers.

From models, Berger was taught to identify British aircraft and warships.

Berger stopped short in horror

From captured weapons he was instructed in the mysteries of British guns, mortars and tanks.

At the same time, he attended a special class in colloquial English. The instructor pointed out that a spy can often pick up fragments of information in public houses—but he would give himself away if he were to say, " May I invite you to partake of refreshment?" Instead, Berger was taught to say, " Have this one with me."

It must have been strange, in the heart of war-time Germany, to hear the discussions between the spy and his tutor. Their subjects were the Derby, Arsenal and Aston Villa, rations, income tax, war savings and other points of ordinary conversation —including, of course, the weather!

Berger was warned about the extravagant use of disguise. He would adopt a certain character and would live it : that was the best disguise. With his steward's background he could pass himself off as a merchant seaman waiting for a ship. This would give him useful access to ports. He must *live* the part of the merchant seaman, and must never forget it.

This point is most important. *A spy can only make one mistake.* A German spy once limped up to a frontier, and was allowed to cross. Once over, he forgot to limp! If he had attended a good spy school, he would have put a pebble in his shoe, to remind him to limp.

" You must remember this, No. 57,"

The attack on the Mohne Dam

said the tutor one morning, talking to Hans Berger. "In wartime a spy's biggest difficulty is not to get information, but to get it home!"

This was the start to a series of lectures on codes and ciphers. The simplest letter code is the sliding alphabet. You write your alphabet out twice, sliding it one letter, like this:—

A B C D E F——
  a b c d e f——

Then you write b instead of a; c instead of b, and so on. Or you may slide your alphabet seven letters, or ten, as arranged with your confederate.

Berger, or No. 57, was given plenty of practice in the use of this code, but was warned that it was not foolproof. The British censor or counter-spy, coming across a jumble of letters, would attack it by means of what is called a frequency table.

Take a couple of pages at random from this book. You will find that the letter E occurs most frequently; next follows T, then A. The frequency table for the English language runs as follows:—

E T A O N I S H R D L C U
F M P B W G Y V K X Q J Z

Of course, it is not quite as simple as this. In your particular pages there might be more F's than C's, or K's than G's. Yet the idea is simple. From the jumble of letters in a spy message, the censor would pick out the one which occurred most frequently, and call it E, the next one T, and so on. In the later stages he would have to resort to trial and error, going down the scale a letter at a time. Yet the method is very sound. It is like doing a crossword puzzle; having found half the letters, it is fairly easy to fill in the rest.

Next, Hans Berger was taught some-

thing about the Playfair code, often used in the British army. It is not foolproof, but it depends upon a code-word which is changed every day.

He drew a large square and divided it into twenty-five smaller squares (I and J being counted as one letter). First he wrote down the code word, ignoring any letter which might be repeated, then followed the rest of the alphabet. As an example, take the code-word CHURCHILL. A covering letter would introduce this word quite naturally several times, and thus give the key to the code.

C H U R I
L A B D E
F G K M N
O P Q S T
V W X Y Z

The working of the code depends on rectangles. If the spy's message began with LY, he would write the letters at the opposite corners of the same rectangles—DV. Similarly, GT would become NP. If two letters come side by side, then those above or below are used. Thus AD would become GM, and MS would become NT. He is a very good spy who can solve this kind of code in his head, without putting anything on paper.

Another useful code is the columnar transposition. That sounds a bit steep but read it again and you will follow me. Here again a code word is necessary, and can be frequently changed.

"Suppose you had picked up information about the British attack on the Mohne dam," the tutor explained. "In your covering letter you mention the code word more than once—an ordinary word, containing all-different letters: SPECIAL, for example. Write down the word, and under each letter its numerical order in the alphabet:

S P E C I A L
7 6 3 2 4 1 5

" Now divide your message by seven, the number of the letters. Your message reads: Attack planned Mohne dam Saturday—29 letters; that is, four lines of seven, the odd one being left out. So write the first four letters under the figure 1, the next four under 2, and so on.

S P E C I A L
7 6 3 2 4 1 5
U M A C D A N
R S N K M T E
D A N P O T D
A T E L H A A

" Thus your message will read: umacdan rsnkmte danpotd atelhaa. That takes a bit of understanding!"

" The columnar transposition code can be worked another way," the tutor went on. " Write out your code word and numbers, then your message, like this:—

S P E C I A L
7 6 3 2 4 1 5
A T T A C K P
L A N N E D M
O H N E D A M
S A T U R D A

Then your message will read downwards, from 1 to 7, kdad aneu tnnt cedr pmma taha alos."

" There's one objection," said Berger. " It is so obviously a code, the censor would know that I'm a spy."

" Quite right, No. 57. Your letter, with the code word, will be quite ordinary. The code message will be in chemical ink—invisible ink, it is popularly called."

" Good."

" But before we pass on, I shall have

to set you an examination on codes. They are important."

Here are some of the questions from Berger's examination. You might care to tackle them.

1. A British spy was caught in France, just after he had tapped out the following message in Morse, on a short-range transmitter. He was acting under pressure and probably encoded hurriedly. Decipher the message:—

VYQP GYDC VVGT KGUY GUVQ HECN CKU.

2. You receive from another agent in England a casual letter in which the word " chose " appears twice. A number of letters are distinguished by tiny blots of ink from the others. They read:—

BIYAE EDBIS WTETC AMTOH RARRM.

Decipher the message.

3. Encode the following message in Playfair, using the code-word HIT-LER. Time allowed, 2 minutes. " British experimenting jet propelled plane."

4. Decipher the following message found on a British spy caught near Amiens:—

UENCOG HFCMLF OGPOND MCOGEQ.

Berger found that the first three problems were comparatively simple. The fourth was not! As a hint (which Berger did *not* get) I will say that it includes all three code methods described, and at one stage the letters were all reversed. The question gives a clue to the dominant code word.

Invisible ink is simpler than codes! You do not buy it at a stationer's shop, but make your own. Lemon juice is admirable for the job. Berger was shown how a sheet written over in

Secret Ink

lemon juice dried absolutely clean, but when a hot iron was run over it the writing appeared, faintly but legibly, in brown.

He was told that he would be supplied with the latest chemical ink. He would not carry it about in a bottle labelled " Secret Ink." Instead he would dip a handkerchief in a concentrated solution, let it dry, and dip it in warm water when he required a supply of invisible ink.

Potato pulp makes a good secret ink. So does a mixture of brandy and milk. Others are far more complicated, but all are dangerous. The censor also goes to school and learns a lot about inks: what the eye cannot see, the microscope can, for a *pen* makes faint scratches on the surface of paper. Berger was issued with a ball-pointed pen, which writes without making scratches. He was warned that it was dangerous, however, for its very possession was evidence that he was a spy.

He was instructed in unusual methods of carrying information. One Alsatian man used to carry messages inside his glass eye; a woman put them inside a hollow tooth, with a layer of gutta percha to keep them in place.

Here is a practical spy experiment which you may like to try out. Get a spot of vinegar from the pantry, and a little alum chipped off father's antiseptic shaving block. Mix the two. Now get a hard-boiled egg and write in large characters on the shell and leave it for 24 hours. There is nothing to be seen on the shell, but what you wrote on it will appear in black on the *white* of the egg when the shell is removed.

Actually, the best method of conveying information is by means of something that looks like an ordinary letter or cable. The following telegram reads like an ordinary business telegram—nonsense to anybody except the recipient but quite intelligible there. " Other sets only obtainable to employees. Obtain ten from Ashton. Atkins twice read inquiry at Lyons. If time, Ogden should attempt sell Irons as is likely extra ton at Sheffield held. Price spoils alliance talk until we ascertain allowance he offers at old basis. Use items on list. Agree this statement."

Now take the second letter of each word, and the hidden message is immediately revealed. Have you got it?

Berger was taught how to use a field radio, but was warned only to employ it on desperate occasions. The spy who has a wireless transmitter concealed in his chimney is a regular feature of rumour, but just does not exist. If the B.B.C. detector vans are delicate enough to discover if you listened without a licence, how much easier to trace the much greater power of an emitter? The spy who uses radio is just asking for trouble.

While Berger was undergoing this series of lessons and examinations, physical fitness was a special subject at the spy school, but he soon passed beyond the range of ordinary physical jerks.

One day he found himself wearing a pneumatic suit, inflated at all joints. He was placed in a contrivance rather like a juvenile roundabout, which began to revolve at a great pace. Suddenly his seat collapsed and flung him to the ground. The rubber suit protected him from serious injury, but after much practising he had to accomplish this feat without its help. Thus he was trained to jump from a moving car or train.

He was taught how to drive a dozen makes of British cars; he studied detonators and explosives for sabotage purposes. He was instructed in the art of spreading rumours which would lower British morale—for in wartime this is a recognized part of the spy's business.

One tutor after another told him to forget everything he had ever read in spy stories. He would pick up bits and pieces of information here and there, and would fit them together like the fragments of a jigsaw puzzle. One agent reports extensive troop movements in the south of England—he has heard a railwayman mention the numerous special trains; another gathers from a docker in a public house that ships are being loaded in unusual fashion; a third has picked up information that all the fighter squadrons are standing to. Each fragment by itself means nothing; together they point to an operation such as the Dieppe landing.

Finally, Berger was prepared for his " cover " profession, living for weeks with sailors so as to refresh his memory of their habits. Then he would be shipped into England, maybe posing as a Dutch refugee.

Would he be very successful? The answer is certainly a very big " No." The average life at large of German spies in Britain has been about twenty-four hours. Why?

There are many answers. The first is that the Germans are very inclined to think along one line, and their spies tend to use the same methods. In the First World War spies were taught to use foreign stamps. If a letter from Portsmouth contained four Peruvian stamps, six Colombian and ten Montevidean, that meant that there were four battleships, six cruisers and ten destroyers in Portsmouth harbour on that date. Unluckily for the Germans, we caught the first man to use this method—which meant almost auto-matically that we caught all his successors.

Secondly, the Germans are a strange mixture of cleverness and stupidity. They do amazing things and then forget some trifling detail. One of their agents completed the most dangerous part of his job—that of being landed on the English coast

He was trained to jump from a moving car

Every time a visitor came to the school the boy looked at his watch

from a seaplane. He wanted to travel about and so stole a bicycle from outside a public house. Then he forgot a detail—that our rule of the road was the opposite to the German. He rode off on the right hand side of the road! He was held up by a village policeman before he had covered a quarter of a mile.

There may be other reasons for German failures too. Let me tell you what happened in the First World War. The Germans established a spy school in Antwerp, where recruits were given a very intense training. The school was in an ordinary house, and the training was good, but every spy sent out from that school seemed to be caught within a week of arriving in Britain or France. The exasperated Germans never thought of looking in the street outside the door of the school, where Belgian boys played marbles. One of them had an ingenious camera which looked like a watch. Every time a visitor approached the school, the boy looked at his watch and took a photograph. Thus, over a period of time, we collected a series of portraits of all visitors to the spy school, and so could arrest all those who ventured abroad.

This was by no means the only example of juvenile aid in espionage. In the First World War Holland was neutral, and one of our biggest tasks was to get information over there from Belgium. The Germans put up banks of barbed wire, an electrified fence, pill-boxes, machine gun posts and the rest, but our information always got through.

One day a small Belgian boy was flying his kite when the string broke. The kite flew over the impassable

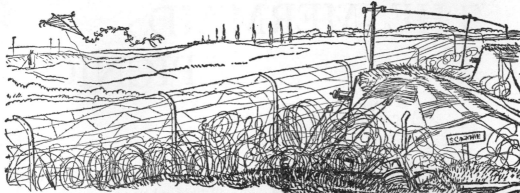

fence at the frontier, and the little boy cried. An elderly German soldier on guard had boys of his own, and gave him twopence to buy sweets for comfort.

After the war we gave him more than twopence. As the kite blew across the Dutch fields, two of our agents chased it. They took the pieces of paper which formed the tail, and ran hot irons over them. In the margins of the newsprint appeared details of German gun positions.

Another reason for German failure lies in the comparatively poor quality of the men they have used as spies. In the countries where they have been most successful they were able to persuade local quislings to work for them, but they found this almost impossible in Britain, where treachery is not one of our failings. The Germans decided to bribe neutrals, or even Dutch and Belgian criminals, to spy for them. Such men—usually poor types—often gave themselves away and sometimes gave their employers away as well!

The hireling spy is almost useless. The dangerous agent is the man who does the job for love of his country, and he needs some things that can never be taught him at a spy school: courage, resource and inventiveness.

The kite flew over the impassable frontier, and the little boy cried

A British spy is selected for these qualities *before* he goes to the spy school. And the course there is far more severe than it is in Germany, and his time at school is very much longer. After that comes a life of danger and interest, but—if he is a good spy—not of particular excitement. So would you still like to become a spy?

THE MERMAIDS' PICNIC

By Meryon Vance

THERE were once three mermaids, Marina, Serina and Fidra, who lived with their father, the Mer-King, beneath the Coral Sea.

Their palace was run like clockwork, for the Mer-King was served by shipwrecked sailors, and none can be more handy and useful than they. The rock gardens round the palace were polished every day and not a seaweed grew out of place. The isinglass windows shone, the floors were as white as snow, the cook was a famous Frenchman, the butler an English admiral.

"I know of no better training than his for such a job," the Mer-King used to say.

Every day the mermaids would take their tame turbots for a swim, wash their collections of coral, and play with their cat- and kitten-fish. In such a well-run household one day was the same as another and the three little mermaids grew bored.

"I think it would be nice to go for a picnic," said Marina one morning at breakfast.

"Well," said the king, "when I was young we found our pleasures at home; but Fortescue can put you up a basket."

"Aye, aye, sir," said the admiral.

"Where are you going, my dear?"

Now it is a well-known fact that human beings like to picnic in a place near water and get wet. Contrariwise, mermaids enjoy a picnic on dry land and getting dry.

"We thought of the Kwang Rock," said Marina.

"Oh well," said the Mer-King, "I don't admire your taste, but I suppose you'll be all right if you take the turbots with you. And you might give my poor old cod a run; he never gets proper exercise."

The cod, who was portly and fat, lay gaping under the table; hearing he was to go for a run, he wagged his tail so vigorously that the cups and saucers rattled. The three mermaids hated him. He swam so slowly and was always getting into trouble, so they determined to lose him on the Great Barrier Reef if they could. However, they said nothing about it.

"One thing I will not have," said the Mer-King, breaking his fourth seamew's egg. "I will not have any more shipwrecked sailors brought home; this house is overstaffed with them, isn't it Fortescue?"

"Aye, aye, sir."

"This egg is stale! Take it away! Why don't you get fresh ones?"

"It's the equinoctial gales, sir. They always upset them. We had them sent specially for you from China, sir."

The old cod wagged his tail so vigorously that the cups and saucers rattled

*He had a fascinating trick of doubling down his little finger flat on the
palm of his hand, whilst all his other fingers remained upright*

" I shall speak to your Uncle Neptune about it; it's disgraceful. Now off
you go and be good girls, and don't
forget the poor old cod!"

So the three mermaids set out with
their picnic basket, their turbots and
the cod.

"And I do wish," said Marina, "we
could find a new pet, for I do think

turbots are the stupidest things and
only want to fetch and carry seaweed."

By going just a little out of their
way they did manage to lose the old
cod on the Great Barrier Reef, and that
was one good thing.

The Kwang Rock is a solitary rock
now famous as the last home of the
kwang, a bird as rare as the dodo. At

the time of the mermaids' picnic nobody bothered about it at all except for Admiralty charts. As the mermaids drew near, they saw someone on the rock waving a flag made of clothing —a tall young man with a pleasant face and curly head, who looked anxious and thin.

"It's another shipwrecked sailor. What shall we do?" said Fidra.

"We can't leave him to starve, and we can't take him home," said Serena.

"We will have our picnic with him and keep him here," said Marina. "I expect there's lots of kwang's eggs for him to eat."

The stranger climbed down to the edge of the rocks and hastened to greet them.

"Why, you must be the mermaids I've heard so much of," he said. Then he helped them on to the rock and looked hungrily at the picnic basket.

"I expect you've been living on kwang's eggs," said Marina.

"If kwangs are the ungainly birds hopping around here, I have," he said. "This morning I came across a nest of such stale eggs I gave it up and I've eaten nothing since."

The little mermaids were sympathetic and soon laid out their sandwiches, and indeed let him eat the lot.

"It's fun finding you here," said Marina. "You aren't a bit like the sailors at home."

"I'm not a sailor, I'm an airman," said the young man, "and I must get back to my base. It was lucky for me I crashed near here and got washed up on this rock. But now that you've come it'll be all right. You'll send a ship to take me off."

The mermaids' faces all grew very long indeed at the thought of this.

"That would be a pity," said Marina, "when we've only just got to know each other, and might have such fun being friends."

"It would be wonderful," said the airman, "if you were always here. But you'll go home, and when I'm here alone living on kwang's eggs, it's different. Any storm might wash me off."

He told them his name was William and that he came from Brisbane, and the picnic was a great success. He showed them how to play ducks and drakes on the water with flat pebbles, and he had a fascinating trick of doubling down his little finger flat on the palm of his hand, whilst all his other fingers remained upright, and this trick no one else could do, although they tried very hard.

He could even induce the youngest turbot to leap out of the water over his hand.

"He's far nicer than catfish or tame cods," said Marina, as they swam home. "Let's keep him for our very own pet."

"I think we ought to go to Uncle Neptune and see he doesn't raise a storm. It would be awful if he got washed off," said Serena.

"And we shall have a picnic every day," said Fidra happily.

When they reached home, they found the old cod had got there first and told the Mer-King all about the Great Barrier Reef.

"Well, I think you girls are perfectly disgusting to treat a poor old cod like that," said the Mer-King. "You can go to bed without supper. Fortescue will send you up some limpet gruel."

They went happily to bed and didn't

care a bit—they were so excited about William.

The following morning Marina wanted another picnic and asked for twice as many sandwiches.

"Oh, I suppose so, if they're determined to make pigs of themselves," said the Mer-King, "but let there be no nonsense with the poor old cod today."

"We're going round by Uncle Neptune's; that's a long way for him," said Marina, "I don't suppose he'll keep up. The ship's doctor says he's got a weak heart."

"Poor old cod! I must have him seen to," said the king.

Marina was very firm with her uncle when they called on him.

"We're making a lovely rock-garden round the Kwang Rock, Uncle Neptune," she said. "When it's finished, you shall come and see it. But we don't want any storms there. It beats down the anemones so."

"Did you say the Bass Rock, or the Kwang Rock, my dear?"

"I said Kwang, K-W-A-N-G, where the funny birds are."

"Oh, there!" said Uncle Neptune. "Only you will remind me, won't you? All these rocks are so alike."

William was just as charming as ever. He had a number of tales to tell and taught them the ballad of Clementine, and how to play pitch and toss with a make-believe halfpenny.

"Now, be good girls, and don't forget to send a ship for me. You say you see lots," he said, when they were going.

"I do think it's rude of you to want to get away when we've only just got to know you," said Marina.

"But we could always be friends," said William. "My home is by the sea, and I could give you a picnic whenever you called."

"But it wouldn't be so nice as having you here to ourselves," said Marina.

"I don't call that friendship!" said William.

"You do make him angry, Marina," said Fidra, on the way home.

"I don't care," said Marina. "I've got him and mean to keep him. And if the Kwang Rock isn't safe, I'll put him somewhere safer."

So every day the mermaids picnicked and William told them tales and asked them to send him a ship, and they wouldn't. At last, they got so jealous of their new pet, they determined to move him. Marina thought he would be safest on an iceberg, and Serena on a

coral reef, and they quarrelled so violently about it that they missed three whole days of picnics; and Uncle Neptune made a big storm off the coast of Papua and wrecked a ship called the *Eleanor Jane*. And when he told them at supper, they yawned; they thought it had nothing to do with them and didn't even bother to be polite. And that was a pity, for it had more to do with them than they thought.

On the coast of Papua lived the good Bishop of Papua in a hut surrounded by palm trees. He had rescued so many sailors, that they built him a special chapel all made of ship's timbers, with a mast instead of a tower. Not only was the good bishop famous for his chapel, but he had the best collection of seabirds' eggs in Australasia, save one. That was owned by the ex-mayor of Brisbane, who had two kwang's eggs in his.

When the *Eleanor Jane* was wrecked, the bishop and his servants ran down to the shore to rescue whom they could. And when every one was going home, the bishop noticed another head bobbing about on the waves. He turned and plunged in, and after great exertion drew an old ship's carpenter to land.

Later, when the crew had recovered their health and strength, they came to thank the bishop, and last of all came the old ship's carpenter.

"Ah, my lord bishop," said the old

The bishop noticed another head bobbing about on the waves, so he plunged back into the water and brought an old ship's carpenter to land

man. " If I could only do something for your reverence."

" That's very good of you, my man," said the bishop, " but there's nothing."

" Not even some little thing, your reverence?"

The bishop wondered if it were possible. He had asked so many times in vain. Sailors didn't seem to notice things.

" I don't suppose you've ever come across a bird called a kwang?" he said.

" Why, your reverence, I was wrecked upon the very rock where they breed—the Kwang Rock—seven years ago!"

" Take me there and you have repaid me seventy times," said the bishop.

So they launched the mission-ship and, steered by the carpenter, they sighted the Kwang Rock on the third day of the mermaids' quarrel. A chill seized the heart of the bishop as they drew near. A figure was jumping over the rocks, waving to them, but it was not a kwang.

The bishop was the first to wade ashore, and William, all radiant with relief and happiness, grasped him by the hand.

" You've saved me, sir!" he said. Indeed, he had been three days without the mermaids' picnic-basket, and that morning had killed and eaten the last of the kwangs.

" I suppose you've found something to live on here, my boy?" said the bishop in a trembling voice.

" Oh, yes," said William. " It's been pretty awful. Kwang's eggs, you know. I ate the last yesterday; horribly stale!"

For a moment an awful temptation assailed the good bishop. This cheerful, destructive young man, the grave of all his hopes, let someone else rescue him —why not push off and leave him? But he put the matter aside and said kindly:

" Well, my boy, I expect you've had enough of it. We'd better be getting home."

Nor did they mention eggs again till William was fed and clothed and looking at his collection.

That very evening Marina, Serena and Fidra came to the Rock and found it empty. They sat down and cried, for they knew it was all their fault. After a time they saw someone walking round the rocks and found it was Uncle Neptune.

" Well, girls," he said, " I've come to see your rock-garden." Then they burst out crying afresh and told him all about it.

" Well," he said, " I don't think it was a nice way to treat a friend. You must give and take in friendship, you know. One can't have it all one's own way. But I'll tell you what I'll do. I'll give you each a nice cinder-fish from the Hawaiian Isles and you can call him William. And I'll take the old cod out every day for a run myself."

And Marina said: " Oh, Uncle Neptune, what a dear you are! I do think we've been perfectly horrid!' So the three mermaids were happy again, for though they had long tails they had very short memories.

And William returned to Brisbane and his uncle, the ex-mayor, gave him an excellent dinner but went to sleep over the wine while listening to his adventures. When William got to the part about the kwang's eggs, he woke up, however, and when he came to the part where the Bishop of Papua saved him, the ex-mayor listened hard. When he heard the words, "Well, my boy, we'd better be getting home," he jumped up crying:

"Is that all he said when you'd eaten the last? I couldn't have done it! I'll have to think this over."

Then he went to his safe and took out the two kwang's eggs, the gems of his collection. He took the one which was perfect, not the one with the almost invisible crack, for his godmother had brought him up well; and he packed it beautifully, and sent it by special messenger to the Bishop of Papua, with a note of thanks for sending his nephew back.

"For," he said, "no one but I will ever know what a good man he was."

The mermaids burst out crying afresh and told him all about it

IT LOOKS IMPOSSIBLE

By Lt.-Com. R. T. Gould, R.N. Retd.

"*I don't believe there's no such creature*"

MANY people make a habit of disbelieving, on principle, any statement which does not come within the range of their normal experience. To be convinced, they must see for themselves. Sometimes, they will not believe even then: you perhaps know the old story of the countryman who went to see the first giraffe ever brought to this country. He spent five minutes or so gazing at it open-mouthed, and when at last he recovered his speech, all he said was: "Well, I don't believe there's no such creature."

There is a story of a man who went out to India in the early days of "boneshakers" — primitive bicycles, mostly built of wood. While in England he had learned to ride one —and he regretted not having taken it abroad with him, since the station he was at possessed plenty of good, level roads. So he made working drawings of what he required (he was an engineer) and commissioned an Indian carpenter to build one for him. The Indian made quite sure that he understood what the sahib wanted; then he politely declined to tackle the job. He would gladly build a *three*-wheeled machine; but one with two only, and those in line, could not possibly stay upright—and he would have no hand in making a machine which was foredoomed to complete failure! It was at about the same period that a west-countryman, who lived miles from anywhere, ordered a "boneshaker"—he had heard of them, but never seen one. It duly arrived. After a time, as his neighbours never met him on the road with it, they began to ask how he was getting on. "Oh, I'm afraid I shall never learn to ride it. I haven't dared to get it moving yet, because I can't even balance it standing still!" Some people are like that—on the other hand there was a gamekeeper in the Isle of Skye who walked eight miles to the nearest town, bought a bicycle, and rode it home—never having ridden one in his life before! But men like that are rare—too many people find it hard to take in a new idea.

When Edison's European representative, Col. Gouraud, was demonstrating the newly-invented phonograph to the Paris Academy of Sciences in 1878, one of the members, Professor Bouilland, made a fearful scene, and finally stormed out, denouncing the machine as a barefaced imposture!

Have you ever seen a rubber ball spinning and balancing on top of a jet of water? One would have expected it to be flung violently away—yet there it stays, rising and falling, but always hugging the jet. The whole thing seems not far short of a miracle, yet of course the ball must balance there—you can prove that mathematically. Incidentally, a very striking feature of one of the early exhibitions at the Crystal Palace was a large ball, a couple of feet or so in diameter, spinning away several feet from the ground and apparently without any visible means of support. It was balanced on a jet of compressed air.

GYROSCOPES

There was a startling side-show in a Portsmouth exhibition some years ago. On the counter of a stall was a small cubical cardboard box, about three inches each way, solemnly balancing itself on one corner and slowly twisting round. When it finally lay down, the attendant took the lid off—and inside was a gyroscopic top! Of course, if anything looks impossible at first sight, it is the behaviour of one of those tops—only supported by one end, and yet sternly refusing to drop down, but slowly revolving in a horizontal circle.

As everybody knows, gyroscopes are much more than toys; they are used to steer ships and aeroplanes and torpedoes. But one of their very cleverest applications, the Brennan gyro-controlled mono-rail, has passed into the limbo of forgotten inventions. Yet it was an almost incredible piece of work. At first sight it looked to be just an ordinary, flat-topped truck, mounted on bogies in the usual way—and then one suddenly realized that all of the wheels (which were double-flanged) ran on a *single* central rail. You could walk all round the truck—which must have weighed a good many tons—and apparently there was nothing at all to keep it from crashing over one way or the other; yet there it stood, bolt upright. And when, at the demonstrator's invitation, about forty people climbed on board and all crowded over as far to one side as they could get, that side quietly tilted *up* a few inches, and so remained. Actually, the whole affair was kept balanced by two small gyroscopes, coupled together and driven by electric motors. It was a most remarkable invention; yet the young engineer who remarked: "You know, if we'd had this mono-rail first, and the ordinary bi-rail afterwards, we'd have said that the latter was a simple and obvious improvement!" probably hit the nail on the head. The old Iron Duke, long ago, took much the same view of Perkins's steam machine-gun. After seeing it in action, his comment was: "H'm . . . it would have been a useful weapon if gunpowder had never been discovered."

"PERPETU-OIL!"

An exhibit at one of the Olympia motor-shows was even queerer. A large glass bottle, about half-full of motor-oil, and tilted mouth downwards, was suspended by very fine wires about a foot above a basin. Naturally, the oil was pouring out at the rate of several gallons a minute; yet the level in the bottle did not alter in the slightest—

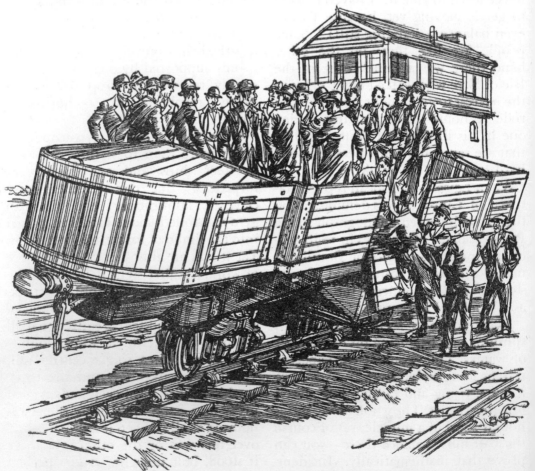

About forty people climbed on board and crowded over to one side

apparently this was fed from some invisible and inexhaustible source. Actually, right in the centre of the gush of oil coming from the spout was a thin, curved glass tube, up which oil under pressure was pumped into the bottle. This tube was invisible, being surrounded on all sides by the falling oil.

SHEER CHANCE

Turning to matters of pure chance, things which would seem to be absolutely impossible have happened more than once. The odds against any one player in a four-handed game of cards getting all thirteen of a suit in any one deal are 635,013,559,599—(a number of which no human mind can form any real idea)—to 1. Yet such a deal has genuinely happened at least half a dozen times—and, to make it queerer, on two of those occasions all four players were dealt a complete suit each! The best-known case is that of Mr. Justice Norris, of the High Court of Bengal. Playing whist in the Calcutta Club soon after he came out from England, he was dealt all thirteen trumps, and promptly threw down his hand. People said how lucky it was that such a thing should have happened to a man entirely above suspicion! At golf, too, an almost equally unlikely event—the halving of a hole in one—has occurred at least twice in recent years.

Very few people would credit, at first hearing, that a man could hold his breath under water, for a longer time than it would take another man to run a mile; yet there is no doubt about the fact. Wooderson's mile record is 4 mins. 6.2 secs. Well, in 1886 an English professional swimmer named Finney, diving in a tank of warm water,

stayed under for 4 mins. 29¼ secs.; in 1893 Beaumont, an Australian, pushed this record up to 4 mins. 35 secs.; and later still an American named Enoch was credited with 4 mins. 46¼ secs.

Most people imagine that the famous Indian rope-trick—in which

Although the oil was pouring out, the level in the bottle did not alter in the slightest

The Indian rope-trick

a length of unsupported rope remains standing upright while a small boy climbs it—is a myth: a trick which no one has ever actually witnessed, because its performance is impossible. That isn't so at all. There must be quite a number of persons from different countries who have seen the trick performed in India. The usual routine seems to be that the performer —out in the open, with no buildings near him—uncoils from round his waist what appears to be a fifteen or twenty foot length of ordinary rope. He throws this up, while holding the last yard or so—and the rope at once stiffens and remains like a long rod, up which the boy climbs and does various balancing feats at the top. Then he slides down, and the rope collapses and is again coiled round the waist.

There is one point about all this— there never seems to have been a case in which the performer would let the rope be closely examined, and there seems no doubt that it covers the secret of the trick—in fact, it *must*, because no other apparatus of any kind is used. Probably it is really a sort of necklace of short wooden rods, with coned ends, threaded on a central gut line, and covered with cloth ribbed to look like the strands of a rope. When the performer throws up the rope, he tightens the gut, which causes the joints to lock and so bear the boy's weight. On the other hand the joints have enough play, when the gut is slack, to let the rope be formed into comparatively small coils.

WALKING ON FIRE

Firewalking — in which the performer walks barefooted over red-hot embers without being scorched—is another feat which used to be regarded as a myth. Professor Langley, of U.S.A., who saw it performed at Tahiti about fifty years ago, was one of the first to confirm that the thing itself was a fact. Tests made by Mr. Harry Price, who experimented with two Indian fire-walkers and several English volunteers, have not only established the fact but shown the reason for it. In the final test (at Alexandra Palace, 20th April, 1937—it was televised) the walkers, one by one, passed unharmed across a trench twelve feet wide full of wood-embers at a temperature of 1,472 deg. Fahr. — *which would melt steel!* Incidentally, the best performance of all was made by a volunteer — a Cambridge graduate. The secret is that wood-embers are a bad conductor of heat; you can be in contact with them for a full half-second before they start to scorch you—and if the walker steps out confidently and smartly, he can get across the trench unscathed.

LOOKING-GLASS MAGIC

There is nothing mythical about the magic mirrors of the Far East; their curious property has been known to Europeans for at least two centuries—but until recent times the cause of this was an unsolved puzzle. Like the old Roman mirrors, they are made of solid metal, not of silvered glass. The face of the mirror is highly polished and quite flat, while the back bears an ornamental pattern. Held in the hand, they behave exactly as an ordinary mirror. But if you stand in strong sunlight, and reflect this from the mirror on to a wall a few feet away, then you'll see, in the bright disc of reflected light, a pattern of dark lines —the same pattern which you will find

The barefoot walkers passed unharmed across a trench of red-hot embers

In strong sunlight the patterned back of the mirror is reflected on the wall

on the *back* of the mirror. Well, seeing that this back is turned *away* from the light, and that the face is perfectly plain, where on earth does the pattern come from?

The explanation is this. In the process of patterning the back of the mirror by hammering and chiselling, the metal immediately under the tool gets hardened right through to the face. Consequently, when the face is afterwards polished, those harder portions—arranged, of course, in the lines of the pattern—resist the polisher more than the rest of the metal; and when the polishing is done they remain standing, as an engineer would say, slightly proud. The difference of level —a matter of a millionth of an inch or so—is impossible to see or feel: none the less, it is there, and it causes the edges of the hard parts to diffract the sunlight slightly as they reflect it—thus repeating the pattern on the wall.

TOPS

The ju-ju top of the Cameroons is another puzzle. Comparatively few white men have ever seen it, and none has mastered the trick—which takes years to learn—of keeping it spinning. Yet some of the natives can keep it going indefinitely. The top is like a large teetotum several inches across, with a thin spindle about a foot long. It is spun with a whip, and *in the air*—it is never allowed to touch the ground. The whole thing is really a fiendishly-difficult variation of that forgotten pastime called diabolo. The performer begins by winding the whip-lash tightly round the spindle of the top. He then gives a sharp upward flick, which causes the top to spin and also rise in the air. As it descends, he gives it another upward flick—and so on. The skill required is extreme— among the natives themselves, only a few can be certain of keeping the top up for more than ten seconds. As it spins, it emits a loud roaring noise, which is supposed to be good for the crops!

ODDS AND ENDS

Many puzzles seem, at first sight, to demand the impossible; but in such cases you will always find that there is some loophole offered by the conditions. Here is a specimen. If you hand someone a length of string about four feet long, and ask them to take a firm hold of each end and *then* tie a knot in the string without letting go of either end, you will probably be told that obviously it can't be done. But all you have to do is to lay the string out straight on a table, cross your arms and, still keeping them crossed, take hold of the two ends of the string (this, by the way, takes a little doing). If you then uncross your arms, lo and behold! there is a knot in the string! Of course all that you really do is to tie the knot in your arms, and then transfer it to the string.

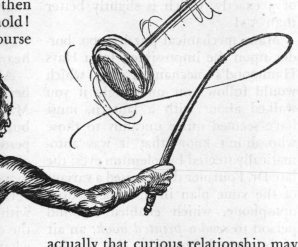

Here is a specimen of another kind. Is it possible for one man to be, simultaneously, another man's uncle *and* his nephew? "No," most people would say, "Of course it isn't." But actually that curious relationship may come about in any of several ways. Here is the simplest. If two men each marry the other's mother, and there is a son of each marriage, then each of those sons is at the same time the uncle and the nephew of the other. It sounds a little complicated, but it's not really difficult to follow.

And then there is the long-standing puzzle of the bowlers' averages—based, I believe, on what actually happened in an Australian match many years ago. Two bowlers, A and B, bowl unchanged throughout the whole of a match, taking all the wickets between them. In the first innings A takes 5 wickets for 30 runs (average 6) and B gets the other 5 for 31 (av. 6.2). In the second innings, A gets 3 for 12 (av. 4) and B gets the other 7 for 29 (av. 4 1/7).

The ju-ju top of the Cameroons

A, then, has slightly the better average both for the first and for the second innings. Which of them has the better average for the whole match?

Well, believe it or not, B has! Look at the totals. A got 5 for 30, and 3 for 12: in all, 8 for 42, making his average $5\frac{1}{4}$. But B, who got 5 for 31 and 7 for 29, has taken, in all, 12 wickets for 60 runs, and so comes out with an average of 5 exactly, which is slightly better than A's!

Many mechanical puzzles, too, border upon the impossible. John Hays Hammond's mechanical dog, which would follow you unerringly if you walked about with a lantern, must have seemed quite uncanny to those who didn't know that it was automatically steered by selenium eyes; the late Dr. Fournier d'Albe used a variant of the same plan in his type-reading optophone, which enabled a blind person to *read a printed book;* an air of mystery hangs over the watches constructed, about 1730, by Thomas Moore of Ipswich, which can be wound with ease and certainty by turning the key *either way;* and good mechanicians are sometimes completely puzzled by James Ferguson's famous mechanical paradox. In this very simple apparatus, which any one can make, a thick toothed wheel engages directly with three thin ones of the same diameter and all on the same axis;

yet, when you turn the thick wheel either way, one of the three thin ones turns the opposite way, another turns the same way, and the third one doesn't turn at all!

IN MINIATURE

But, of all such machines, one stands out high above the rest. That is the Peters machine for microscopic engraving — whose feats, although well-attested, are (quite naturally) regarded by almost every one who hears of them as being incredible.

About 1850, William Peters, a member of the London banking firm of Masterman & Co., designed and had built a machine in which one of two pens was made, by means of a system of levers, to follow the other pen's movements quite faithfully, but on a very much reduced scale. You wrote with one pen in the ordinary way—and the other produced a very tiny copy of what you had written. Peters's idea was that banks should use machines of this type for endorsing bills of exchange, and similar documents, in a way which

A mechanical dog which will unerringly follow a lighted lantern

could not possibly be forged unless the forger possessed a similar machine—which, of course, he wouldn't.

But this plan failed. Using pen-and-ink, there is a definite limit beyond which it is impossible to reduce the size of the writing while still keeping it legible; and, so long as it remains legible, it can be imitated by hand. Having settled this point, Peters, not wishing all the time and trouble he had spent on the machine to be wasted, modified it to write—or rather engrave—with a diamond point on a glass plate. And he was delighted to find that, using this plan, he could produce writing which, while beautifully clear, was *absolutely invisible* to the naked eye, and could only be read with a high-power microscope. As finally completed, the machine could reduce writing to 1/6250 of its natural size.

In one of his early experiments, Peters engraved the words, " Matthew Marshall, Bank of England," in the two-and-a-half-millionth part of a square inch. The machine's most triumphant feat was to engrave the Lord's Prayer (short version) in 1/356,000 of a square inch. It has also engraved the second chapter of the fourth gospel on the same scale.

What was that scale? Well, the answer, as a little calculation will show, is startling. The Lord's Prayer (short version) contains 223 letters. The Old and New Testaments, together, contain 3,566,480. It follows that, on the same scale that the machine wrote the Lord's Prayer, it could engrave, on a piece of glass one inch square, the whole text of the Bible *twenty-two times!* Or, to put the matter another way, on a disc of glass the size of a silver

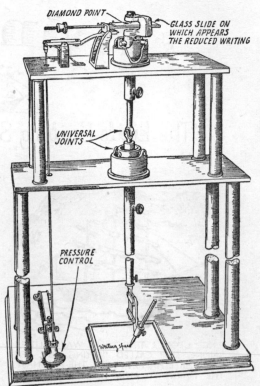

The Peters writing machine

threepenny-bit (0.6 in. diameter) it could engrave the whole text of the Bible *six times,* and there would still be a little blank space left over!

In 1921, Mr. A. McEwen of New York and the Rev. J. G. Crawford of Saunderstown, R.I., completed an improved form of the Peters machine. There is a photograph of the Lord's Prayer engraved by this machine on the scale of forty-nine Bibles to the square inch—in other words, the whole text of the Bible could be similarly engraved on a tiny square of glass *one-seventh of an inch* each way. And the machine can write legibly, if little more, at seventy-four Bibles to the square inch. On this scale, you could engrave, on a piece of glass the size of an ordinary 2½d. stamp, the complete text of the Bible *thirty times!*

"Flying Jib"

The Little Sailing Ship by Eric Joysmith

1 ONCE UPON A TIME THERE WAS A LITTLE SAILING SHIP CALLED "FLYING JIB". SHE HAD THREE MASTS . . . . . THE FOREMAST, THE MAINMAST AND THE MIZZEN MAST.

2 SHE WAS VERY TIRED OF BEING TOSSED ABOUT BY THE BIG WAVES.

3 SHE WAS CHASED UP THE SIDE OF ONE WAVE

4 ONLY TO BE CHASED DOWN THE SIDE OF ANOTHER. IT WAS VERY WEARING

5 SO THAT "FLYING JIB" WAS OVERJOYED WHEN THE HARBOUR ENTRANCE HOVE IN SIGHT . . . .

96

6 AND SHE COULD LIE SNUGLY BERTHED ALONGSIDE THE QUAY, VERY GLAD TO HAVE ALL THREE MASTS STILL STANDING.

7 SOON IT WAS TIME TO PUT TO SEA AGAIN AND "FLYING JIB" BECAME VERY UNHAPPY, BUT WHEN SHE TOLD HER TROUBLES TO AN OLD SAILOR WITH A WOODEN LEG

8 HE SAID, "YO HO, I'LL SOON FIX YOU MATEY." AND HE GOT A PIECE OF WOOD AND SOME PAINT IN A CAN, AND WITH HIS JACK-KNIFE

9 HE CARVED A BEAUTIFUL MODEL OF "FLYING JIB" AND PUT IT IN A BOTTLE,

10 AND *THAT* IS THE STORY OF HOW "FLYING JIB" SAILED, HAPPY EVER AFTER, ON A NICE, STILL, BLUE, PAINTED SEA,

San Fairy Ann

by ELEANOR FARJEON

CATHY GOODMAN was picking peas in the front garden of the Corner Cottage on the village green. She picked them as though she hated them. For four years, ever since she had been evacuated, her face seemed to have a permanent scowl. This was a pity, for Cathy Goodman had been born with a nice face.

Old Mrs. Vining was peering through her window in the cottage. She spent most of her time peering at what went on round the green. Just now she was peering at Cathy, to see she didn't eat too many peas; and she also peered at Mrs. Lane, the doctor's wife, and at Miss Barnes, the schoolmistress, who were standing on the green staring into the duckpond.

Miss Barnes was saying: " It's a disgusting sight."

"And smell!" said Mrs. Lane, screwing up her pretty little nose. " Oh, *mon Dieu*!"

Doctor Lane had married her in London, a year ago. Everybody in Little Medham liked Doctor Lane, and was curious about his French wife.

Would she be plain or pretty? She was pretty. Pleasant or stand-offish? She was pleasant. Young or old? She was neither. Mrs. Lane was thirty-five, just betwixt and between, a very suitable age, thought Little Medham for a doctor of forty-four. Soon they liked her as much as they liked him for all her foreign ways. She was lively, and kind, and practical, and interested in everything and everybody. Her clothes were plain, yet there was something different about them; it was a treat to see her walking up the street. Then, if her ideas and ways were not quite what Little Medham was accustomed to, Little Medham found it liked them. Life was somehow more amusing since the doctor's wife had come to live among them. She was always up to something, which was why Mrs. Vining, peering between her lace curtains, wondered : " What's she up to *now*?"

Mrs. Lane was asking: " When was the pond last cleared out?"

" Not since the evacuees came in 1939," said Miss Barnes. " We'd never let it be a dump for rubbish before. But some of the evacuees were rather a rough lot to begin with; they were at a loose end, and used to sit on the rails chucking in anything they could get hold of, for the fun of the thing. They settled down, of course, and now they like being here."

"Not Cathy Goodman," said Mrs. Lane, glancing towards the Corner Cottage.

The schoolmistress sighed. Cathy Goodman was a problem. She didn't fit in. She didn't try. She had no parents, and seemed to belong to nobody. From her first day in Little Medham she had got into the habit of being unhappy, and resisted all attempts at friendliness. Miss Barnes had made every effort, but Cathy's case had got her beat, she said.

"It's a pity she was put with Mrs. Vining."

"Can it not be changed?" asked Mrs. Lane.

"Who would take her? She seems to hate us all." Miss Barnes shook her head impatiently, and stared at the pond again. "Goodness! I'd no idea

*Old Mrs. Vining was peering through her window
at Cathy, to see she didn't eat too many peas*

The lady was sewing at a table strewn with brocade and silks, while San Fairy Ann lay amongst the finery

how much those children threw in, till this drought."

Little Medham was suffering badly from the drought. The wells were dry, the gardens were parched, and the ponds were showing their very bones. The duckpond had shrunk to a smear of green duckweed on the slime in the middle, with a crust of mud all round, in which was embedded a number of most disagreeable objects. Salmon tins, sardine and soup tins, rusty kitchen things, and broken bottles; in one part an old boot, hard as iron, had thrust its wrinkled toecap through the caked mud, and in the very middle a wooden chair-leg stood up like the mast of an ancient wreck.

"It is not nice," said Mrs. Lane, emphatically. "It is not sanitary.

And it is very ugly. It ought to be cleaned out."

"I've spoken to the vicar," said Miss Barnes, "but what can he do? With labour so short there's no men to spare for it."

"*Eh bien!* If there are no men there are women, I hope!" cried Mrs. Lane. "I shall clear out the pond myself."

"When?" asked Miss Barnes.

"After supper," said Miss Lane.

"I will help," said Miss Barnes.

"We'll want rakes and shovels," said Mrs. Lane. "I shall put on shorts and the doctor's wellingtons. After we've had our *café*. Eight o'clock."

"I'll be here," laughed Miss Barnes. She went off gaily to her cottage near the school, and Mrs. Lane crossed to the pretty white house that overlooked the village green. They both seemed merry, and walked so energetically that old Mrs. Vining asked herself again: "What *are* they up to?" She called through the window to Cathy: "What was Mrs. Lane doin' by the pond?"

Cathy did not answer.

"Ain't you got a tongue in your head?" rapped out Mrs. Vining.

Cathy put it out at her.

"Get on with them peas!" shouted Mrs. Vining; and added to herself: "One might have thought she were expectin' to find a treasure in the pond."

Cathy crammed peas in her mouth to stop herself from crying. A treasure! Only she knew about the treasure in the duckpond. Oh, how she hated the duckpond!

The duckpond was the reason why, for four years, her nice little face had been puckered with a scowl.

The treasure in the duckpond was San Fairy Ann. She lay in the mud under the broken chair in the middle. When it settled on her chest and pushed her deep down, she gave up all hope of seeing daylight again. She hadn't seen the light for nearly four years. Her frock, made of fine old silk, in blue and white stripes with rose-buds dotted down the white stripe— by now her lovely frock was simply ruined. Her sawdust body felt sadly limp and soggy. San Fairy Ann hoped that her face was still all right. She had been born with a shiny pink and white china face, glossy black hair, big blue eyes and a little rosy mouth —born long ago in France.

Lying under the mud in the green duckpond, San Fairy Ann had lived on her memories. She thought she must be nearly eighty years old. She remem-bered a lovely little château with turrets and a bridge over a dry moat, and rose gardens and peaches that ripened in the sun; almost a fairy castle, with a lady as pretty as a fairy to live in it. The lady was sewing at a table strewn with bits of brocade and reels of coloured silk, and a fine lace flounce. San Fairy Ann lay amongst the finery, with nothing on. The lady was finishing making a blue-and-white striped bedjacket for herself, with lace ruffles on the sleeves. A scrap of lace, and a piece of the silk, were left over. "These will just do for Célestine's doll," said the lady. She cut the garments deftly, and with exquisite stitches made a petticoat of the lace and a frock of the silk. Next day the doll was given to the lady's little girl; it was her *jour de fête*, her birthday. The child called the doll Célestine, after herself. She kept her

carefully, and twenty years later gave her to her little girl, who was also called Célestine. Thirty years later there was a third little Célestine, and she in her turn treasured her grand-mother's doll in its rich dress of old French silk and real lace. The doll supposed she would go on living for ever in the fairy castle, belonging to one little Célestine after another. Then the time came when she learned that things do not go on for ever.

It was the year of the first World War. Guns boomed all round the castle, then holes appeared in the walls, and some ceilings fell in. One night her little mistress ran and clutched her out of her cradle, saying: "We're running away, Célestine, *maman* says we must hurry, but I simply won't go without you."

One night her little mistress ran to take her from her cradle

" Quick, *chérie*, quick!" called her mother from below. The little Célestine of flesh and blood flew down the stairs, clasping the sawdust Célestine in her arms. Out into the starry summer night, through the sweet-smelling gardens, and across the bridge over the moat—suddenly the child stumbled; the doll fell out of her arms, and a servant who followed kicked it into the moat. " Célestine!" cried the child. " Hurry!" called her mother. " But Célestine is down there!" " *Ma pauvre petite,* we cannot wait——" The last thing the doll heard was her little mistress weeping for her.

She did not know how long she lay in the moat. Her next memory was of a man in a sand-coloured uniform fishing her out of the dead leaves and dusting her. " Coo!" he said. " Just the ticket for my Kitsy!"

The guns were still booming, the roses were trampled to bits, and the fairy castle was fuller of holes than before, when the English Tommy carried the doll away. That was her last memory of France.

Next she remembered the soldier unpacking her from his haversack in a little room in England, where his wife was clinging to him, crying for joy, and on his knee was the little girl he called Kitsy.

" See what daddy brought you all the way from France, ducks."

" Oo!" said the little girl. " Wot's 'er name?"

" Let's see," said the soldier. He didn't know her name was Célestine, and he said: " Her name's San Fairy Ann."

" Wot's it mean, dad?"

" It means she's a fairy, see, and you'll find she'll bring you luck."

And San Fairy Ann she became, first to Kitsy, who loved and treasured her as three little French Célestines had done, and then, many years later, to Kitsy's only little daughter, Cathy Goodman. Nobody, not Kitsy, not one of the three Célestines long ago, had loved her so much as Cathy Goodman did. She loved every bit of her. No doll in the world had such a happy face, or such beautiful clothes. Miss Higgins the dressmaker said about her dress: " That's a very fine sample of silk "; and about her lace petticoat: " Well, I never! I do believe it's *real* lace!" But San Fairy Ann herself was what Cathy loved most.

Before the Second World War broke out, sad things happened in Cathy's life. She was left without parents, and the people who were supposed to take care of her neglected her. All she had in the world was San Fairy Ann, and San Fairy Ann was all the world to her.

In 1939 came the Second World War, and Cathy, with a crowd of other children, was evacuated. She fell to the lot of old Mrs. Vining in Little Medham, and that was bad luck, because Mrs. Vining was selfish and crotchety, and had no notion of making a child happy. Still, Cathy would have found friends in the village and things would have been very different but for a bit of worse luck that happened on her very first day.

There was in Little Medham a boy who was not bright in his wits. Johnny sat in school with the youngest when he was well-grown, and Miss Barnes was especially careful and kind with him. There was no harm in Johnny, but he had a weakness for bright things, and when a child complained of missing this or that, Miss Barnes would take Johnny into her room and say: "Now then, you squirrel, let's see what you've hidden away!" Johnny grinned and turned out his pockets readily—and there to be sure was Doris Carter's hair-slide, mixed up with somebody else's ribbon, bright rose-hips from the hedge, and a glass button.

The morning the evacuees arrived they were welcomed with cups of tea in the women's institute, where Johnny loitered to gaze at his face in the metal tea urn. "Keep an eye on the tea-spoons," whispered Miss Barnes to her helpers. She knew that Johnny's fingers would itch for them. But soon those fingers itched for something else. Johnny had caught sight of Cathy, sitting forlorn in a corner, hugging San Fairy Ann. She was miserable in this strange new place, wondering who would choose her to go home with them; but she got comfort from knowing that she and San Fairy Ann would go together, and sleep in the same bed.

Johnny came up and grabbed the

Suddenly the child stumbled, the doll fell out of her arms,
and the servant who followed kicked it into the moat

*Suddenly Johnny hurled San Fairy Ann
far out into the middle of the pond*

S. van Abbé

doll's silk dress. " Gi'e oi 'er!" he said. Cathy could only stare at him, and hold San Fairy Ann tighter. " Gi'e oi 'er!" repeated Johnny, and this time Cathy gave him a violent push, crying: " Go away, you horrid little boy!"

Lady Blackwater, who was choosing five children and had paused by Cathy, passed on, remarking: " I'm afraid you're one of the troublesome little girls." And somehow her ladyship's words had stuck. Nobody chose Cathy, and in the end she was given to old Mrs. Vining.

That evening she stood inside the gate of the Corner Cottage, showing their new world to San Fairy Ann. It was quiet on the green, everybody seemed to be at supper. Johnny came by, and stared from the other side.

" Gi'e oi 'er!" he said.

" Go away, or I'll tell the pleeceman on you," said Cathy angrily.

She never knew how it happened— Johnny had made a long arm over the fence, snatched San Fairy Ann out of her arms, and scampered off. Cathy flashed through the gate after him, shrieking: " I'll tell the pleeceman! I'll tell the pleeceman!"

Did her threat frighten him out of his small wits? Suddenly Johnny hurled San Fairy Ann far out into the middle of the pond. For one moment she swam on her stiff silk skirt; then it got drenched, and she sank out of sight. Cathy's cries brought people to their doors. They saw Johnny lying on his back on the green, being scratched and pounded by a furious little evacuee.

The children were pulled apart. Johnny couldn't, and Cathy wouldn't explain. She would not show her broken heart to these unfeeling strangers. She would suffer in silence

—but oh! how she would suffer. Her pain went deep, and shut her lips. She scowled at Johnny. She scowled at the duckpond. She scowled at Little Medham and everything in it.

It was a bad start for the "troublesome little girl" from London. It was why Cathy Goodman had never fitted in, and never tried to. But nobody had ever known the reason.

At eight o'clock in the evening, double summer-time in July, there are still three good hours of light. Old Mrs. Vining peered at children and grown-ups gathering in increasing numbers round the pond, and heard the jokes and chatter, and the occasional shouts, with which they filled the air. In the middle of the pond stood Mrs. Lane, her sleeves rolled up, her cotton skirt tucked into her shorts, her legs encased in the doctor's rubber boots, her capable

hands raking the slime as she passed her findings to Miss Barnes, on the hard caked mud. The children framing the banks made rubbish piles.

"Biscuit tin, pre-war!" announced Mrs. Lane. "Cricket ball belonging to William the Conqueror. Tea-kettle used by Noah in the Ark." Each find was hailed with laughter and applause. It was as good as a play. "The wooden horse from Troy!" called Mrs. Lane.

"Thur be my owd 'orse," cried Bobby Maitland. "I niver knowed what 'ad become of 'e."

On the edge of the crowd, with all her heart in her eyes, stood Cathy Goodman. If Bobby Maitland's wooden horse were found, why not San Fairy Ann?

The hunt went on. Nine o'clock chimed. Mothers began to chase their children to bed. Cathy slipped

behind a bush and hid. When ten o'clock chimed there was no one left but Mrs. Lane and Miss Barnes. The village green showed three big dumps, and not a tin was visible in the pond. San Fairy Ann had not come to light. Mrs. Lane pushed her hair off her forehead with a muddy arm.

"That is all, I think," she said, raking idly in the slime. ("Don't stop! don't stop! don't stop!" prayed Cathy silently.) Doctor Lane leaned over the garden wall of the white house, smoking his pipe. "That's quite enough, Tiny! Come along in," he called. ("Oh, please, go on! go on!" prayed Cathy Goodman.)

"*Pouf!* it has been fun!" laughed Mrs. Lane. She pulled herself slowly out of the sucking mud.

"Great fun," said the doctor. "If I have you sneezing tomorrow."

"And do my shoulders ache!" Mrs. Lane wriggled them, and crossed the green to her house.

Miss Barnes said: "We'll clear the dumps in the morning." She too went away.

The village green was empty, except

Mrs. Lane could hear a muffled sobbing, and saw a child in the middle of the pond for Cathy, crouched under the bush.

San Fairy Ann still lay under the mud in the middle of the pond.

Twelve o'clock chimed. The doctor was asleep. Mrs. Lane slipped out of bed to smell the jasmine and look at the moon shining on the village green. It was one of the prettiest sights in Little Medham, but not many people bothered about it. Standing in her pyjamas at the window, Tina Lane gazed at the square church tower behind the peaceful elms, at the quiet grass where children had played their games for hundreds of years, at the darkened cottages, asleep in silver light. The elms, thought Mrs. Lane, ought to be poplars; but the church tower might almost be the turret of a fairy castle.

She caught her breath. What was that muffled sobbing?—*and what was that in the middle of the pond*? Had a dog or a sheep floundered in? " Oh, *mon Dieu*! it's a child!"

Mrs. Lane was down the stairs and out of the house in a flash. She snatched up the muddy wellingtons in the porch, and thrust her pyjamaed legs into them. Within two minutes of seeing her from the window, Mrs. Lane was lifting Cathy out of the slime. They stood clutching each

other in the middle of the pond.
Cathy was soaked with mud, her wet
hair streaked with weed.

"San Fairy Ann! San Fairy Ann!"
she sobbed.

"Cathy—*chérie*—what is it?"

"San Fairy Ann!"

"Tell me, *pauvre petite*!"

"I want San Fairy Ann!"

"Who is she, San Fairy Ann?"

"You never fished her out. You
fished out Bobby's horse, but you left
San Fairy Ann."

"A doll!" cried Mrs. Lane, like one
inspired. "Stop crying, *chérie*! We'll
find her if we have to fish all night."

Cathy stopped sobbing, and stared.
Were people kind after all, then?
Regardless of her pyjamas, Mrs. Lane
knelt in the mud and groped with both
her hands. What was this? Only
another tin. She must be careful. Ah!
here was something smooth and round
and hard. A stone? She brought it
into the moonlight. Not a stone, a
china head, with glossy black hair,
blue eyes, and a rosy mouth.

Cathy Goodman turned red with

*Cathy turned red with happiness.
"San Fairy Ann!" she cried*

happiness. "San Fairy Ann!" she cried. But Mrs. Lane turned white, and said: "*Célestine!*"

Doctor Lane, in his pyjamas, met Mrs. Lane in hers at the front door. She dripped with mud, and clasped in her arms a child and a doll, even muddier.

"Tiny! what on earth——"

"Don't stand asking questions, *mon cher.* Please run a hot bath and heat some milk."

They all three went into the bath, Mrs. Lane, Cathy and San Fairy Ann, whom Cathy would not let go. Her china face and arms and legs soon shone again—but oh, her poor limp body! and oh, her dress! What did it matter? Presently, wrapped in a towel, she was lying on Cathy's pillow in a clean bed, while Cathy sipped hot milk. Mrs. Lane, also sipping, sat by her in a dressing-gown. Only then did she ask a question:

"Cathy—tell me, *chérie*—tell me, where did you get my Célestine?"

"She's *not* your Célestine. She's *my* San Fairy Ann."

"Yes, I know. But when I was a little girl in France, long ago, I think she was mine."

"She *wasn't*."

"Wasn't she?" Mrs. Lane let her dressing-gown slip off her shoulders. Under it she was wearing a little bed-jacket in blue-and-white striped silk, with rosebuds on the white stripe, and lace in the sleeves.

"Why—you've got San Fairy Ann's dress on!" cried Cathy Goodman. So then Mrs. Lane was sure.

Her eyes were full of tears as she took the little girl's hands and said: "Tell me, Cathy. Tell me how you got San Fairy Ann."

"My granddaddy bringed her from France for my mummy. He found her in a castle and my mummy gived her to me."

"Listen, Cathy! My mummy gave her to me. And I cried because I lost her, just like you."

"She's *mine,*" said Cathy Goodman, very fiercely, very appealingly.

"Yes, she is yours. She always shall be till you give her one day to *your* little girl. Tomorrow I will make her a new body and a new dress. Can you guess what San Fairy Ann's dress shall be?"

Cathy shook her head.

"It shall be my little jacket," said Mrs. Lane. "Oh!" gasped Cathy. "It belonged to my great-grandmother. It was made from out of *her* granny's dresses. Her granny danced in it when she was a princess in France, and lived in a fairy castle."

"Oh!"

"Tomorrow," said Mrs. Lane, "we will cut it up again for San Fairy Ann, with a lace petticoat underneath."

Cathy stared at her, unable to speak. Suddenly the scowl came un-puckered from her face, and her face was so nice when it smiled that Célestine Lane's eyes filled with tears again. She put her arms round the little girl and the doll, saying: "And Cathy—would you and San Fairy Ann like to stay here and live with me?"

"*Oh!*" gasped Cathy Goodman.

HOW TO MAKE A
By E. Keil MODEL GLIDER

A MODEL glider is a fascinating toy to fly, and here are the instructions for one you can make quite easily.

Materials Required.

One sheet each of 3/32 in., 1/16 in. and 1/32 in. balsa wood (this wood is extremely light and can be bought in any model or toy shop); balsa cement for gluing the wings and tailpiece of the fuselage; and plasticine clay for weighting the nose.

Instructions for Making.

1. Trace the plan of the glider on to thin paper, and then transfer it to the sheets of balsa wood by re-tracing the plan over carbon paper, using the 3/32 in. sheet for the fuselage, the 1/16 in. for the wing panels and the 1/32 in. for the tailplane and fin. Be careful to see that the plan is laid over the correct grain of the wood, as indicated on the diagrams. Carefully cut out the different parts.

2. Using a sheet of sandpaper wrapped around a matchbox, which makes a very good sandpapering tool, taper the thickness of the fuselage down towards the tail, as shown in the plan view.

Cut out a shallow V-shaped slot on the top edge of the fuselage, as indicated on the diagram, where the wings will be glued in at their correct angle.

3. Using the sandpaper, round off the front edges of the upper sides of the wing sections and taper off the upper sides of the back edges, so that they will present as little resistance as possible to the air. Cement the two halves of the wing together, achieving the necessary dihedral angle by placing one part of the wing flat on a table while resting the tip of the other on the edge of an upturned matchbox (this will be approximately 2½ in. in height—that is, twice the dihedral angle shown on the diagram).

When dry, glue the complete wing assembly into the small V-slot which has been cut into the fuselage, and for extra strength, run a line of glue between the base of each wing and the fuselage.

4. Glue the rudder and tailpiece in position, as marked on the plan. Allow to dry. The model is now ready to fly and must be balanced.

Both model and full-sized gliders must be weighted at the nose to become " nose-heavy," otherwise they cannot gather air-speed and fall flat to the ground. To obtain this balance, add a small amount of plasticine to weight the nose — adding or taking away the weight until you have discovered the correct amount.

When launching your glider, do not throw it up into the air, but launch it gently in a downward direction, and you will find as soon as it becomes airborne, it will lift itself up and sail along on an air-current for a considerable distance, in a most exciting way

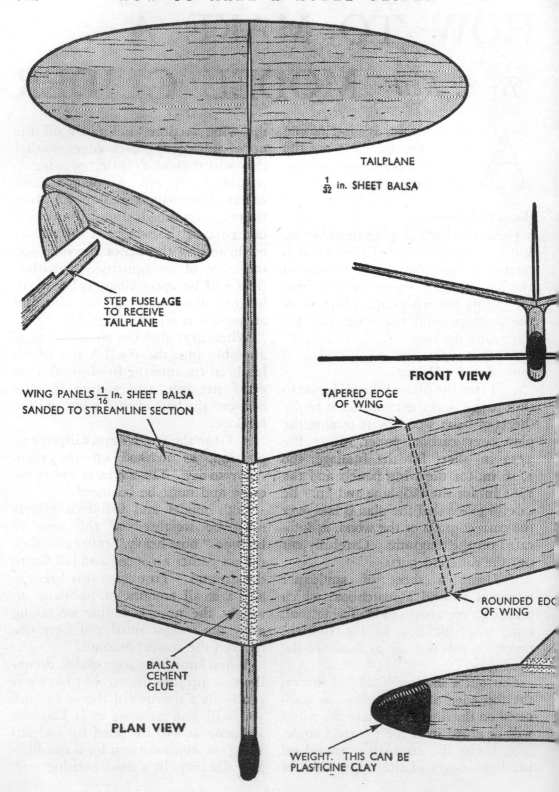

TAILPLANE

$\frac{1}{32}$ in. SHEET BALSA

STEP FUSELAGE
TO RECEIVE
TAILPLANE

WING PANELS $\frac{1}{16}$ in. SHEET BALSA
SANDED TO STREAMLINE SECTION

FRONT VIEW

TAPERED EDGE
OF WING

ROUNDED EDGE
OF WING

BALSA
CEMENT
GLUE

PLAN VIEW

WEIGHT. THIS CAN BE
PLASTICINE CLAY

THE
"CADET"
GLIDER

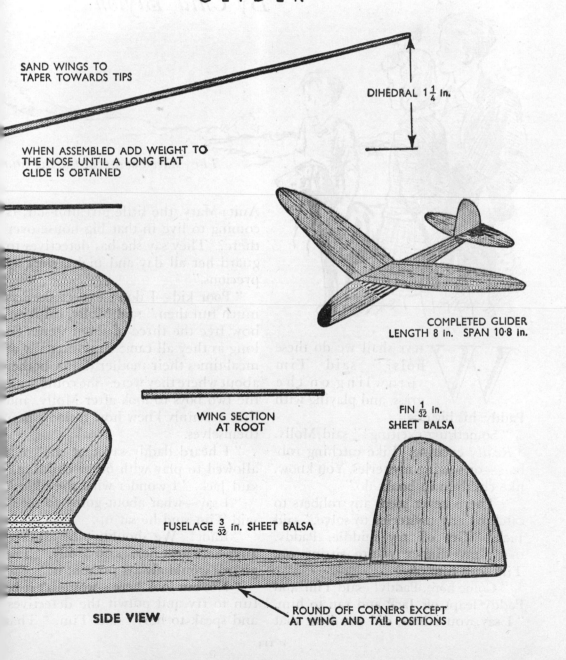

SAND WINGS TO
TAPER TOWARDS TIPS

DIHEDRAL 1¼ in.

WHEN ASSEMBLED ADD WEIGHT TO
THE NOSE UNTIL A LONG FLAT
GLIDE IS OBTAINED

COMPLETED GLIDER
LENGTH 8 in. SPAN 10·8 in.

WING SECTION
AT ROOT

FIN $\frac{1}{32}$ in.
SHEET BALSA

FUSELAGE $\frac{3}{32}$ in. SHEET BALSA

ROUND OFF CORNERS EXCEPT
AT WING AND TAIL POSITIONS

SIDE VIEW

WHAT HAPPENED OVER THE WALL

By Enid Blyton

They stared across at the big hou

"Anita-Mary, the little girl film-star, is coming to live in that big house over there? They say she has detectives to guard her all day and night, she's so precious."

"Poor kid—I don't expect she has much fun then," said Molly, thinking how free the three of them were. So long as they all came in punctually at meal-times their mother didn't bother about where they were. She could trust the two boys to look after Molly, and they certainly knew how to look after themselves.

"I heard daddy say that she's not allowed to play with other children," said Jack. "I wonder what she's like."

"I say—what about going to see?" said Tim, and he sat up.

"Idiot! We shouldn't be allowed anywhere near her," said Molly. "The guards would always prevent it."

"No, but look here—wouldn't it be fun to try and outwit the detectives and speak to her?" said Tim. "Tha

"**W**HAT shall we do these hols?" said Tim sprawling on the grass, and playing with Paddy, his big dog.

"Something exciting!" said Molly. "*Really* exciting. Like catching robbers—or solving mysteries. You know, like children in books do."

"There never seem any robbers to catch or any mysteries to solve," said Jack. "Get off my middle, Paddy, that's my dinner you're sitting on. Tim, call him off."

"Come here, Paddy!" said Tim, and Paddy leapt off Jack and ran to him. "I say, you others, did you hear that

would be something exciting to do."

"I don't expect she would be a bit of fun to know," said Molly. "She'll be stuck-up and vain and dressed like a princess. Don't let's do that."

"Yes, do let's," said Tim. "Shall we, Paddy? Will you come and help too?"

"Woof," said Paddy in his doggy voice and he licked Tim's nose.

"Wonder if Anita-Mary is there yet," said Jack. "Yes, do let's go and find out."

"Molly doesn't need to come if she doesn't want to," said Tim. But Molly wasn't going to be left out. She got up too, and all three children stared across at the big house they could see on the hill beyond them, its windows winking in the sun. They started to walk up the hill towards it, Paddy capering around in his usual excited way. He was a big retriever, quite mad, very loving, and he adored the children with all his heart.

The big house stood in its own grounds. A high wall ran all round it. Set on the top were wicked-looking iron spikes.

"Shouldn't like to climb over *those!*" said Tim. "Mother would have something to say about torn shorts, I bet."

They walked cautiously round the high wall. There was a drive that led up to the house, and at the gate stood a burly man, leaning against the gate-post.

"Hallo," said Tim.

"'Lo," said the man, not moving. "You can't come in here without a permit, so move on."

"Why? Is Anita-Mary here then?" asked Tim.

"Little boys shouldn't ask questions," said the man, aggravatingly. Tim hated people who said things like that. He gave the man a glare and the three of them walked on, with Paddy at their heels.

"That was one of the guards, I expect," said Jack. "Tough-looking fellow, wasn't he? I bet he guards Anita-Mary all right."

They walked on round the wall again, meaning to go right round the grounds, which were entirely enclosed by the stout wall topped by its vicious-looking spikes.

They came to a small door, but it was locked, and had barbed wire

wound across it. No one could possibly get in that way.

Then they heard a clear voice singing a song, and they saw a ball rising high in the air. Someone was singing in the garden behind the wall, and playing ball at the same time. It must be Anita-Mary.

Suddenly the ball was thrown badly, and it sailed right over the wall, landing by Paddy. He was startled and he growled. Tim picked up the ball.

"Hey!" he called. "Do you want your ball back?"

"Oh!" said the voice that had been singing. "Is there somebody there? Yes, please send my ball back. Thanks awfully."

"Are you Anita-Mary?" called Molly, rather liking the sound of the voice.

"Yes. Who are you? Can't you come over and play with me? I'm bored," called back Anita-Mary.

"We'd like to—but just take a look at the spikes on top of the wall!" shouted Jack.

"Can't you get a ladder?" called Anita-Mary. "A rope-ladder would be best—a long one that could hang down this side as well. A pile of sacking put

Suddenly the ball was thrown badly and it sailed right over the wall

on top of the spikes would stop them from sticking into you. The only thing to worry about is Ricky the dog. He's about somewhere, and is awfully fierce. He'd never let any one come over the wall if he could help it."

The children didn't like the sound of Ricky. "We've got a dog too," called back Jack. "He's Paddy. Can't you tie up Ricky somewhere?"

"Well—I might be able to," said Anita-Mary, her voice coming clearly over the wall. "Can you go and get a ladder? Wait a bit though—I think this evening would be the best time. I might be able to shut Ricky up somewhere then, and you could come over safely. We could have a game. It's so dull here."

"Someone's coming!" suddenly whispered Tim. "Hide! We'll be back this evening, Anita-Mary. Look out for us."

The three children sank under a thick bush as footsteps came near. It was another guard patrolling outside the wall. Paddy began to growl, but stopped as he felt Tim's hand over his nose. The guard went by quite unaware that there were three children and a dog crouching under the bush nearby.

When he had gone the children crept out and whistled softly. But there was no answer from the other side. The little girl must have gone.

"Come on," said Tim, in excitement. "This is going to be quite an adventure. Fancy climbing over this spiky wall into a forbidden garden, under the very nose of the guards, to play with the famous Anita-Mary."

"I hope that Ricky won't bite us," said Molly, feeling rather nervous.

"Paddy will see to *him*!" said Tim.

"He's going to come with us, aren't you, Paddy? You'll eat up any dog that so much as growls at us, I bet."

"Woof," said Paddy, agreeing, and wagging his tail.

"Where can we get a ladder?" said Molly.

"Have you forgotten the rope-ladder that daddy had made?" said Jack. "Don't you remember how, when we first came to our house, and had a nursery at the top of it, mummy was afraid of fire. She thought we mightn't be able to escape—so daddy had a fine rope-ladder made, that reached from our nursery window to the ground."

"Golly! I'd forgotten all about that!" said Molly. "Where is it?"

"Well, ever since we've been big, and haven't used the nursery, the ladder's been stored in the loft," said Tim. "We'll get it out. I bet it will go over that wall nicely, and down the other side too."

"We must take piles of sacking to put over those awful spikes," said Jack. "I should just hate to sit on them!"

They found the rope-ladder. It was a perfectly simple one, with light wooden rungs that slipped into knots of rope. It could be coiled up easily and carried.

"Good! Just what we want!" said Tim. "Now let's go and bag some sacking from the gardener's shed."

They waited till the surly old gardener had gone. Then they slipped into the shed and found a pile of sacking used to cover up potatoes in winter.

"Pooh! It's smelly," said Molly. "*I* shan't carry it."

"I don't mind smells," said Jack. "I'll carry it and you and Tim can carry the ladder between you. Isn't it tea-time yet? I'm awfully hungry."

A bell rang and told them that Jack was right—it *was* tea-time. They ran indoors, washed and brushed themselves, and appeared at table looking very clean and good and proper.

"Does any one want to go across to the farm with me this evening?" asked their father, at the end of tea. Usually there were shouts of joy at such a question, because there were horses to ride at the farm. But today the children felt they had better things to do.

"Well," said Tim, "we'd rather planned to do something exciting, daddy. We've got a—a sort of appointment."

"Dear me. Who with?" said mother, laughing.

Molly opened her mouth to say "Anita-Mary" and the two boys each gave her a kick under the table. They knew Molly's way of letting out secrets without thinking.

"Oooh," said Molly, and rubbed her ankles.

"I see it's a secret," said mother, and she laughed again. "All right, I won't ask any more questions. But keep out of mischief, please."

"Of course!" said all three together, and they looked as innocent as old Brer Rabbit when he was up to something.

They slipped away from the table, and Molly had a few words to say about her bruised ankles.

"Sorry," said Tim, "but you do give things away without thinking, Molly. Now—what time shall we start off?"

"Not yet," said Tim. "You can't really call it evening yet. Say at half-past six. That's really evening. Any-

way we've got our bikes to clean—you know we promised to do them today."

"Golly, so we did!" said Jack. "Let's go and get them now. That will be something to do whilst we're waiting."

At half-past six they all felt rather excited. Paddy pranced round, feeling that something was in the air.

"I'll get the sacking," said Jack. "You two get the rope-ladder."

It wasn't long before they were all on their way to the big house. Paddy kept sniffing at the sacks as if he could smell mice or rats. Molly did hope there weren't any hidden in the smelly old rags.

Tim went on in front to make sure things were safe. He came back and reported that there were now two guards or detectives at the front gate, but he couldn't see or hear any one else.

They walked to the wall, just about where they had stood in the afternoon. Molly noticed something and pointed to it.

"Look!" she said. "Doesn't it seem as if somebody else has been trampling about since we were here? And what are those two deep marks in the ground?"

"Funny," said Tim, looking hard. "I'd say those two marks had been made by a ladder—but there's no ladder here now—and anyway, who would go over the wall on a ladder with guards about and a fierce dog? It must have been one of the detectives messing about here. Perhaps he saw our footsteps, and was looking round."

"Let's whistle for Anita-Mary," said Molly. "She said she'd be here. We'll have to know if she's shut up that fierce dog."

So they whistled softly. But nobody

whistled back. They whistled more loudly, and then Tim called. But there was no reply at all.

"Perhaps she's been locked in the house," said Molly. "Maybe when evening comes they won't let her out. Now, what are we to do?"

"Well—we'll just have a peep over the wall, anyway," said Jack. "Help to heave over the ladder, Tim."

It wasn't easy to throw the ladder so that half of it went over the wall, and the other half hung down their side. But they managed it at last, though the rungs all hung crooked.

"I'll go up first," said Tim, and up he went, climbing carefully rung by rung. He came to the top, and looked over, the ladder swaying a bit.

"Look!" she said. "Doesn't it seem as if somebody's been trampling about?"

He stood staring over the top. The others grew impatient.

"Tim! Is Anita-Mary there? What are you staring at?" called Jack.

"Well—I can see something queer," said Tim. "I can't quite make it out."

"What do you mean — queer?" asked Molly.

"I can see something that looks like a big dog—but he's lying down on his side, not moving—and it seems to me jolly queer that he's not barking at us," said Tim, in a low voice.

"Come on down and let me up," said Jack, impatiently. Tim came down, and Jack climbed up, and he too stared for a long time.

"I believe the dog's poisoned," said Jack, coming down, looking rather pale. "That must be Ricky, the big fierce dog Anita-Mary told us about. He'd never lie still like that if he was all right. You know—I think there's something peculiar going on."

"What do you mean?" asked Molly, suddenly feeling out of breath.

"I think somebody's gone over this wall—you know where we saw those footmarks—and I think they've poisoned Ricky—and maybe they're going to kidnap Anita-Mary," said Jack. "Film-stars are rich, you know, and people sometimes kidnap them for their money."

"We'd better go home," said Molly. The two boys looked at her scornfully.

"Don't you want an adventure? Don't you want to solve this mystery yourself?" said Tim. "Isn't it just what we were wishing for today? You go home if you want to."

'No. But what are you going to do?" asked Molly, her heart beating fast.

"We're going over the ladder, of course—and Paddy's going with us," said Tim. "We're going to find that little girl. I bet she's somewhere in the grounds, all tied up ready to be kidnapped and taken away. Maybe the kidnappers are going to wait till it's dark."

"I'm coming too, then," said Molly, feeling better when she knew that

Paddy was coming. So one after another they climbed up the rope ladder, sat for a moment on the pile of sacking over the spikes, and then climbed down the other side.

Paddy was half-pushed, half-dragged up by the two boys. He leapt down the other side in one bound. Then he stood staring at the furry heap of dog

"Look—here's a tiny hanky," said Molly she picked up a small blue square

that lay beneath the tree not far off. He put up the hairs on his neck and growled softly. Then, stepping very stiffly, he walked slowly up. He sniffed, then looked round at the children, as if he was puzzled.

Tim went up to the dog that lay so still. He sniffed too. He touched the dog. It was warm and living.

"I believe it's just been knocked on the head and stunned," he said. "I can't smell any drug or poison. Now, let's go very cautiously, and see if we can spot where Anita-Mary is."

"Look—here's a tiny hanky," said Molly, in a low voice, and she picked up a small blue square. In the corner were the letters A.M. "She was here too."

The children wondered where to look for the little girl. Then Tim saw curious marks on the ground, in a long, irregular line. The earth was slightly scraped up.

"I say—I believe they got Anita-Mary and dragged her off through the trees here," he said. "See that scraped-up line? I bet that's where her feet dragged. Poor kid! What a shame! She must have been waiting for us here. She couldn't have shut Ricky up though, because he was here too."

"Let's follow the track her dragging feet made," said Jack. "But we must be jolly careful. We don't want to be caught ourselves."

So, very cautiously, they followed the track. It took them to an old tumble-down shed. The children stopped and peered about to see if any one was near. But they could see and hear nothing.

Tim went to the shed and peeped inside. He looked back at the others. "Nothing there," he said. "Only a barrow with some old sacks inside it."

But Paddy was not satisfied that there was nothing there. He bounded up to the barrow and began to sniff in excitement. Then he suddenly pulled at the sacking—and lo and behold, a little bare arm was uncovered.

"Why! Anita-Mary is hidden in the barrow!" cried Tim, as he pulled away the sacking. Sure enough, there was a pretty little girl there, with dark curly hair, and fat little cheeks. Her face was white, and her eyes were shut. There was a funny sweet smell hanging about. Tim sniffed.

"She's been drugged or something. Hark how loudly she is breathing. I bet the kidnappers meant to wheel her out of the grounds. A gardener could easily wheel this barrow to the gates, and not make any one suspicious. Then if a car could be pulled up just by the barrow—why, Anita-Mary could be popped into it as easily as anything, almost under the noses of the guards."

"But Tim—the gardeners have gone by now," said Jack. "Perhaps they meant to . . ."

"Sh!" suddenly said Molly, and Paddy growled. A whistling could be heard in the distance. Tim peeped out of the shed to see who it could be.

"Why! Anita-Mary is hidden in the barrow!" cried Tim as he pulled away the sacking

"It's two men. They look like electricians or something. They've got a little van in the drive. I bet it belongs to the kidnappers. I bet those men are the ones. One of them must have climbed over the wall and caught Ricky and Anita-Mary."

"Quick—get Anita-Mary out of the sacks," said Jack, and they all helped to drag the limp little girl out. They hid her under a bush.

"Paddy! You get into the sacks, quick," said Tim, his eyes gleaming. "Go on—good dog. They'll take *you*, instead of Anita-Mary—and what a shock they'll get when they find what's in the sacks. Now, lie quiet. Lie still. Sh! Sh! Good dog."

Paddy was used to games of all kinds. He thought of this as half a game, and half something queer.

He was quite ready to enter into it, however, whatever the game might be, and so he lay buried in the heap of sacks, perfectly still, so big that he made about the same sized lump as Anita-Mary had made.

Just in time the three children slipped into hiding. The two men who looked like electricians came up, and took the barrow. They wheeled it off

The two men who looked like electricians wheeled away the barrow

to the little van that stood in the drive. They bundled the sacks—and Paddy too—into the van, slammed the door, and pushed the barrow into the bushes.

Then both the men climbed into the van, and drove along the drive towards the gates. The guards let the van out, quite unsuspectingly, thinking it was merely the electricians who had come in earlier, saying they had been called to mend fuses.

As soon as the children saw the van drive towards the gate, they came out of hiding. They went to Anita-Mary and wondered what to do for her. There was a water-butt nearby, and Tim filled a watering-can he saw. Then

They helped Anita-Mary, who was a little shaky but very plucky

BERTRAM PRANCE

they all splashed the water over the little girl's face.

To their great delight she slowly opened her eyes and gave an enormous sigh. Then she sat up, clutching at Tim as she did so.

"Who are you?" she said wonderingly. "What's happened?"

The children told her all that had happened. She frowned a little. "I'm just beginning to remember something," she said. "Let me see. Yes—I was just going to take old Ricky to shut him up, when a man came up to me. Ricky began to bark and he hit him with a brick. Then he put something all round my face, and it smelt horrid. I don't remember any more."

"Poor Anita-Mary," said Molly. "That man hid you in his barrow, meaning to wait his chance to run you away in the van that his friend had ready in the drive. Well—the van has gone—and Paddy's gone with it."

"Who's Paddy?" asked Anita-Mary, looking much better now.

"Our dog," said Tim. "He'll give the kidnappers a lively time when they take off the sacks, meaning to find *you*."

"Anita-Mary had better come home with us," said Molly. "She'd be safe with us. There aren't any kidnappers at home. There might be some more here. Can you climb over a rope-ladder?"

"Yes, of course," said Anita-Mary, cheerfully. "If you can, I can."

They helped her to where they had left the rope-ladder. It was still there. Poor Ricky still lay beneath the trees, breathing slowly, a limp heap of dog. The children decided that they couldn't do anything about him. He would just have to look after himself when he woke up. They couldn't drag him over the rope-ladder.

They climbed over the wall, Anita-Mary a little shaky, but very plucky. All the children liked her. Molly thought she would make a fine friend —she wasn't a bit stuck-up or vain.

They took her home with them. It was getting late, and they heard the head-lines of the news on the wireless as they went in at the door. They stopped in surprise, and listened.

"A police message has just come in. Little Anita-Mary, the child film-star, has been kidnapped. A search made of her garden a short while ago revealed a rope-ladder flung over the wall. She——"

Daddy snapped off the wireless as they all came in. He looked annoyed.

"Why are you so late?" he said. "You know quite well I don't like——"

"Daddy! It's all right. We've not been into mischief," broke in Tim. "We've only been rescuing Anita-Mary. Look, here she is."

Mother jumped up in surprise. Daddy stared too. Anita-Mary burst into tears. The excitement had suddenly been too much for her. The children's mother put her arm round her.

"It's all right," she said. "You're safe here. Children, what *has* been happening?"

Tim, Jack and Molly told the whole story in bits. Their parents listened in amazement. "You put yourselves in great danger," said their father. "But anyway, you're safe—and poor little Anita-Mary is too. We'd better ring up the police and tell them."

"Oh and daddy—we didn't tell you about Paddy," said Tim. "We stuffed him into the sacking where Anita-Mary was hidden—and the kidnappers took him away thinking he was Anita-Mary herself. Won't they get a shock when they find out?"

They certainly *did* get a shock. They drove on for a good way before stopping the van, when one of the men climbed inside to pull back the sacking to give the kidnapped child some air—but to his great alarm he saw, not Anita-Mary, but the face of a large dog looking up at him—a face that seemed full of bare teeth and gleaming eyes.

He gave such a startled yell that the driver came rushing round to the back to look inside.

Paddy had pounced on the man inside and was chewing the sleeve off his coat, occasionally nipping the arm inside as well. He welcomed the other man with loud barks, darted at him, caught hold of his coat and dragged him inside the van too. There they lay, not daring to move, for the loud growls that Paddy gave were enough to frighten anyone.

Meantime the children's father had telephoned to the police to say that Anita-Mary was safe.

"Please will you keep her with you for the night," said the police-inspector. "We think she would be safer with you than with any one just now. No one knows where she is and they wouldn't dream of looking for her at your home."

Then the children's father told about the van that had driven off with the dog in the sacking. The inspector chuckled.

"What will those children of yours do next?" he said. "All right. We'll send out a wireless message to the police everywhere to keep a good look out for that van."

The van was soon found by a policeman cycling along the road. Surprised to see a van with no driver, he looked inside. Paddy welcomed him, for he was getting tired of chewing sleeves and trouser legs, and his throat was sore from growling. Both the men were there, scared out of their lives, and puzzled to know how a small girl could apparently have changed herself into a large and fierce dog.

Anita-Mary had a lovely night at the children's home, sharing Molly's bedroom. Molly was sorry for her, for the little rich film-star child had no mother or father, just an uncle who cared only for her money.

"You must come and play with me every single day now," said Anita-Mary earnestly the next day. "I do like you all so much, and I think you're very clever and brave. As for Paddy guarding those wicked men and keeping them prisoner till a policeman turned up, I think he's just wonderful. I'm sure he'll make friends with poor Ricky, and we'll all have a lovely time together."

And now, each day of the holidays, Tim, Jack and Molly set off to the big house with Paddy. The guards stand at the gate as usual. There are spikes all round the wall, and a man patrols the grounds. But always the three children are allowed inside with polite salutes, and Paddy rushes off to find his firm friend, Ricky.

"We looked for an adventure and we found *you*, Anita-Mary," says Molly. "You have all kinds of wonderful adventures when you act for the films, don't you—but you had the biggest one of all in real life.'

They are greeted with polite salutes

BEACH an

A WIDE sandy beach, though pleasant as a playground, is not the best place to see something of the life of the sea shore; the stony and rocky parts of the shore hold far more interesting things. Perhaps best of all are the pools left on rocky shores by the retreating tide, for they are happy hunting grounds where one may spend many hours always finding new and strange things and creatures.

A sandy beach has little cover and very little food for any kind of plant or animal, but often at low tide when the softer and perhaps more muddy sands are uncovered, it pays to look closely among the wavy ripple marks. You see, quite a number of shell animals which live just below the surface of the sand can then be found. Razorfish and cockles of many kinds live in muddy sands and there are strange and beautifully coloured worms. The sand-worm tubes are sometimes many inches long, boring

Rock Pools
By William Aspden

deep into the sand. If water lodges among the ripple marks then quite often the creatures give themselves away by showing the little net or other apparatus by means of which they catch their food when the tide is in. One can often find cockles by such traces.

Razorshells are far more interesting than cockles. Their long and often beautifully coloured shells are frequently found lying on the sand, but the living animal is not so easy to see.

The shells are shaped rather like the handle of an old-fashioned razor—the two halves of which form a cylinder, the ends being open. From one end of the cylinder the creature can extend its single foot, and from the other the two siphons by means of which it takes in and sends out again the sea water from which it extracts food. The razorshell has no mouth or teeth. It takes in a constant stream of sea water and any particles of matter floating in the water are either digested or rejected as the stream passes through the siphons. The fact that they and millions of other creatures who feed in a similar manner, extract all their food from sea water shows what an immense amount of material there is floating about in it, even though to us it may appear quite clear.

Razorshells have another peculiarity which they share with most bivalves. They, that is, creatures with hinged double shells, have only one foot, but they can get along quite well. The long hinge along one side enables the two halves of the shell to be opened in order to allow a greater freedom of flow for sea water when the creature is needing a really hearty meal.

The shell is covered with a silky sort of skin which has a pearly sheen and shows lovely soft colours rather like wet silk.

When the creature prepares to burrow down into the sand, it will lie on the surface for several minutes and nothing happens. Then, slowly and cautiously the foot begins to extend from the end. The end is pointed and very soon is pushed down into the sand. This happens very slowly at first until a good grip is obtained. This grip is secured in a curious fashion. When the animal has pushed its foot downwards, as far as it can, an extra amount of blood is forced down into the foot and that causes the point to swell into a bulb. Thus the creature gets anchorage and immediately gives a sharp pull which shortens the foot. The whole shell suddenly stands up on end on the surface of the sand. Almost at once the foot is pushed further down below the surface and with another heave, half the shell slides below. One or two more pulls and the

The whole shell suddenly stands upright on the surface of the sand

whole thing disappears below the surface. All this is done very quickly and the razorshell goes on down and down until it feels itself out of danger. The speed at which it can burrow is surprising.

Sea-urchins and starfish are among other creatures which are sometimes plentiful on muddy shores. They are quite closely related, and if you examine the shell of a sea-urchin it is really very like a starfish with the arms closed up. There are many kinds of starfish, some of which have only five arms, while others, like the sunstar, have anything up to twelve or

When a starfish travels, it appears to slide along the sea-bed

fourteen. Brittle-stars and feather-stars are beautifully coloured creatures with long feather-like arms which look as though they could not be of much use except as decoration. This is far from true because all starfish have thousands of tiny suckers on the under sides of their arms and, by wrapping themselves round the shells of mussels and other shell animals on which they feed, they can quite literally force the shells of their victims open. If you have ever tried to open a mussel shell without a knife or something similar, you will realize how very strong both the arms and the tiny suckers must be.

Starfish travel along the sea-bed by means of these suckers which are all interconnected by a series of canals containing water. Watch a starfish travelling and you will notice that it appears to *slide* along the sea-bed, *pulling* itself along by the tiny suckers. Sea-urchins are even more odd for they pull themselves along by means of their teeth.

Perhaps one of the most interesting things about simple creatures living in the sea is that so many of them make the most curious uses of their different limbs.

For instance, the little grey barnacle —the acorn-barnacle—which is often found in dense masses on rocks, sea-walls and the wood and stonework of piers just about high-water mark, makes a curious use of its legs. Acorn-barnacles are distant relatives of crabs and lobsters and, when very young, they swim about in enormous numbers, as active as a cloud of gnats. After about a month of this busy life they get tired and settle on any convenient thing which happens to be near. The odd thing is that they rest by standing on their heads, and they like being in that position so much that they glue themselves down firmly. Next, they begin to grow a shell to protect themselves from fish, crabs and other creatures who like to make a meal of baby barnacles. Soon the cone-shaped shell sets hard. There is an opening at the top, but this can be closed by means of two hinged doors when the tide goes out and leaves the barnacle uncovered. These trap doors serve not only to protect the barnacle from birds and insects, but also to retain a certain amount of water inside the shell so that the barnacle has sufficient oxygen to

*As soon as the tide returns, the barnacle opens the door and sticks out
its legs which it waves to and fro in the water*

live on until the tide covers it again. As soon as the tide returns the barnacle opens the doors and sticks out its legs —legs rather like tiny feathers—which it waves to and fro in the water. What is actually happening, of course, is that the creature is constantly kicking little particles of food into its mouth with its feathery legs.

A weedy and rocky seashore is one of the best places to study what are termed associations, for so dense is the population and so fierce the struggle for life that all kinds of strange friendships for mutual assistance are to be found.

Association means that certain groupings of animals are usually found living and working together just as people who work at many different trades live together in towns.

Such associations may consist of widely differing creatures. There are some which feed on plants and live on or amongst seaweeds; others consist of attached forms of life—sponges, sea anemones, corals and corallines or rock burrowers; whilst others may be carnivorous creatures which prey on the other communities or attach themselves to a particular community for purposes of obtaining food.

Some most interesting and close associations are found in which two very different creatures depend on each other so much that one just could not live without the other, or at least would find things very difficult. An interesting case of this kind can be seen in some rock pools round our coast where one may find hermit crabs. There is often a close association between sponges and hermit crabs. One species of hermit crab which lives in shells up to whelk size, often has a large sea anemone attached to the shell it uses, and frequently there is also a particular kind of tube worm living on the shell. The three very different kinds of creatures are so frequently found together in this queer companionship that it just cannot be an accident. Another, smaller hermit crab nearly always carries a large mass of sponge on the shell which it inhabits.

The association between the crab, the sea anemone and the worm is interesting and there is no doubt that the stinging tentacles of the anemone help to keep away certain enemies of the crab, and the crab, when feeding, almost certainly supplies little particles of food for the anemone. Where the worm comes into the party no one yet knows, but there can be no doubt that there is some advantage to all concerned from the association.

There is a small pea-crab which lives inside mussel shells and sometimes inside sea anemones.

It appears to be a rather helpless kind of creature and it lives entirely upon its host. Its shell is round and smooth, and its legs fit in so closely to its body that there are absolutely no sharp edges or corners which would irritate the mussel. If there were it would either try to get rid of the crab, or try to grow a covering of pearl over it as mussels do when a grain of sand happens to get into their shell.

One species of hermit crab often has a large sea anemone attached to the shell it uses, with perhaps a tube worm also living on the shell

The common mussel does not, however, form pearls which are of any real value. The so-called pearl oyster from which valuable pearls are taken, is not really an oyster at all. It is more closely related to our common sea mussel.

If you wish to look for pearls in Great Britain it is no use wasting time over mussels on the shore or in rock pools. Valuable pearls are often found in freshwater mussels, and at one time British pearls were collected on a big scale. One of the finest pearls in the royal crown came from a freshwater mussel which was dredged up in the River Conway, and about a hundred and fifty years ago there was a considerable trade in pearls between this country and India.

Many creatures besides mussels and oysters produce pearly nacre. Even the silvery appearance of fish scales is caused by a similar substance. This is principally lime which has undergone certain chemical processes within the body of the creature concerned, and is very like the material out of which the protecting shells and armour of shell animals are formed.

Armour is an important matter among sea-living creatures as there are so many savage enemies always on the prowl, and any soft-bodied creature must either have a coat of armour, or some other means of protection. The hermit crabs, mentioned earlier, are not provided with armour on the body and so are forced to make use of discarded shells built by other creatures, but other crabs have a full suit of jointed armour which is sufficient to protect them against most of their enemies.

Although this armour has many

One of the finest pearls in the royal crown was found in a freshwater mussel in the River Conway

advantages, at the same time there are very grave disadvantages. A crab, the common shore crab for instance, grows fairly rapidly from a tiny thing about as big as the head of a glass-headed pin to three or four inches across the back. Unlike bivalves such as cockles and mussels, and univalves such as periwinkles and whelks, crabs cannot increase the size of their shells by adding a bit to the edges. A crab goes on feeding for some weeks and his shell is hard and cannot expand. After a time he gets more and more uncomfortable and must feel like a swollen foot inside a shoe which is too tight.

Soon the crab begins getting rid of his hard shell. All the elastic joints of his legs and nippers turn bright yellow, or orange, in colour and the shell itself changes from greeny bronze to dull red. He leaves his regular hunting ground and seeks out a nice, safe hiding place, usually under weed-covered rocks, where he can find a few inches of soft mud. Then he begins to cast his shell. The leg coverings are gradually worked loose and he shakes them away. Next the hard covering across his back and the underplates come away and finally the covering of his nippers.

He can stretch himself again and feel remarkably free and, in fact, he does get much bigger, but there is one serious matter which requires immediate attention. His shell is now soft all over, even to the tips of his nippers. He couldn't fight even if he wanted, couldn't feed and couldn't protect himself from enemies in any way. He is compelled for a matter of a few days to keep well out of sight and so creeps into his hiding place and burrows down into the soft mud under the weed and rock.

Fishermen often search for him at such times for he makes a favourite bait for certain methods of fishing.

Often you will find these soft crabs when you look under stones for sponges and anemones.

Sea anemones are among the most beautiful things one can find in the sea.

Many live in rock pools, usually well down shore below the half-tide line. They are actually very simple animals, simple in structure that is, for they consist of a bag or stomach, no limbs, eyes or ears. Round the opening to the stomach there is an elaborate arrangement of tentacles, usually of some beautiful colour, and these tentacles can be opened out until they look very like the petals of a flower. Indeed the very name anemone suggests that they are flower-like in shape. It is not easy, perhaps, to think of them as animals at all. The commonest forms found in rock pools are the

Crab casting its shell

beadlets, usually bright red, orange or purple in colour. When the tide is out beadlets close up and look like little knobs of coloured jelly, but when open they are quite beautiful.

The finest anemones, however, live in that part of the shore which is just about the lowest tide mark, what is termed the laminaria zone. Laminaria is the long, leathery seaweed often ten or twelve feet long, of a brownish-olive colour, which grows far down the beach and is only partially uncovered at low spring tides. Among the great tough roots of laminaria countless myriads of creatures spend their whole lives, among them the finest and most beautifully coloured anemones. Some are pale mauve, others pink and soft green or yellow; some are purple, and some have brilliant cobalt-blue fringelets round the main fringe of tentacles.

A few live on sandy beaches, making long tubes rather like big caddis tubes, but built upright in the sand, and the entrance is well camouflaged with grains of sand. When the tide covers the beach the anemone comes to the surface and puts out its fringe of tentacles to catch food. The tentacles of anemones are armed with stinging cells which can quickly paralyse any small fish or other creature on which they seize. These stinging cells are tiny cavities filled with fluid, and inside is a miniature harpoon attached to a fine thread which is coiled like a spring. The instant any creature touches a tentacle of an anemone out shoot scores of the tiny harpoons injecting the poison into the victim. It dies at once and the lovely petal-like tentacles draw it into the stomach to be digested. Anemones also feed on a great deal of dead matter which is floating about in the water, little broken scraps of fish, shrimps and other creatures. In fact, they are extremely useful scavengers and do their share in helping to keep sea water clean.

Closely related to sea anemones are

Sea anemones

Jelly-fish

the so-called jelly-fish. Indeed they are, in structure, almost exactly like anemones except that they have a more elaborate system of stinging tentacles, and long thread-like and invisible trailers also armed with stings. It is with these trailing threads that jelly-fish often cause stings like nettle-rash on the arms and legs of those unfortunate people who happen to be bathing when a shoal drifts close inshore.

Jelly-fish, unlike anemones, have the power of free movement but nevertheless they are not really able completely to control the direction in which they travel.

Among the more common objects found in rock pools are shrimps and prawns. The shrimp's colour is rather sandy (when it's alive, and before being boiled!) and it is covered with tiny dark brown specks so that on sand, and especially when half buried in the sand, it is far from easy to see. There are, however, other kinds of shrimps in rock pools. One is so well camouflaged that it can hardly be seen at all. It has the very best kind of camouflage, being practically trans-

parent. Only the creature's eyes are really visible, two specks of black which appear to be jerking about as though attached by an invisible thread. Only when the shrimp takes a meal can it be seen, for then the food inside its stomach is clearly visible.

Lobsters and crabs are related to shrimps and prawns, and if you

Shrimps

A lobster will lie in a pool by the rocks, half-camouflaged by seaweed, with long antennæ waving about in the water

happen to be studying a rock pool down near the water's edge and notice two long antennæ waving about from under a bunch of weed, don't put your hand in to find out what is there. It may be a lobster, and to shake hands with a lobster is a somewhat painful business.

He is always so "hearty" in his greeting and so glad to meet you that he just won't let go! Poke him out, if you want to, with a stick or an iron hook but be very careful how you handle him. Hold him behind the shoulders and he cannot nip you at all. Live lobsters are often beautifully coloured, deep blue with red and purple feelers, and the edges of their pincers and legs are nicely picked out in reddish orange or terra-cotta.

Under stones on a rocky shore, one often finds a small eel-like fish with two rows of dark spots along its back. This is the gunnel, or butterfish, and sometimes it is found inside an oyster shell curled round a bunch of pearly-looking eggs.

In pools with sandy bottoms you can find baby flat-fish, both dabs and plaice.

They are not at all easy to see, partly owing to their colouring which exactly matches the sand on which they live, and partly because of the quickness with which they can almost cover themselves with sand. If you happen to notice a small "puff" of sand suddenly appear on the bed of such a pool you may be certain that it is either a shrimp or one of the baby flat-fish.

Sometimes in rock pools near the mouths of rivers, one finds stickle-backs. The ten-spined stickleback normally lives in the sea but our friend, the tiddler, can also adapt himself to life in salt water. In order to do this he has to grow a protective covering over his scales, and when one meets with him in a rock pool he is bright silver in colour. That colouring is due to the special covering material which he puts on—just as salmon and sea trout do—when he decides to go for a holiday in the sea. He has the curious power of retaining the water in his body. Normally, if a freshwater fish is placed in sea water it quickly dies owing to the fact that there is more salt dissolved in the sea than there is in the fluid of the fish's body.

As a result much of the moisture in the fish's body is drawn out through the skin, and the fish simply dies of thirst even though it is swimming about in sea water. The silvery coating stops this process of losing moisture which would render the fish incapable of life in salt water.

When the fish returns to live in fresh water the silvery appearance fades just as it does with salmon and sea trout which have been in a river for some considerable time.

Many of these creatures can easily be kept and studied in a sea-water aquarium, but unless one lives near the sea this is not very satisfactory as sea water is not easy to obtain inland and just dissolving salt in fresh water will not do. There are other substances in sea water which are important to the lives of creatures living in it. Perhaps the easiest things to keep are anemones. They are easy to feed on scraps of animal matter and do nearly all the work of keeping the water free from decaying matter themselves. Therefore, there is little risk of the dreadful smelly business which results from a badly managed sea-water aquarium.

A small net, a glass jar, a warm sunny day and a nice rocky beach will provide you with almost endless interest, for nowhere else is it possible to find more exciting things and more beautifully coloured creatures.

TREASURE AND SCAVENGER HUNTS

By David Rodney

INDOOR TREASURE HUNT

Treasure hunts are always very popular. The players usually prefer to seek the clues in couples, since two heads are better than one in puzzling things out. Therefore, to start the hunt, first divide the party into twos, and give each couple the first clue written on a piece of paper.

The clues should not be too easy; keep the players guessing for a bit, so that the hunt is made more exciting. As the various couples solve the clues

Two heads are better than one

they should proceed cautiously and try to read the clue without letting the other couples know the secret. The clues should be hidden all over the house, and consist of quite short sentences so that they can be easily memorized. No clue must be removed from its place, but players may write it down if it helps them to remember, making sure that they get well away from the clue before starting to write it down, or they will surely give the game away to others. An umpire should watch the couples to make sure they do not jump clues by stumbling on one accidentally.

Here is a specimen list of clues and hiding places from which you may get some ideas for a treasure hunt of your own : —

1. *Count six as you go up.* This is the first clue which is given to all the couples.

2. *Where the waters flow.* This clue is placed on the sixth stair, either between the banisters or tucked under the stair carpet.

3. *I am trodden underfoot.* The clue is placed under the bath.

4. *The answer is in books.* Place this clue under the door mat.

5. *Seek behind a closed door.* To be placed in a book on the bookshelf, with part of the clue showing.

6. *The keys to this clue are many.*

This should be inside a closed cupboard.

7. *Where your head rests.* The clue should be on the keyboard of the piano, with the lid down, of course.

8. *Where distant voices are heard.* Pinned to the pillow on one of the beds.

9. *Where you sit at ease.* This clue should be placed behind the wireless.

10. *Seek fuel for the fire.* To be put under an arm-chair.

11. *Shuts out the light.* The clue is placed behind the coal scuttle.

12. *Seek the treasure in a top drawer.* Pin this clue behind a curtain or blind.

In the top drawer of a dressing table, or chest of drawers, a small prize representing the hidden treasure is triumphantly found by the winning couple.

This clue is pinned to a pillow on one of the beds

GARDEN TREASURE HUNT

In the summer a garden treasure hunt is good fun. The same rules are followed as for an indoor hunt, the only difference of course, being that all the clues are hidden in the garden. Here is a suggested list of clues and hiding places, though it can only be used as a guide, since gardens differ.

The first clue, written on a piece of paper, is given to each of the couples.

1. *Keep to the well-marked track.*

2. *Danger—rocks ahead.* This clue is placed somewhere on a garden path.

3. *Seek on the boundary line.* Place this clue on the rockery.

4. *Where the queen of the flowers is found.* Pinned on to the fence with a drawing pin.

5. *Under the plant protector.* Fasten this clue to a rose bush.

6. *Search along the row of flowers.* This clue is placed under a glass frame.

7. *At the entrance to the garden.* Hidden among the front flowers of a border.

8. *Seek where things to eat are grown.* Fasten the clue to the gate with a drawing pin.

9. *Look among the branches.* This clue is placed in the vegetable garden.

10. *Follow the mower's track.* Hide this clue among the branches of a tree.

11. *Here you may be tempted to linger.* Place this clue on the edge of the grass.

12. *Seek the treasure where the implements are kept.* Put this clue in a fruit bush or tree.

The treasure is carefully hidden among the tools in the shed in the garden for the winning couple to find.

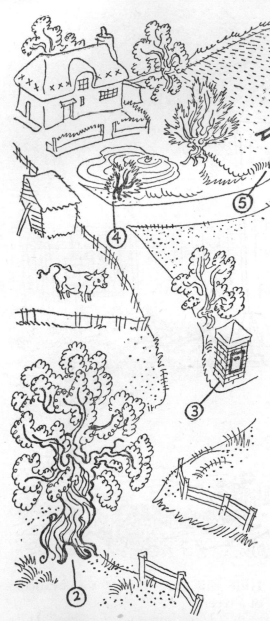

COUNTRYSIDE TREASURE HUNT

This kind of treasure hunt needs a little more preparation than the others, as you must first go out for a walk in the neighbourhood and find suitable hiding places for your clues. Do not go too far afield, or you will find some of the treasure hunters will get lost when you turn them loose to look for the clues.

When you have discovered about twelve good spots where you can hide the clues, make them up and write them out, and then on the day you have planned for the treasure hunt, you will have to take another walk to hide the clues in the places you have chosen.

As with the indoor treasure hunt, the first clues are given on slips of paper to the couples, and they must follow the rules already given for indoor hunts. It is a good plan to have the treasure hidden indoors, and for the last clue to send the couples back. If you plan the clues carefully, you can send the seekers on a circular tour, starting out from home and gradually working back again.

Here is a specimen list to give you some idea for clues and hiding places, though of course, the clues you make up will depend on the country near you. They must be a little more helpful and easier to find than the indoor clues, or you will find some of the players wandering much too far from the route and getting lost completely!

The first clue to be given to all the couples could be:—

1. *Turn left at the gate and seek the hollow oak at the fork.*

2. *Look near the place where letters are put.* This clue is tucked into the hollow of an oak tree.

3. *The bush by the pond holds the secret.* This clue is placed as near as possible to the letter box.

4. *The signpost at the crossroads may point the way.* The clue is fastened to a bush near the duck pond.

5. *Go to the church gate, but do not enter.* Conceal this clue at the foot of the signpost.

6. *Try the nearest stile to help you on your way.* Hide this in a convenient spot just in front of the church gate.

7. *Walk along the lane until you come to the farm gate.* This clue should be fastened somewhere on the stile where it cannot easily be seen.

8. *The old barn has many secrets behind its door.* Fasten this clue somewhere on the farm gate.

9. *Seek the third tree in the lane that leads home.* Pin this clue somewhere behind the barn door.

10. *Look for the treasure in a dark cavern in the house.* This clue is pinned or fastened to the trunk of the third tree along the lane.

The treasure is hidden in a closed cupboard at home.

It is a good idea for the umpire to go out with the seekers and keep an eye on them as far as possible, to see that none go too far from the track.

SCAVENGER HUNT

This is a form of treasure hunt which has become very popular. The players are paired up, as for treasure hunts, and each pair is given a list of about twelve articles to be collected. They all set off in search of these articles at the same time, and the first couple to bring back the complete list gets the prize.

The articles in the list should not be too easy to find, though not, of course, impossible. Here is a suggested list for a scavenger hunt in the country: —

1. A bird's feather.
2. A fir cone.
3. A twig (or leaf).
4. A certain flower which you know grows in the neighbourhood.
5. A catkin.
6. A piece of straw.
7. An ivy leaf.
8. A piece of flowering gorse.
9. A wisp of sheep's wool.
10. A shell (any kind, such as a snail's, or fancy garden shell).
11. A toadstool.
12. A piece of bramble.

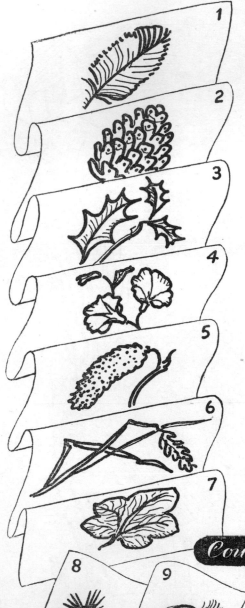

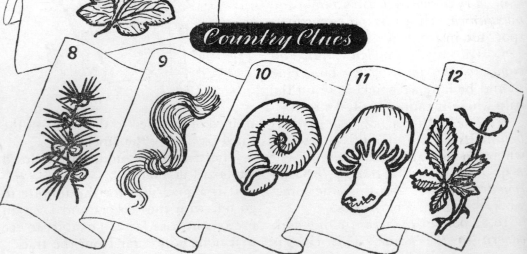

Country Clues

The items on this list will vary, of course, according to the seasons of the year, and you must make sure that everything on your list can be found locally.

For a town scavenger hunt, it is best to give a list of articles which are to be found mostly in the house, or in the players' own houses if they live near, but they need not be restricted in their search, and may go anywhere where they think they might be able to find the articles on their lists. Here are some suggestions for a scavenger hunt in a town:—

1. A bus or tram ticket.
2. A used stamp.
3. A daily newspaper.
4. A small piece of coal.
5. A used match.
6. An empty cigarette box.
7. A shoe button.
8. A pencil.
9. A reel of cotton.
10. A hair ribbon.
11. A marble.
12. An umbrella.

You will be able to think of many other lists to set for the scavengers.

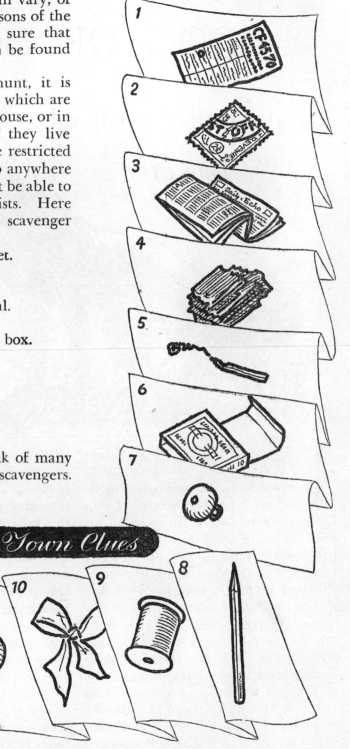

Town Clues

DOG OF GOLD

An Australian bush tale

By John Ein

DAVID HOLME was riding round his fences, or boundaries, on a dreary night with blustery storms of rain lashing down. Not a thing could his keen bushman's eyes see, save the black limbs of trees tossing against the lesser blackness of the sky. So he left everything to his mare, knowing well that her eyes could pierce through any darkness. In the great Australian bush one has to take many chances—what with snakes, bush fires, floods, falling timber, and riding buckjumpers.

Tonight the howl of a dingo from the virgin bush beyond David's paddocks had called horse and man into the night. A dingo or Australian wild dog is a thing of terror to the sheepfarmer, a very cruel beast once it gets among sheep. It kills, not from necessity as other animals kill, but for the sake of killing. It is so cunning that it is rarely seen and much less shot at, so cunning that it will eat nothing that smells of man. That's why David Holme never touched with his bare hand the pieces of poisoned meat he was fixing outside his fence. But if any dingo did chance to gobble one of those baits he was a goner.

A whimpering cry brought the man to a standstill. Nothing could he see but a great black shadow outside his fence where the trees of the virgin bush reached out for countless miles, rolling on and on like a tree-clad sea until they became a vast loneliness which men called " out-back " or the " never-never " lands. Then the cry came again. Some creature was in trouble—in pain! Such a cry never went unanswered by David. In a moment he was off his horse. " Sounds like a dog that's been hurt bad," he muttered.

Then came another whimper, very pitiful to hear. David clambered over his fence and felt his way to the creature; then struck a match, revealing a sorely hurt dog. He knelt and very tenderly felt the creature's body over. " Seems about all in," he

thought, and then carefully carried the dog home to the bush hut where he lived. She proved to be an Australian kelpie sheep bitch, but she had been cruelly bitten and torn. " Looks to me as if them dingoes had set about you, poor lass," he said, and she feebly wagged her tail in answer. " Maybe one of them male dingoes took a likin' to ye and then the females got jealous and tore ye about. Poor lassie, it's little I can do for you now."

That night the creature gave birth to three puppies. Although David did his best, she died towards morning. Only one puppy survived, a strong and lusty male of a curious yellow hue, that

David struck a match, revealing a sorely hurt dog

howled bitterly, and then attempted to lick David's hand as if it already felt its loneliness. Something in the puppy's helplessness touched David.

In this manner the dog Bonz was born. His fame as a sheep dog eventually reached across Australia, over into New Zealand and South Africa. Of his rearing, his training and his epic deeds this story will tell.

How did he come by his name and what does it mean? Well, young Boomer really christened him when he dropped in upon David one day. They called the man " Boomer " because he made a living by shooting the big red or " boomer " kangaroos for their skins out in the never-never bush, at the back of beyond. For weeks at a time Boomer would camp alone, twenty, fifty, a hundred miles from the nearest settler, his big dogs running down and Boomer shooting the big " kangar " or " roos." Then he would return laden with skins for sale. When Boomer saw the puppy, he whistled. " I lay a pound," he said to David, " that that pup's father was a dingo! Look at that ruff along the pup's neck and spine. Look at that plume of a tail and look at that colour. It's dinkum gold, I tell you. I seed a big dingo just like him once—a bonza bloke."

" Ah," said David, who liked better to listen than to talk. " Did you indeed?"

" I had just rounded a big rock when we two came face to face. There he stood, bold and proud, looking at me with eyes golden where the sun struck glints out of 'em. Then, as I grabbed for me gun, he whisked around and was gone, and I never saw him since. I lay a pound that a dingo fathered this pup. Born of a kelpie mother, you say? Shouldn't be surprised because a kelpie is a wonderful dog for sheep. The kelpie breed has been bred and trained for nothing else."

David was too intent on the puppy to answer. Barely able to walk itself, it had been playing with some chickens which were scratching around; and then with guile and with set purpose the pup selected one special chicken and started to edge it towards its coop with the idea of driving it in. Oh, the perversity of that chicken! It wouldn't go anywhere, least of all where it was driven. Quietly, working to a plan, the tiny, ambling, leggy pup started again and yet again to drive it. Nearer it got, nearer and yet nearer and then with a rush and a shrill yapping the chicken was jostled inside the coop, protesting vigorously. It was a triumph for the puppy's skill and patience.

" Born in him," said David then. " Natural for him to drive sheep. That li'l feller can no more help shepherdin' something than he can help breathin'. He's made a start a-driving chickens but some day he'll be a marvel at shepherding sheep. That dog will be worth his weight in gold when he grows up."

" If you trust that pup when he's big among your sheep, David Holme," said Boomer earnestly, " you'll be a ruined man. He's been fathered by a killer and he'll surely grow to be a killer hisself. Knock him on the head quick, I say. But I'm sorry because he'd grow into a bonza li'l feller with his gold jacket."

" A bonza little feller, to be sure. A great little dog at shepherding sheep," said David thoughtfully. " Maybe I'll keep him and we'll call him Bonza."

The alarmed Boomer just gaped at him. This was madness.

"Seriously, you mustn't keep that pup, David," persisted Boomer.

Then David said, "I tell you, Boomer, that there li'l dog has been sent for me to train. For why? Because them dingoes has killed a terrible lot of my sheep one time and another and lots of sheep belonging to other poor farmers. He's going to make up for some of them losses. That's why I'm keeping him, and that's why I'm calling him Bonza, which means *good*. He's a good-hearted pup."

Now what could Boomer, who was short and slight, say to a remark like that from David Holme, who was tall and stringy and quick with his hands beyond belief, and who had a reputation for gentling horses or dogs that no other man could handle? So Boomer went off without another word, and the yellow pup became Bonza, which means good and true.

The pup selected one special chicken and started to edge it towards its coop

Very soon Bonza became shortened to Bonz. He idolized his master, and bred in his bones was that other passion—for sheep of all sorts and sizes, any kind of sheep—lambs, ewes, rams, hoggets, wethers, store sheep, fat sheep. Bonz and his master both thought, talked and lived sheep. Within limits at present, Bonz was allowed to ride around with his master, to watch his master and other dogs of which he was tormentingly jealous, working with the sheep. But the tempestuous, untrained and head-strong puppy had to learn to trail along behind, and was quelled if he even barked. How he would have loved at that time to get one good bite home on those sheep and scatter and chase them.

Yet all the while Bonz was being taught by a master of sheep-dog craft and by a method known only to a few. Fewer men still could have trained a dog like Bonz, because the whole scheme was based on the fact that a dog has a sixth or an extra sense—a sense of knowing what is going to happen. Inexhaustible patience and affection were the main things, but not the sort of affection which expresses itself by pattings and pettings. David could be stern. Neither he nor any other man might break the rule that Bonz must never be caressed—by any one. Nobody might touch Bonz except David and only David fed him. If Bonz did well he was given a word of approval; if ill, a sharp rebuke— never any bribes or titbits, never any other sort of reward. Bonz grew to trust David more and more as the days passed, because he never experienced injustice, never suffered unkindness. Above all things Bonz had to learn to understand exactly what his master wanted him to do. Everything had to be as carefully explained to Bonz as if he were a human being.

So when the day's work was over the two would sit in David's wooden-walled hut. Sometimes the rain drummed or thundered upon the galvanized iron roof while they sat before a fire of logs. Sometimes in the summer they would lie under a tree and talk.

" No, Bonz," David would say, " none of your snuggling up, currying favour or begging attention. None of your smoodgings, lad. Set you down over there, quiet and dignified and listen." Bonz lay with his head between his paws, his eyes fixed upon his master, listening for all he was worth. " You see, Bonz, I aims to make a real dog out of you. I aims to trust you with everything I've got. I wants you to help me, day in, day out, year in, year out." Bonz made a little sound at this, as if his affection for his master must burst out some way.

David would relight his pipe and wait. Not too much at a time was his method with Bonz.

One day David noted how quickly Bonz was growing out of puppyhood. The yellowness had grown out of his coat and was replaced by a rich light brown which in the sunlight shone brightly golden; at certain angles his eyes would flash with gold, giving him a queer illumined look. A ridge of fur grew on his neck and his tail was a proudly carried plume. Beautiful, lionlike almost, Bonz had grown, yet his heart was subjected by love for his master.

One hot day they rested beside a billabong—a natural water hole. That day was a scorcher. Bonz had cooled himself by a swim and lay steaming. Around them the ranks of the great gum trees stretched for countless miles, plentiful as the waves of the sea. Overhead was the blue, blue sky, bright with sunlight, while below heat stabbed down violently. The leaves of the big red gum tree above them fairly

like a tiny dragon hissed at man and dog and then withdrew. Yes, it was hot.

But not too hot to teach Bonz. "Them sheep has been out of the ordinary cussed today, Bonz lad. I see you thirsting to get a bite in. But you mustn't never, never bite a sheep with them bright teeth of yours, although you and I both know that a sheep can

Bonz lay with his head between his paws, listening for all he was worth

dripped with sunlight. Heat had cracked open its bark and treacly gum, bright red at first but soon darkening, oozed down the trunk, forming a big brown splodge. In the branches a kookaburra bird laughed rudely, jeeringly, as is the way of kookaburras, and a bob-tailed iguana

be the most maddening creature ever."

Not a word missed Bonz, his ears cocked and watching David with all his soul in his eyes. David was as mindful of the dog. This was his method, and do you think Bonz understood and remembered this talk? Not altogether. Perhaps the actual words passed him by; the tone meant far, far more because it indicated what David was thinking and feeling, so it went deep and stuck in Bonz's memory.

That was perhaps why he learned to watch a mob of sheep going down to drink with a jealous eye. Maybe that mob had grazed for some twenty-four hours without a drink and when they came near water they fairly rushed it. Bonz would then hustle them from the muddy places where they might bog themselves, and make them drink from some clear sandy pool. Or perhaps Bonz would find a sheep lying flat on its back kicking helplessly, when he would gently roll that sheep back on to its feet. Or maybe he would free some sheep which had become tangled up in a fallen tree or fence or scrub, or if he couldn't do so, go and fetch David.

Another story of Bonz tells how once a ewe and lamb climbed a great granite bluff in David's hill-paddock, up and up until they stood at its very crest. Vast and magnificent was the panorama which lay beneath the vault of blue sky. The bush reached out to the horizon, a great vista of trees—those nearby brown-green in hue, deepening to an indigo in the middle distance, then changing to a clear bright blue and at the horizon to a brilliant purple, clear, bright and shining in the marvellous atmosphere. It was a sunscape rather than a landscape that that ewe might have gazed on. But not she: she was browsing on the scanty grass that grew between granite boulders. The lamb followed, complaining, after her.

Alone up in that tremendous vault something with wonderful eyes watched the doddering white speck which was the lamb. Then the great eagle swooped earthwards in a dive a mile deep; at that same moment a dog streaked up the hillside after the ewe, so that the swooping bird met a snarling dog with battle-red eyes and bright ferocious teeth. Three times that eagle swooped, and three times Bonz drove it off. Once its talons sank deep into the dog while Bonz bit into a scurry of flesh and feathers. The eagle soared away and Bonz hustled that foolish old ewe and her lamb back to the scrublands where they were safe.

This simply goes to show that Bonz did learn something from those talks, and also that his gift of *knowing* was increasing; else how had he known about the eagle, the ewe and her lamb?

Not that Bonz didn't have sad, sad lapses from grace. Once he streaked off after a kangaroo, forgetting his duty to the sheep and to his master—forgetting everything but the chase. Not that he caught anything, because the kangaroo could hop two yards while Bonz ran one. But he made himself ridiculous and then came sneaking back to camp mighty ashamed of himself. Not a bit of notice did David take of Bonz for a while, giving time for the enormity of his offence to sink home. At last David broached the subject, talking and talking to Bonz but never raising his voice in anger. Then the flames of the camp fire revealed an abject Bonz, his tail drooping, his belly flattened to earth. No need for harsh words. Little pitiful whines were heard until at last Bonz could stand it no longer and faded away into the darkness. Then David heard Bonz cry out, telling the silent trees, the creeks and ranges, the wide bushlands and the moon of his grief

As the great eagle swooped earthwards, Bonz streaked up the hillside after the ewe

and shame in that dingo wail, that dingo howl, come down from generations of killer ancestors. At last David called him in a changed voice and poor Bonz crept back with feebly wagging tail and ventured to lick David's hand and was forgiven.

Such lapses were few. Afterwards a host of kangaroos might dart up from

of them and of their mother at first, but soon he forgot everything except his master and his sheep. Shepherding, mustering, droving, helping in the dipping and shearing of sheep had again become the one interest of his days and nights.

No man then dreamed that those sons of Bonz—aye and their sons and

*Bonz was devotedly licking
the lamb back to life*

under his very nose and not an eyelid would Bonz blink, nor would he stir a muscle.

One spring when Bonz had grown big and strong and very leonine in appearance, David made a journey and came back with a young kelpie sheepdog bitch. Soon she settled down with David and Bonz; soon she and the latter became friends.

Later, six tiny puppies were born to the bitch. Bonz seemed quite proud

grandsons and great-grandsons and all the generations descended from Bonz would some day be famous because of their great forebear.

The full story of the feats Bonz accomplished with sheep, his canniness and wisdom would fill a whole book. Some of the stories seem incredible but they are nevertheless true. For instance, the neighbours still tell the story of the drowning lamb. It seems that one winter David and Bonz found a score or so of their ewes and lambs marooned on a sandbank by the floods. Each sheep had to be caught, its legs bound, lifted into a cart and carted away into safety. It was dangerous work for the horse and cart, for the floods were deep and rapid and both might have been swept away. Then, when a cartload of sheep had reached

to reach the two he found Bonz devotedly licking the lamb back to life and looking immensely pleased with himself and none the worse for his adventure.

Bonz had to learn to obey absolutely, and when his puppies grew to be dogs, Bonz was made to feed them himself by carrying their bones to them. David

Bonz would hand over a bone to each of his offspring in turn

midstream, a frightened lamb flung itself out of the cart into the flood and went whirling downstream battling feebly. In a flash Bonz had dived and was swimming after it, often nearly submerged by the rushing waters. When he overtook the lamb he seized it and headed for the bank, carefully keeping it above water in an effort which almost drowned him. However, once ashore again he soon recovered and when David managed

would hand out a juicy bone saying, " Take this one to Peg, Bonz." Peg was the kelpie mother of the puppies. Bonz would duly lay that bone down before Peg. " Bone for Sam," and Sam would get his in the same way. In this manner Bonz would hand over a bone to each of his offspring in turn and last of all would receive his own bone and then retire to eat it.

Perhaps it is little wonder that the tales of Bonz's feats went round.

Perhaps the tales got added to after a while. By and by even the newspapers heard about Bonz. "The miracle sheep-dog" they called him. But his greatest feat had nothing whatever to do with sheep—which sounds a bit Irish. But never mind; Bonz saved the life of seven-year-old Polly Jones; and anyway it all happened because Irish Sergeant O'Brien of the Mounted Constabulary came to ask for the help of David and Bonz. And oh, the sergeant was a worried, bothered man that day!

"Ye see how it is, sor," he explained to David. "The little lass has been lost thirty-six hours, and her mother is beside herself at the thought of her darling wandering in the bush without food or drink. Half Mudgerup township is out searching for the lass, and niver a thing can they find."

"Ah, it's thick scrub country around Mudgerup," said David, sympathetically, "where a little lost lassie would take a deal of finding."

"Mr. Holme, if that lass wanders in the bush for another twenty-four hours it's dead she'll be."

"But why don't you get a black fellow, an aboriginal, to track her down?"

"Sure, and haven't I scoured the blessed bush for a black fellow! It's gone into the mountains kangaroo hunting they are, and would take a week to find," cried O'Brien. "Mr Holme, we shall never find that child

Bonz would jump up and run across the backs of the sheep to bark at the leaders

without the help of that dog of yours."

"Do you mean Bonz?" said David, and he was troubled. "Ah, no; Bonz would never find her. It wants a dog trained to scent and follow people, like a bloodhound. Bonz has only worked with sheep. He'd never understand what was wanted."

O'Brien laid his hand on David's. "Mr. Holme, Bonz is our last chance. Fifty men can't find the lass. They can't follow her scent. But that wonderful dog of yours might. You say he'd never understand what is wanted? But can't he read the very thoughts you're thinking? Doesn't he know everything what you want done without a word from you? Can't he go and muster sheep in a paddock thick with scrub

and bushes, and maybe two or three square miles in extent, and scour it clean of sheep in half the time a dozen men and horses would take, and bring them sheep home and yard them all by himself, and this without ye saying a blessed word?"

"Yes, that's the sort of thing he's trained to do."

"And when he brings them sheep to the bridge, sometimes the front sheep just won't budge and the rear sheep jam up behind them. What does your Bonz do then? Why, it's himself that jumps up and runs across the backs of the sheep to bark vicious just behind the leaders, and sends them tearing across the bridge; and then runs back again across the backs of them sheep

The master said, "Smell this shoe, smell it boy, deeply. Now find . . . find"

and rounds up the stragglers in a trice. Holy saints! A dog with twice the sense of a man ought to find the little maid! For the love of mercy let's try!"

The two gripped hands on it. A few moments later they were in O'Brien's ancient car tearing over bush tracks, with Bonz in the rear seat. But already Bonz, with his trained sixth sense, was uneasy. He didn't like cars, he didn't like strangers; and most of all he sensed that David was uneasy and worried.

For miles they bumped onwards, and now great karri and jarrah trees towered overhead, and dense scrub grew around the fallen timber. This was bad country for a child or for any-one else in which to get lost. Soon they came to the scattered galvanized-iron and timber houses of Mudgerup town-ship. Anxious people hastened to meet the car, but David pleaded with O'Brien, saying he could do nothing

with the dog once he became upset by a crowd. So O'Brien didn't stop until he reached a cottage which he entered. He came out with a child's shoe in his hand—"Polly's shoe," he explained. "Her mother gave it me." And then, addressing the dog, "Sure, and it's broken-hearted she'll be if ye don't find her Polly in time, Bonz, me lad, and half the township will be weeping, too!"

The two men and Bonz now left the car and walked to where the child had last been seen by her companions. Nobody was allowed to follow. Then David knelt down before Bonz. Very carefully he explained everything. Bonz listened. Over and over again, David told the dog about the lost girl, Polly, and each time he said "girl" Bonz was given the shoe to scent. At last David hoped he had made Bonz understand what was wanted, although somehow David could not rid himself of the fear that Bonz would fail. This same feeling communicated itself to the dog, who was restless and inclined to whimper. "It's my fault, dear old Bonz, and not yours," David thought, and bent down to whisper certain secret things into Bonz's ear. And then again proffering the shoe, "Scent this, Bonz. Good dog, *smell* . . . again, again. Now find, boy, find!"

Bonz tried to be interested but he wasn't really keen about the smell of that shoe. What he wanted was a good old sheep smell; *that* he did understand. Meanwhile dozens, hundreds of other smells distracted him; a booby-rat had crossed the track here, a bush kangaroo had lain down over there. He would like to have investigated both smells. Also an ant-eater was hiding within that dead log. He dragged at the leash, pulling towards a rare smell which proved to be only a dead bird. Ah! An iguana had just fled up that tree trunk. A lesser dog than Bonz would have loved to scratch and bark at its foot and terrify that iguana. As it was even he had been tempted.

Then came master's voice again, oh! so sad, so worried. "Bonz lad. Smell this shoe. Smell it boy, deeply. Good dog. Now find . . . find . . . *find!*"

Bonz couldn't guess what it was that his master wanted! Something to do with the smell of that shoe? That shoe —*that* smell? Why, he'd already found a smell like that, a human, a *child* smell. He hadn't bothered about it. If master actually wanted him to follow that little-girl-smell . . . well, perhaps he'd go back and smell around again and maybe find it.

Bonz tugged at the leash. David

Bonz tugged at the leash

They could see Bonz, his tail waving exultantly, and a little figure wearing a torn and crumpled dress

made a sign to O'Brien to keep well behind. Bonz took them back again some quarter of a mile and sniffed around, this time with interest and then with a whine set off, snuffling at the ground, following a scent that seemed to wander here, there, any-where and might well have been that of the straying child. Through a wilder-ness of scrub and dense thickets and rocks and gullies Bonz led them.

Then, when crossing a stony ridge Bonz lost the scent. At last the dog had fully grasped what his master was feeling and thinking. At last he *knew*. Here, there, Bonz cast about, growing ever more desperate as he found nothing, and then at last lifted up his voice and howled woefully. David and O'Brien looked at each other with despair. " Maybe he'll pick up the trail in the creek beyond," David mut-tered and dragged the unwilling Bonz onwards. Then came an excited yelp. Bonz had found the scent again and with a great tug tore the leash out of David's hand and was tearing along with his nose to the ground, his tail waving and jubilant. The two men looked at each other, hardly daring to breathe, to hope, then broke into a run. Down through the bed of the creek where kangaroos hid in the scrub until the last moment and then jumped from beneath their running feet—up along the far bank where great outcrops of granite lay—bursting through the scrub and ironstone that crowned the ridge. Now a joyful exultant barking reached their ears and thrilled them.

" If he's found the little lass he's found her alive," thought David, knowing well that had it been other-wise Bonz would never have given

tongue. " My heavens above, I believe he *has* found her ! " he cried to O'Brien who was puffing along behind. " I've never known Bonz like this before. Look, there he is ! "

Now they could see Bonz, golden against a patch of brown-green scrub, his tail waving exultantly. Now they could see a little figure wearing a torn and crumpled dress—it must be, it *was* the little lass, lying at the dog's feet !

They drew closer and David called. A hand feebly waved in response. When they reached her she was sitting up trying to smile at them, and her arm was clasped so tightly around Bonz that it seemed it would never let go; and even as he had licked the half-drowned lamb back to life, so was Bonz's rough tongue licking the face of little Polly Jones.

.   .   .   .   .

Give a dog a bad name, they say, and hang him; but give a good dog a good name, let a David Holme rear and train him, and what happens? . . . Bonz happened ! And now in the sheeplands of Australia many a descendant of Bonz works the sheep. Some have golden coats, some have eyes which glint with gold, some have hearts of gold. All are honoured because of the fame of their great forebear. Millions of sheep are under their charge. The wool from those sheep clothes millions of people each year. So it was a big job of work that David did with Bonz; but then in his quiet way David was a big man, the sort that does big jobs quietly.

So that's how Bonz paid back the debt owed by his long line of killer forebears, and dog of gold that he was, he certainly gave good measure !

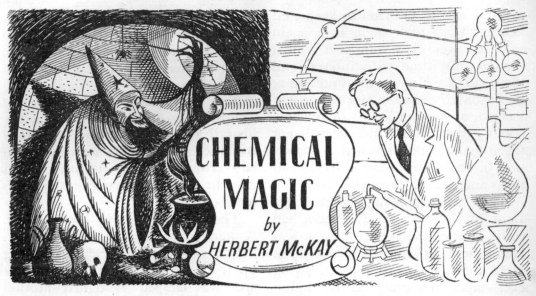

CHEMICAL MAGIC

by
HERBERT McKAY

THE old magicians were the chemists of their day. We should now think them rather crude chemists, but that is because they lacked the great store of chemical knowledge that was not then available. The wonders they performed seemed like magic to people who saw only the results, and did not know how they were achieved.

The match suddenly bursts into flame

Chemical magic is now an open book that all may read. But chemical results seem just as magical as ever.

There is that magical gas, oxygen, that keeps life going and fires burning. We usually see it at work in a diluted form, its activities curbed by being mixed with four times its own volume of nitrogen. Even then it can be spectacular enough, as every one knows who has watched a great fire. But the chemist produces oxygen neat, and even stores it in iron bottles. A spray of this pure oxygen, in the oxy-acetylene flame, creates the intense heat that bites through refractory metals. That is the kind of thing pure oxygen can do, even when it is used on a small scale.

On a very small scale we can get an exciting result with a little potassium chlorate. We put a little of the chlorate on a tin lid, and heat it over a gas flame. It melts and bubbles; we hold the glowing end of a match over it, and the match suddenly bursts into flame. We crush a little of the chlorate, and mix it with sugar, then put the mixture on a tin lid, and put a match to it. Suddenly flames spring up, and there is the not unpleasant smell of burnt sugar. The chemist can even put a drop or two of sulphuric acid on the mixture and start the flames apparently by magic.

We never let potassium chlorate and sulphur get together, except in very small quantities; the mixture can be too exciting; and, in spite of its harmless appearance, it can be dangerous. If you do mix a very small amount, always crush the materials beforehand, and never on any account after they are mixed. Put a little of the mixture in a small square of thin paper, together with one or two small stones; screw up the corners of the paper, and you have a home-made cracker.

Potassium chlorate is a storehouse of oxygen; so also is saltpetre. We can use either one or the other to get fierce burning. We make a mixture consisting of half sulphur and half powdered charcoal, both of which burn. Then we powder some saltpetre and add it to the mixture of sulphur and charcoal; three times as much saltpetre as sulphur and charcoal together, is needed. We mix the three substances thoroughly with a wooden rod, and thus get a mixture which should burn fiercely; the sulphur and charcoal burn, and the saltpetre supplies pure oxygen. It is best to burn this mixture out of doors, because the smell is apt to hang about the house if it is burnt indoors. It was this mixture of sulphur, charcoal and saltpetre that produced the old magic of gunpowder. The difference between gunpowder and the mixture obtained is that the materials in gunpowder are very finely ground, very thoroughly mixed,

wetted, compressed, dried and broken up. The explosion of gunpowder is due to extremely rapid burning, and the sudden production of large masses of hot gas which press out in all directions.

We can make a strong solution of saltpetre in water. If we soak string in the solution and dry it, this string will slowly smoulder away like touch paper. We can use the solution to draw a picture with a paint brush on very thin paper; all the lines of the picture should join up. We let the picture get thoroughly dry. Then we touch one point on the picture with a glowing match. The paper begins to smoulder and the glow spreads all along the lines where the saltpetre supplies oxygen. Finally the black smouldered paper reproduces the whole picture.

The chemist can take harmless substances and, with a wave of his wand as it were, can turn them into deadly

A glow spreads along the saltpetre line

explosives. Cotton waste is, of course, quite harmless. Nitric and sulphuric acids need careful handling, but boys are allowed to use them in school, so they are not so very dangerous. The chemist treats cotton waste with nitric and sulphuric acids, and the harmless cotton becomes guncotton. In the open air a piece of dry guncotton will burn quickly but harmlessly. Damp guncotton does not even burn; but if we use a detonator to start it off, then indeed, it is a powerful explosive. Fulminate of mercury explodes wildly, and that is the stuff we want as a detonator. Suppose we have to blow up a bridge. We can carry as much damp guncotton as we need, and pack it away where it will do most damage —we are quite safe so far. Then we put a small quantity of dry guncotton in the damp guncotton—we are still fairly safe. Then we put a detonator in the dry guncotton—we are no longer safe. A spark will detonate the fulminate, and in a split second the whole mass of guncotton goes up, dry and damp alike, and with it the bridge.

Glycerine is another harmless stuff that chemical magic can change to an explosive. Again it is treated with nitric and sulphuric acids, and it becomes deadly and dangerous nitro-glycerine. Nitro-glycerine is too dangerous to handle alone as an explosive; a mere knock may set it off. So it is absorbed into sawdust, or into a special kind of earth and then it is much safer to handle. In this form it is the well-known and useful explosive, dynamite.

The art of the chemist is, of course, not entirely destructive. The production of crystals is also part of his work. It is easy to get tiny crystals; we can get them in a few minutes, but it is a longer process to grow big crystals. We get a small jam jar and half fill it with lukewarm water, but not more than lukewarm. We stir saltpetre into it until no more will dissolve; there should be a little left after much stirring. Then we pour off the clear liquid into another jar, put it where it will not be disturbed, and leave it till morning. There should be a small crop of crystals. We fish them out with a spoon, and carefully put back four or five of the largest. Then we put the jar in a cupboard, and forget about it for a week or two. When we look again we should find that the crystals are much bigger, and we can leave them to grow bigger still. Quite large crystals of copper sulphate and potassium chlorate may be grown in this way.

We can also grow sugar crystals. We make a very strong solution of sugar in lukewarm water. Then we damp several pieces of thread, and let them dangle into the solution over a small rod. When the crystals have grown to a good size they are very pleasant to crunch between the teeth.

The methods of the chemical magician are indeed simple. He powders substances, and mixes them in suitable proportions; he dissolves substances, usually in water, but sometimes in alcohol, benzene and other liquids; he distils liquids, by boiling them and cooling the gases that come over; he heats substances either gently or strongly; he may heat them under pressure. By these simple methods, and others like them, he obtains his astonishing results.

Of course, the chemist must have raw materials to start with. These materials come from mines, or forests, or the sea, or even from the air. And very often the finished products are not at all like the raw materials. The rubber that comes from tropical forests is soft and plastic; it is so soft that we can mould it in our fingers. The chemist mixes it with a little sulphur and heats it up to boiling point, and so he obtains rubber hard enough to be used as an eraser; we say the rubber is vulcanized. He adds other substances in addition to sulphur, and when the rubber is heated it is the hard tough rubber used for motor tyres. He puts more sulphur with the rubber, and heats it for a long time. And lo—a change like magic! We get the hard black solid known as vulcanite or ebonite. The rubber can be moulded into any shape we like whilst it is still plastic, and then we have that shape fixed permanently by long vulcanizing.

Another of the raw materials is coal. We have to begin by separating it into different substances; indeed a lot of the chemist's work is separation. The coal is shut up in a retort and heated strongly. Little or no air gets at it, so it does not burn. But gases are given off—hydrocarbons we call them,

because they are composed of carbon (pure charcoal) and the inflammable gas, hydrogen. These hydrocarbons are the coal gas we burn in our homes.

We can imitate the method by which the chemist distils coal. We want a one-pound treacle tin for a retort, and we use a nail to make a hole in the lid. We break some coal into small pieces, and fill the tin with it. We press down the lid and heat the tin over a gas flame. Smoke begins to pour out of the hole in the lid, and after a time the coal-gas will burn merrily.

But that is a dirty, wasteful flame. For coal-gas contains ammonia, and so when it is being manufactured, the gas is allowed to bubble through water, which will dissolve the ammonia, and the chemist can then recover and purify it. In the retort there remains the clinkered coke, hard and free from gas. The coke can be used for domestic fires and for smelting iron.

There is still another important product that comes from coal; this is the black, sticky coal-tar. When coal-gas was first made, it seemed that nothing much could be done with coal-tar. Some of it was burnt as fuel, and some was used for surfacing roads, but on the whole it seemed to be little more than a waste product.

And then the magic wand was waved! The tar was re-distilled. It was made rather hotter than the boiling point of water; gases came over which condensed into benzene, toluene and other liquids. When it was made still hotter, carbolic oil came over, then creosote oil, and lastly anthracene oil. Finally we were left with a stiff pitch which could be used on roads.

The chemist has obtained a wonderful series of new materials on which to

You can also grow sugar crystals

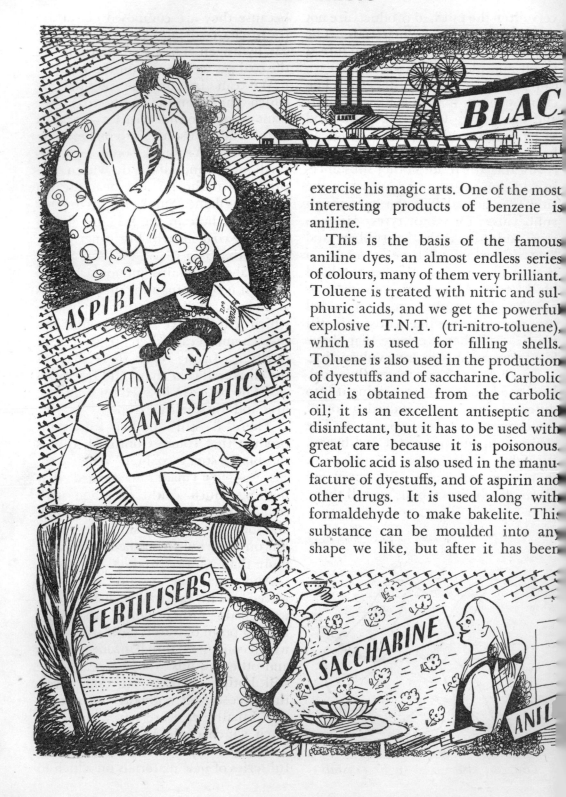

exercise his magic arts. One of the most interesting products of benzene is aniline.

This is the basis of the famous aniline dyes, an almost endless series of colours, many of them very brilliant. Toluene is treated with nitric and sulphuric acids, and we get the powerful explosive T.N.T. (tri-nitro-toluene), which is used for filling shells. Toluene is also used in the production of dyestuffs and of saccharine. Carbolic acid is obtained from the carbolic oil; it is an excellent antiseptic and disinfectant, but it has to be used with great care because it is poisonous. Carbolic acid is also used in the manufacture of dyestuffs, and of aspirin and other drugs. It is used along with formaldehyde to make bakelite. This substance can be moulded into any shape we like, but after it has been

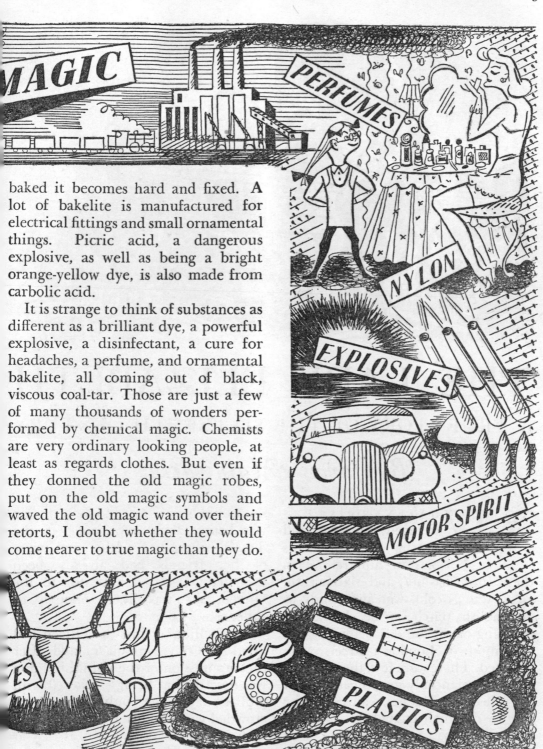

baked it becomes hard and fixed. A lot of bakelite is manufactured for electrical fittings and small ornamental things. Picric acid, a dangerous explosive, as well as being a bright orange-yellow dye, is also made from carbolic acid.

It is strange to think of substances as different as a brilliant dye, a powerful explosive, a disinfectant, a cure for headaches, a perfume, and ornamental bakelite, all coming out of black, viscous coal-tar. Those are just a few of many thousands of wonders performed by chemical magic. Chemists are very ordinary looking people, at least as regards clothes. But even if they donned the old magic robes, put on the old magic symbols and waved the old magic wand over their retorts, I doubt whether they would come nearer to true magic than they do.

THE LADY ELIZABETH

A TRUE STORY OF THE SIXTEENTH CENTURY

By James Mainwaring

WHATEVER else has changed in England during the last three or four hundred years, the weather has not; and March 18th, 1554, was as cold, wet and windy as an English March can be. It was the morning of the Sunday before Easter, and most of London's streets were deserted. There were few, therefore, to see the melancholy group gathered at the side of the Thames, waiting for the tide to rise high enough to carry the barge safely past London Bridge. One of the group was a girl of twenty, tall, pale, a little afraid perhaps, though she would have scorned to show it. She was being taken, a prisoner, to the Tower, where her mother and many of her friends had already been executed. Declared a traitor to the Queen, she was likely enough to suffer a similar fate.

A rebellion against the Queen had filled the Court with alarm, and, after the suppression of the rising, London was described as being " covered with gibbets, and the public buildings crowded with the heads of the bravest men in the kingdom." It was easy at that time to heap suspicion on the innocent, so it was a great opportunity for the members of the Queen's Advisory Council to rid themselves of private enemies. The girl who stood shivering at the Thames' side, and whose mother had once been a maid of honour at the Court, had many enemies. Of her friends, some of whom had undoubtedly been involved in the plot, some had already been executed, some tortured, and others were awaiting they knew not what fate in the Tower.

Her guardians had long grown impatient at the delay. One of them cried angrily to the cautious boatmen: "The tide is high enough! Why must we wait longer? If this proves a trick I'll have you flung where you shall see neither sun nor moon!"

"It is not yet safe, my Lord," one of the boatmen answered. "Another quarter of an hour, I beg of you."

"Not another minute," he replied, and in a few moments the miserable party had begun the last stage of its melancholy journey to the Tower. The tide was still too low for the barge to pass under the bridge without great peril, and the stern of the boat struck the starling, the ring of piles which support the pier of the bridge, and cleared it only with great difficulty.

The Tower, always grim and forbidding, looked especially grey and gloomy on that Sunday morning, in the rain which had begun again to pour, as the barge arrived at the foot of the stone steps leading up to the Traitor's Gate. The Lady Elizabeth, for such was her name, was a girl of spirit. "No person more innocent or loyal than I," she said, "has ever landed, a prisoner, at this gate for traitors."

"If that be so," one of the nobles answered, "you have little to fear, Milady."

"Fear!" she cried, "I fear nothing save to wet my feet by wading through this water to the steps!"

One of them would have flung his cloak to cover the steps down which the water poured, but she brushed it aside, and walked up unaided.

Warders and soldiers were lined in ranks at the Tower entrance under Lieutenant Bridges, Lieutenant of the Tower. Before the gate Lady Elizabeth stopped. "I will not enter by the Traitor's Gate, for I am no traitor," she said, and sat down on a stone, cold and wet as it was.

"Madam, you had best come out of the rain, for you sit unwholesomely," said the Lieutenant.

"Better sit here than in a worse place," she replied, "for God knoweth, not I, whither you would bring me."

At this one of her attendants began to weep, whereupon she jumped up angrily. "Is this how you would cheer me?" she cried, and walked into the Tower with no further word. A few minutes later, the locks and bolts of her room were made fast upon her.

For some weeks the Lady Elizabeth knew not whether she was to die or to live. Her imprisonment was at first so rigorous that she was allowed neither air nor exercise other than what her locked rooms afforded. It was about the middle of April, when winter was noticeably turning to spring, that she was permitted to walk in a little walled garden in the grounds of the Tower. Her only companion during these walks was a young boy, the son of one of the Tower warders. He would wait for Lady Elizabeth at the gate of the garden, always with a

The child was questioned closely

bunch of flowers that he had already gathered for her.

If one of Elizabeth's friends, Robert Dudley, with whom she had played as a child of eight, and who was now, like herself, a prisoner, sometimes succeeded in hiding a note in the flowers, and if Lady Elizabeth occasionally sent one in reply, by the same messenger, it is no business of ours. If they did, they were wise enough to do so without the child's knowledge, which was fortunate for them; for the child was brought before the Council which was debating Milady's fate, and questioned closely. But he replied that he had brought nothing but flowers to Milady. Nevertheless, he was not allowed to bring any more, and the garden gates were locked in future when Milady took her exercise.

It was but a few days later that Lieutenant Bridges received an order from the Council commanding him to have the Lady Elizabeth executed without delay. It was signed by Bishop Gardiner, one of her most determined enemies. It should, of

course, have been signed by the Queen, but Gardiner, taking advantage of an illness of the Queen, had issued the order without her knowledge. Fortunately for Milady, Lieutenant Bridges refused to obey the order without the Queen's signature and sent a messenger to the Court to ask what were the Queen's wishes.

A few more weeks had passed, when a hundred of the Queen's Guard, under Sir Henry Bedingfield, arrived at the Tower. Lady Elizabeth saw them as they were lined up in the Inner Court, and presumed it to be in preparation for her execution. She enquired the meaning of what she saw, and was told that they had come to conduct her to a safer keeping. This answer did little to relieve her anxiety, for she recalled that two brothers of her grandmother, after whom she had been named, had disappeared under similar circumstances.

"I know not this Sir Henry Bedingfield," she said. "Is he a man who maketh conscience out of murder, if such an order be entrusted to him?"

On 19th May she was taken from the Tower by boat to Richmond, where all her own servants were dismissed. "Pray for me," she said to them as they departed, "for this night I think I must die."

The Lady Elizabeth was not yet to die, though she was to have alarms enough. Her enemies were cunning, ruthless, and determined. A messenger arrived with a basket of apples for the Lady Elizabeth's journey, with the compliments of one known to be a foreign spy. The object was, of course, to throw further doubt on Milady's innocence. The messenger was searched with extreme thoroughness—he was in fact stripped to the shirt—but, fortunately for Milady, no message was found.

Nevertheless, the incident was sufficient to arouse the suspicions of Elizabeth's stern guardian, Sir Henry Bedingfield, and when, on the journey, people drew near to see the unfortunate girl, they were driven back by the soldiers, and called rebels

*When she walked in the garden
the gates were always locked*

the last stage of the journey, she asked to be allowed to await the end of a game of chess in which she was interested. Even this was thought to be another of her tricks, for a game of chess may be extended to last for days, or even months! So she had to set out forthwith.

The last day's journey was the worst, for there arose a storm of wind and rain, so violent that Milady lost her hood and veil; but she was permitted neither rest nor shelter.

At last they reached Woodstock, where the unfortunate girl was lodged in the gate-house, with sixty soldiers to guard her by day, and forty by night! When she was allowed to walk alone in the garden the gates were locked with five great keys. This last precaution was a duty which Sir Henry himself performed, and once the Lady Elizabeth reviled him angrily for it, calling him her jailer. Sir Henry knelt before her, and said, " I pray you, Madam, not to give me that harsh name, for there are so many that would have you dead that I am determined to save you from the dangers by which you are beset."

That there were enemies even within the palace of Woodstock was soon to be demonstrated. A mysterious fire broke out between the floor of Elizabeth's bedroom and the ceiling of the room below. Only by chance was it discovered in time, as she was on the point of retiring. Once, when Sir Henry had to leave for a few days, a hired traitor, with twenty-five disguised ruffians, demanded admittance, on serious and urgent business. Fortunately, Sir Henry's brother, who was left in charge, refused to admit them.

and traitors. Some who rang bells in a village church were set in the stocks.

By the evening of the second day they arrived at Windsor. The next night they spent at Ricote in Oxfordshire. When on the following morning Milady was ordered to make ready for

The Lady Elizabeth was not even permitted the use of pen and ink, but with a piece of charcoal she wrote the following lines on the shutter of her prison window:

O Fortune! How thy restless
    wavering state
  Hath fraught with cares my
    troubled wit,
Witness this present prison,
    whither fate
  Could bear me, and the joys I
    quit.
Thou caus'dst the guilty to be
    loosed
From bands wherein are innocents
    enclosed,
Causing the guiltless to be strait
    reserved,
And freeing those that death had
    well deserved,
But by her envy can be nothing
    wrought,
So God send to my foes all they have
    wrought.

At last, after some months of anxious peril, the Lady Elizabeth was taken to London, to the Tudor palace of Hampton Court—and once again, the doors of her room were locked and guarded. A few hours later they were opened to admit three members of the Queen's Council, including Bishop Gardiner, who had plotted so determinedly to bring about her death. Before they could announce their mission the girl addressed them.

"My Lords," she said, "I am glad to see you, for methinks I have been kept a great while from you, desolately alone. Wherefore I would entreat you to be a means to the King's and Queen's Majesties, that I may be delivered from my imprisonment, in which I have been kept a long time,

The Lady Elizabeth wrote with charcoal on her prison shutter

as to you, my Lords, is not unknown."

"Then," replied Gardiner, "you must confess your fault, and put yourself on the Queen's mercy."

"I shall, then, lie in prison all my life," replied Elizabeth, "for I have never offended against the Queen, in thought, word, or deed. I crave no mercy at Her Majesty's hand, but ask only for justice."

Gardiner and his colleagues came again on the next day. " The Queen marvels at your boldness," he said, " in refusing to confess your offence, as if Her Majesty hath wrongfully imprisoned your Ladyship."

" Nay," replied Elizabeth, " she may punish me as she thinketh good."

" Her Majesty willeth me to tell you," retorted the Bishop, " that you must tell another tale ere that you are set at liberty." Elizabeth answered, " I would as lief be in prison, with honesty, as to be at liberty suspected by Her Majesty. That which I have said I will stand to."

After they had withdrawn, Milady was left alone for a week, seeing only her own attendants. Then suddenly, one night, just as she was about to retire, for it was already ten o'clock, she was startled by a summons to appear at once before the Queen. Believing herself to be in great peril, she turned to her attendants. " Pray for me," she said, " for I cannot tell whether I shall ever see you again."

It was a strange meeting. Philip of Spain, husband of the Queen, stood hidden behind a screen, possibly, it has been said, to protect Elizabeth from the violence of the Queen! On entering the royal bedroom Elizabeth fell on her knees, protesting her loyalty and innocence.

Queen Mary replied, with some anger, " You will not confess your offence, I see, but rather stand stoutly on your truth. I pray God your truth may become manifest!"

" If it is not," answered Milady, " I will look for neither favour nor pardon at your Majesty's hands."

" Well, then," said the Queen, " you stand so firmly on your innocence, belike you have been wrongfully punished?"

" I must not say so to your Majesty," replied Elizabeth.

" But you will report so to others, it seemeth," rejoined Mary.

" No, an' please your Majesty," replied Milady, " I have borne, and must bear, the burden thereof; but I humbly beseech your Grace's good opinion of me as I am, and ever have been, your Majesty's true subject."

After some minutes' silence, save for a whispered " God knoweth!" the Queen commanded Elizabeth to rise. " When I became Queen," she said, " I gave you a ring, promising, should you return it to me when you were in danger, I would see that no serious harm should befall you. You sent it to me and, though I believed you false, this promise have I kept. Here is your ring. Whether you be guilty or innocent, I forgive you."

It was nearly four years after Queen Mary had forgiven Milady for an offence which she swore she had never committed, that news came to Elizabeth, in her retreat at Hatfield, that the Queen was dying. Even then it was possible that such rumours were made to tempt her into some act which could be interpreted as treason; for though some called her Elizabeth Bullen, she was, like the Queen, daughter of Henry VIII and, as Mary had left no heir, next in succession to the throne.

Amongst her attendants was one Sir Nicholas Throckmorton, who had been exiled at the time of Elizabeth's imprisonment, but who had since

On entering the royal bedroom, Elizabeth fell on her knees

returned, to be secretly employed by Milady on many dangerous missions. Now he was to ride as fast as horses could carry him to the palace, to request one of the Queen's attendants who was in the confidence of Elizabeth to take from the Queen's finger, if she were really dead, the black enamelled ring which she always wore.

The Queen died on 17th November, 1558, but before Throckmorton could reach Elizabeth with his proof of Mary's death, a deputation from the Court had already arrived at Hatfield to offer their homage to Elizabeth as their Queen!

On the same day the Speaker of the House of Commons received a message from the Lord Chancellor, "that he, with the knights and burgesses of the nether house, would without delay adjourn to the upper house, to give their assents, in a matter of the utmost importance." It was to proclaim the Lady Elizabeth Queen of the realm, "without any further tract of time." On hearing the speech of the Lord Chancellor, the Lords and Commons replied, "God save Queen Elizabeth! Long may she reign over us!"

Six days later Elizabeth journeyed in state to London and on 28th November, she took formal possession of her royal fortress, the Tower of London.

It was a very different journey from that which, more than four years before, she had made in the barge. Now, in a rich chariot, she was carried to Cripplegate, where the Lord Mayor received her. Mounting on horseback and led by the Lord Mayor, who carried her sceptre, she joined the awaiting procession to proceed with ceremony through the city. Next to

her, as Master of the Horse, rode Lord Robert Dudley who, like the Queen, was returning to the scene of former imprisonment.

As she entered the Tower, she immediately recalled to the assembly her visit to the fortress, and asked to be taken to her former prison apartment. "Like Daniel," she said, "I have been saved from the den of lions."

Fortunate it was for England that she had been so saved. Having learned to defend and guide herself through years of danger against the plots and wiles of ruthless, cunning and unscrupulous enemies, she was for forty-five years to guide England with equal courage through many dangers, to make her nation for a time the greatest nation in the world.

Led by the Lord Mayor, who carried her sceptre, she joined the waiting procession to proceed with ceremony through the city

Bamboo
by

IN prehistoric times man lived very much with nature. The first musical sounds he heard were probably birds singing, the wind in the trees, rolling waves and rippling water. One day the cave man discovered something wonderful. While he was carving a piece of bone he put it near his mouth and accidentally blew across the top, causing a sound to come forth. Later he found that by boring another hole and stopping one hole with his finger he could get two sounds. At a later date shepherd boys played pipes made from the reeds that grew by the side of streams where they took their flocks to drink.

In 1926, Miss Margaret James was sent a Sicilian goatherd pipe. How thrilling it would be, she thought, if her class of children could play a similar instrument. Miss James found a piece of bamboo and started off on the adventure of pipe making.

The exciting news that young people were making lovely-toned instruments from a few old pieces of bamboo, cork and match sticks soon spread beyond the Cotswold village. Perhaps you have not yet experienced the thrill of making this simple, inexpensive musical instrument. If not, here is your chance to begin. By following the directions and the diagrams you should be able to make a sweet-sounding pipe.

Well seasoned bamboo, Indian cane and birch tubes make good toned pipes (length, eleven inches, with inside diameter three-quarters of an inch). Also you want some corks to fit the tube. Do not dry your wood by the

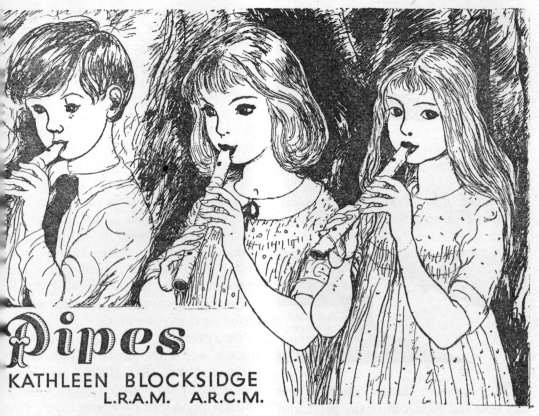

Pipes

KATHLEEN BLOCKSIDGE
L.R.A.M.   A.R.C.M.

fire — let it dry naturally indoors.

Only simple tools are needed—a small sharp penknife, wood file, medium-sized hacksaw and a ruler and pencil. When using a penknife on bamboo be sure to hold the blade firmly between the finger and thumb; then when making a hole twist it steadily to prevent the bamboo cracking. The same twisting movement applies when using a file to enlarge a hole. In sawing bamboo, or whatever material you have chosen, the difficulty is to keep the pipe length steady. Try placing it on an old chair and putting your left knee firmly but gently on top. Then with your right hand using light pressure, move the saw to and fro evenly.

Clean out the inside of the bamboo by means of a poker or long auger. File the inside if there should be a rim, until you have a hollow tube. Decide which end is to be the head of your pipe. If there is a joint, see that it is at least two inches from the head or top of the tube.

Every head has a mouth, and a pipe is no exception. If your tube has a groove, place the mouthpiece so that the groove runs down the side of your pipe. When you have decided which end of your tube the head is to be, mark with a pencil one-third the circumference. Shade that section so that later you will not cut the wrong part away. Cut a thin wedge each end of your pencil marks to act as a guide for the saw. Measure down the pipe from the head three-quarters of an inch and saw half-way through the tube. Now turn the pipe on its side and

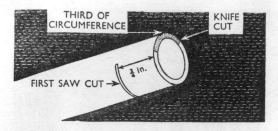

saw both edges of the circumference where you marked it, so as to join your first cut.

A piece of bamboo should now fall away and leave a shaped mouthpiece.

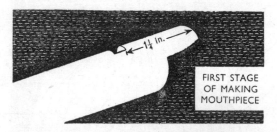

FIRST STAGE OF MAKING MOUTHPIECE

The opposite side of the first saw cut is called the front of the pipe, and it is on that surface that the window is placed. The window in your house

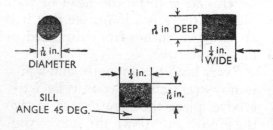

THE WINDOW AND SILL IN PROCESS OF MAKING

is to let air in, but in the case of a pipe it is to let air or wind pass out. For this reason it is extremely important, so be sure to make it neatly and accurately to size, then you will be quite certain to have lovely tone later. Measure one and a quarter inches down the front of the pipe (that is half an inch lower than the first saw

cut, but on the reverse side). With a penknife make a small hole and continue to enlarge it to three-sixteenths of an inch in diameter by using the small, pointed end of a file. Make a hole oblong in shape, that is a quarter of an inch in width and three-sixteenths of an inch deep, by cutting with a penknife small v-shaped wedges, finishing off with a small file.

A sill is required for the window and this you can obtain by shaving off the bottom edge until it slopes at an angle of forty-five degrees. Be sure not to touch the inner side for that should remain fairly sharp in order to catch the wind (your breath) coming down the mouthpiece, via the channel which is the next part to make.

Be sure that the channel is very smooth and only one-twentieth of an inch in depth, then the air will pass along easily and give a good sound. With a pencil, draw a line *inside* the tube from each side of the window to the top of the mouthpiece. Using a penknife, cut along the pencil marks and remove a thin layer of wood between the lines. File the floor of

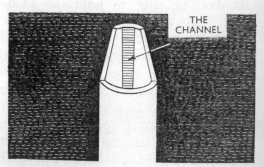

THE CHANNEL

the channel smooth. It must be exactly a quarter of an inch wide at the window end, but it may be a little wider at the mouthpiece. Soon you will reach the thrilling moment when you will know if your handicraft has been accurate and neat, thus producing a lovely sound.

Find a cork, the smaller end of which will fit tightly. Remove it and make a passage on the cork to correspond with the one in the pipe. The best way is to cut off a thin layer of cork with the penknife and then file the surface smoothly. This is rather intricate and most important, for the cork should have a slight dip, the path widening about a quarter of the way down. The illustration should help you to do this correctly. Replace the

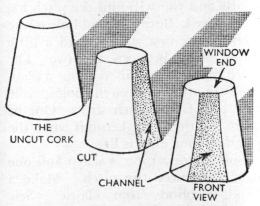

THE UNCUT CORK

CUT

CHANNEL

WINDOW END

FRONT VIEW

cork, making sure that it fits tightly and level with the window. Blow gently, and what you have been longing for should come—a sweet-toned sound. Finally, to make the mouthpiece comfortable for the lips, shape the back part of the cork as in the illustration.

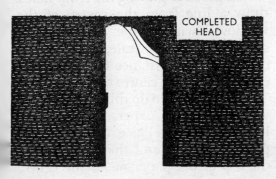

COMPLETED HEAD

If you blow too hard you will get what are termed harmonics. The first one being a sound an octave higher, and the second a twelfth higher than the fundamental keynote. This will help you to understand the technique of the brass instruments in an orchestra. The harmonic series are the only sounds they can produce.

Tune your pipe to the sound D, that is one octave above middle C, not the D next to it. If you do not know the keyboard names study the chart. Be

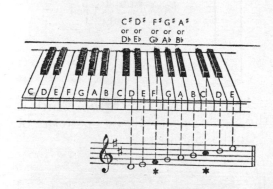

PIANOFORTE KEYBOARD

*THE BLACK NOTE HERE INDICATES A BLACK KEY F# or C#

sure to blow *very* gently. If your pipe is too low in pitch it can be raised by sawing off a piece of bamboo from the end of the pipe. About a half-inch will raise the pitch a semitone. The sound is written on the staff one octave lower than it sounds.

Hold the pipe as if all the holes were made, with the right hand at the bottom, three fingers in front covering imaginary holes, thumb at the back and little finger at the side. The left hand should be in a similar position above. It is important that your right hand is at the lower end of the pipe in case you later play a flute or similar wind instrument.

To produce the keynote place the pipe between the tip of the lips and blow very gently, saying " te " for each note. This is called tonguing. There are other syllables, too, that give clearness and varied phrasing. " Tit " gives a clear cut-off sound, which in musical language is called staccato.

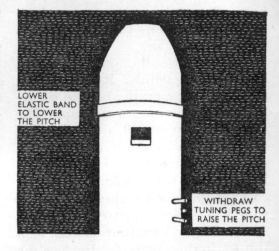

LOWER ELASTIC BAND TO LOWER THE PITCH

WITHDRAW TUNING PEGS TO RAISE THE PITCH

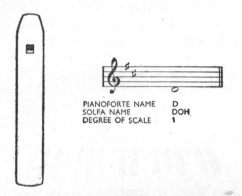

PIANOFORTE NAME	D
SOLFA NAME	DOH
DEGREE OF SCALE	1

Play the following rhythm which is the opening rhythmic pattern of " Golden Slumbers " :

SAY   TE, TE, TE.   TE   TE,   TE   TE,   TE—

Now try tonguing various rhythms of your own invention. Before you go any further with the making of the scale, it is important that you make tuning holes, then when you play with the piano, or accompanied only by other pipers, your pipe, and I hope theirs, will be exactly the same pitch. Atmosphere will vary the pitch of the pipe, and unfortunately all pianofortes are not the same pitch.

Down the side of your pipe, about one inch from the centre of the window, make a very small hole by using the point of your penknife. Blow

gently and you will find the pitch has been raised. Bore a second hole to the right of the first, and a third a little lower down between the two. The pitch will now be raised about a semitone. In order to close the holes, make tiny pegs from match sticks. One or more can then be taken out when the pitch of your pipe is flat.

Sometimes a pipe is sharp and one needs to lower the pitch. Make a window blind from elastic. Sew together the ends, making a band that can be lowered over the top of the window when required.

Learn to play the pipe as you make it, then you will be able to play proficiently more quickly than if you wait until your pipe is finished.

As a guide to placing the front holes, draw a line from the centre of the window down the pipe. To obtain the second note of the scale, measure one quarter of the distance from the base of the pipe to the centre of the window. The easiest way to do this is to measure with a piece of paper, and fold the length in four. Place the quartered paper at the base of the pipe. Where the top of the paper meets the centre line is the position of the first hole. Pierce a small hole with a penknife, then enlarge it by using the narrow end of a file. The larger the hole the higher the pitch. Constantly test the pitch with the pianoforte.

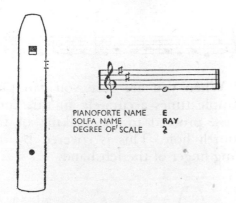

If you completely cover the hole with the ring finger of your right hand, the sound should be exactly the same as before you made the hole. Uncover it and you have the second note of the scale. When replacing the finger be sure to cover the hole with pressure from a flat finger.

Here is a short melody you can play with two kinds of tonguing. Follow it up with a tune of your own.

To obtain the position of the second hole, mark out, but do not make, the places for the remaining front holes. The top one should be two and a quarter inches below the centre of the window.

The five remaining holes are equal distance between the top mark and the centre of the lowest hole. You will find that this will make them about seven-eighths of an inch apart. There is one back hole that is immediately behind the top front hole.

Now to return to the making of the holes. The second hole, which gives the third note of the scale, is the largest on the pipe. If you have small fingers and you think the hole is getting too large to cover easily, enlarge it by undercutting the under surface of the top part of the hole. This is done with a round file or penknife. Instead of making a large fat hole, make it oblong in shape. The second hole is covered by the middle finger of the right hand. When the two holes are uncovered the pipe will give F sharp.

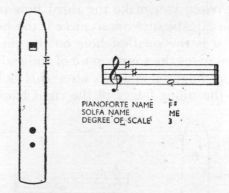

"Que le jour me dure" by Rousseau can now be played. It is a lovely melody and must be played slowly with careful tonguing. Try tonguing these notes ♫ to "te re."

Make up a tune of two phrases. Let the first phrase end on *ray*, and the second on *doh*. Practise playing the interval of a third, that is D, F sharp, D. Be sure and lift up the two fingers together and replace them simultaneously. Here is an exercise that will help you to overcome this slight difficulty :

The first time say " te " to each sound, then repeat saying " tit."

When you make the third hole on the pipe be sure not to make it too big as it is the smallest hole on the pipe and gives the fourth note of the scale. The finger that looks after this hole is the index finger of the right hand.

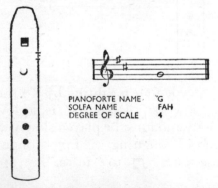

Play the jolly tune, " Peas Porridge Hot." Then try this melody by Dvorak :

Practise the new intervals especially in this exercise and repeat it with varied tonguing.

When you are sure you can play simple tunes accurately in this compass, proceed to the making of the fourth hole. This is covered by the ring finger of the left hand.

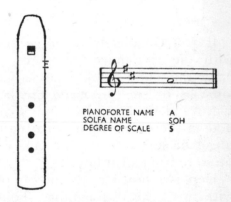

Compose exercises to include the new intervals that this hole gives you. There are many traditional tunes you can play such as: " Ring a Ring of Roses," " Hush-a-Bye Baby," " Little Bo-Peep," " Little Jack Horner " and " Come to the Cookhouse Door, Boys."

The fifth hole will be about the same size as the preceding one, unless you have a groove near this part of the pipe. The middle finger of the left hand covers it.

Remember to make up exercises that will include the various intervals.

Play them with varied tonguing. Then improvise little tunes just for the joy of making music.

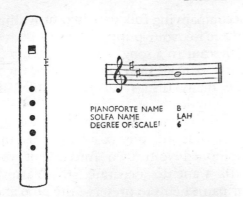

PIANOFORTE NAME   B
SOLFA NAME   LAH
DEGREE OF SCALE   6

One more hole and the making of your pipe is complete. This is rather small and is placed immediately behind the sixth hole. Being on the reverse side of your pipe, the thumb of the left hand is used to cover the hole. Make quite sure when closing the hole (as with all holes) that no air escapes

There are now many tunes available. Perhaps one of the loveliest is that old carol, " I Saw Three Ships." The sea shanty, " Blow My Bully Boys," and the folk tune, " The Keys of Canterbury " are written within the compass of our six notes. The latter tune is in the key of E minor and is a pleasing change from D major.

The top hole which is two and a quarter inches from the centre of the window gives the seventh note of the scale. The index finger of the left hand is used to cover it.

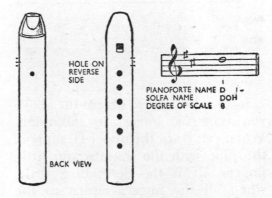

HOLE ON
REVERSE
SIDE

BACK VIEW

PIANOFORTE NAME D
SOLFA NAME   DOH
DEGREE OF SCALE 8

Now you have a little instrument which I hope gives lovely tone and is capable of playing at least seventeen different sounds. As you have progressed from note to note when making your pipe, advance gradually with the remaining sounds. A chart is given to

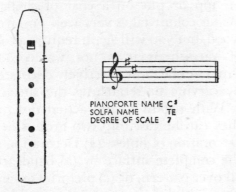

PIANOFORTE NAME C♯
SOLFA NAME   TE
DEGREE OF SCALE 7

You can now play the beginning of a Brahms waltz:

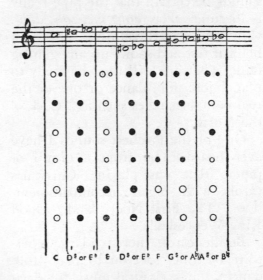

CHART SHOWING NOTES
NOT PREVIOUSLY MENTIONED

show you how they are obtained. A black ring indicates a closed hole.

To be a proficient player of a completed pipe you should first be able to play the scale of D major with varied tonguing and at different speeds.

PIANOFORTE NAME	D	E	F♯	G	A	B	C♯	D'
SOLFA NAME	DOH	RAY	ME	FAH	SOH	LAH	TE	DOH'
DEGREE OF SCALE	1	2	3	4	5	6	7	8

Remember that to obtain the above you raise the fingers in succession. When you reach the upper D, support the pipe with the thumbs and little fingers. It is the descending scale, when all the fingers return to the closed position that is sometimes found difficult. Make quite sure every hole is completely closed with pressure from a flat finger—that is, the pad of the finger that lies half-way between the top joint and the tip.

Having completed your scale of sounds be certain that the pipe really is in tune. Play *doh, me, soh, doh'*, with soft even breathing. This is a helpful test and shows up any glaring fault. The pipe will then be ready to play a jolly folk dance or one of the regimental marches such as " Cock o' the North."

One of the loveliest sounds I have ever heard came from a group of pipers that was playing Christmas carols with organ accompaniment. Try " The First Noël " and " Good King Wenceslas."

Besides carols, there is a large repertoire of tunes for you to play—folk dances, songs, classical music, modern music. You will find pipes ideal for accompanying folk dancing, providing music for your puppet show or giving a descant to a song. They blend, too, with stringed instruments. Yes, there are many things for this wonderful pipe to do.

I think you will feel as many pipers have felt in the past, that having fashioned your own instrument you will want to decorate it. Varnish or paint helps to preserve the pipe and improve the tone. There are many ways of doing this. Whatever method you use, first remove any bumps on the surface by filing and then sandpapering the complete pipe.

If the bamboo is mottled and has especially pleasing markings, you may like just to use varnish and paint on your initials to give the pipe individuality. Perhaps you wish to paint on a design, using the natural wood as a background. In this case use cellulose paint. You may prefer powder or paste colour, but you will need to varnish on top or put on a coat of shellac. Water colour takes very well on birch wood, but you will again require a coat of varnish as it is not waterproof. Pipes can be most effectively decorated by carving or scratching the surface.

With regard to the actual designs, they can be cast into two groups: (1) Decoration of holes. (2) Decoration of the complete surface by (a) bands, (b) all over pattern, or (c) pictorial design. On a child's pipe the holes could be made to represent burrows and rabbits painted outside. Another pipe can have the holes for tunnels and trains running round the pipe.

To hold your pipe, make a case of material lined with cotton wool, or a wooden box with a green baize lining. This will help to prevent it cracking.

PIPE DESIGNS

DECORATION OF HOLES
YELLOW PIPE WITH BLACK DESIGN

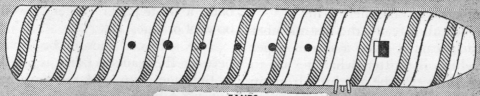

"ALL OVER" PATTERN
BLUE PIPE WITH CREAM PATTERN

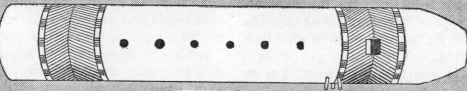

BANDS
GREEN PIPE WITH CREAM AND RED BANDS

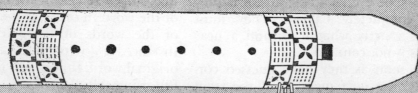

SCRATCHED SURFACE
BROWN PIPE YELLOW CUTS

BANDS
NATURAL WOOD BACKGROUND WITH PAINTED BANDS OF CRIMSON AND BLUE

Pencil and Paper Games

DRAWING RACE

THE party is divided into two or more teams, with about six players in each team.

Both teams are first provided with pencils and several sheets of drawing paper, and then they decide between themselves in what order the members will take their turns.

When all is ready, the first member of each team is given a slip of paper on which is written what he has to draw. This may be anything from an apple to a shipwreck! After looking at it, he must return the slip, and then his task is to go back to his team and, without speaking, draw the given object with as much speed as he can. The rest of the team try to guess what he is drawing, and to all their guesses he is only allowed to answer either "Yes" or "No."

If they cannot guess it, he must try to help them by adding more details, or even starting afresh if they are completely baffled. They must guess exactly what it is, and a near guess is not counted.

As soon as they have guessed correctly, the next member of the team dashes off to get his slip, and comes back to exercise his artistic skill in turn, and so on until each member of the team has had a turn, the winning team being the first to finish.

When writing out the slips, the subjects that are chosen should be mainly things which might look like something else when drawn, so that they are not too easily guessed, such as a bath, a waste-paper basket, a wolf, a bowl of oranges, etc.

The subjects should be divided between the teams as fairly as possible, so that one team does not have more difficult subjects than another.

TELEGRAMS

Each player, after being provided with pencil and paper, is given a word of about eight or nine letters, such as "wireless," "aeroplane," or any other that you may choose. The players write down this word, but they leave a large gap between each letter.

You now tell them that they must make up a telegram using the letters of the word in order as the first letters of the words of the telegram. For instance, if "wireless" had been the original word, they might make up the following telegram:—

"Wilhelmina In River. Everything Lost Except Spectacles. Sebastian."

CROSSWORD MAKING

Everyone begins by drawing on a piece of paper a square as shown below, with five squares down and six across, though not filled in like the example.

O	C	E	A	N	S
A	L	L	D	A	Y
T	A	F	D	I	E
W	I	N	D	L	T
E	M	A	L	S	O

Now the game begins by one of the players calling out a letter of the alphabet. This letter may be any one he likes and he places it in one of the squares in his diagram. The others do likewise, each placing the letter where they like, but bearing in mind that it is to form part of a word.

The next player then calls out another letter which, of course, will form part of the word he has in mind, and then the next calls out his letter, and so on round the room. Each player fits in as best he can the letters called out by the other players, hoping to be able to complete words by adding a suitable letter when his own turn comes.

The diagram gives an example of a finished " Crossword." The scoring is as follows : words of two letters score one point, three-letter words score three points, four-letter words score six points, five-letter words score nine points, and six-letter words score twelve points. Words are counted across and down, but the letters in a row may be used only once, so that if there is an alternative it is better to count the longer word, which scores more points. In the example, for instance, it is better to count the word " yet " than the word " to " in the last line down. We count the score, therefore, as follows : —

Words across : oceans, 12; all, 3; day, 3; die, 3; wind, 6; also, 6.

Words down : oat, 3; we, 1; claim, 9; elf, 3; add, 3; nails, 9; yet, 3.

Total score : 64.

OBSERVATION TEST

First give the players five or ten minutes to look around the room they are in and to notice carefully the objects it contains, and where these objects are placed.

Then turn them out while you make changes, such as moving a vase, putting a chair in a different place, removing an ornament, and so on. When you are ready, call in the players again and tell them to write down as many of the changes as they are able to discover. You will find that very few players will notice all the changes.

n w.

HEAD AND TAIL RACE

Write down two columns of letters, with a good space between them. The letters in the left column are to form the first letter of a word, and those in the right column the last letter, so make sure they are suitable ones.

Here is an example:—

L	Y
E	N
T	S
H	D
S	S
B	M
M	W
A	R
P	T
I	E

Give each player this list and then, when they are all ready, tell them they must fill in words between the letters, using the left-hand letter as the first and the right-hand letter as the last letter of a word. For instance, the first word could be " lorry." The first player to complete his list is, of course, the winner.

CONSEQUENCES

This is always a favourite game at parties, and everyone gets a great deal of fun out of it, particularly when the names of those at the party appear in the little " stories."

The players begin by writing down a word describing a boy. They then fold over the paper to hide the word and pass the paper to the left. Next the name of a boy is written and the paper folded and passed on, then a word describing a girl, and next a girl's name. Each time the paper is folded as before and passed to the left.

Now we come to where they met, what he said to her, and what she said to him, followed by what he gave her, and what she gave him. The last two items to be written are what the consequence was, and what the world said. Each contribution to the story is written by a different player, so that the results are usually very funny, and read something like this:

" Lazy Dennis met hideous Jane in the dustbin. He said: ' May I share your umbrella?' She said: ' I never speak to strangers.' He gave her a bar of chocolate. She gave him a kick on the ankle. The consequence was they fell overboard into the sea and the world said: ' They deserved it!' "

When complete, the slips are collected and either read out by one player, or each one reads a slip in turn.

ANAGRAMS

These are good for all who like to puzzle their brains a little. First make out a list of about twelve anagrams, which are words with their letters rearranged to form other words, leaving enough space for the solutions. Each player is given a copy of this list and allowed about twenty minutes to solve the anagrams. Here is one list as an example, with the solutions given on the right, and you will be able to think of many others.

MY ROME	MEMORY
WHERE AT	WEATHER
LEARNT	ANTLER
SLOW REF	FLOWERS
BLEAT	TABLE
SO NEAR	REASON
THE STAR	HATTERS
OR SITES	STORIES
HEN CLANS	CHANNELS
ANY CAR	CANARY
THE RATE	THEATRE
SMITE	TIMES

SCRAMBLED WORDS

First make a list of about twelve words, which are all flowers, or countries, or animals, or anything else you like to choose. Now mix up the letters of each of these words and write out a list of the mixed words and make copies of it so that there is one copy for each player. Leave enough space beside each word for the solution.

Allow the players a quarter of an hour to puzzle out the correct words after you have given out the lists. Here is a list of jumbled flowers, with solutions, as an example: —

NYSPA	PANSY
TRUBECPTU	BUTTERCUP
CLALI	LILAC
NOOWCRELFR	CORNFLOWER
SIYDA	DAISY
FALDIFOD	DAFFODIL
UPLIT	TULIP
OLIVET	VIOLET
SIRPMORE	PRIMROSE
LULLEBEB	BLUEBELL
TIRACANNO	CARNATION
ROLLWEFLAW	WALLFLOWER

ALPHABET LISTS

Eight subjects are first chosen, such as flowers, animals, towns, birds, etc. The players make a list of these subjects, leaving a space beside each.

Now give them a letter of the alphabet and tell them they are allowed three minutes to write down an example of each of the subjects beginning with the chosen letter. For instance, if the letter were G, they could write giraffe for the animal, geranium for the flower, Glasgow for the town, goose for the bird, and so on.

For the next round a different letter is chosen, and so the game continues for as many rounds as may be desired.

BATTLESHIPS

This is a game for two players. Each of them must first draw a large square, divided up into small squares and numbered and lettered as shown in the example below. This square is the ocean and each player now puts four ships on it, not letting the other see where he has placed them. The ships are marked by crosses as follows: —

Battleship	xxxx
Cruiser	xxx
Destroyer	xx
Submarine	x

They can be placed across or down or diagonally, though they must be in a straight line.

When all is ready the players take it in turns to fire at each other's fleet. They do this by calling out the number and letter of a square, such as B4. Each time the other player has to say if it has scored a hit on one of his ships, and which ship, so that, of course, after a hit the enemy will keep firing near that square. It is best for each player to put a mark on his own square after firing each shot so that he will know where he has fired. When each

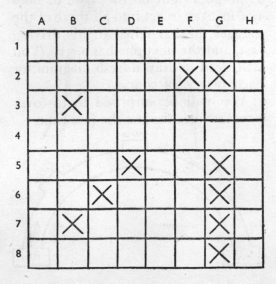

square covered by a ship is hit, it is announced as sunk. The players keep firing at one another until one of them has lost his whole fleet.

DRIVING TEST

Draw a road as shown in the diagram, with three squares to represent garages. (The diagram should measure about eight inches across the bottom.) Now seat a player with this diagram in front of him and tell him he is going to be put through a driving test. He must " drive " along the road, starting from the arrow, and he has to call in at each of the three garages for petrol or repairs, and finally drive into the car park at the end of the road.

Then you give him a pencil and place a mirror facing him, and just behind the diagram so that he can see it in the mirror. One of the other players holds a newspaper or book above his hand so that he cannot see the diagram except in the mirror.

You will find his efforts to keep a straight course very amusing and he will be very clever if he passes the test. If he goes right off the road, or does not manage to get into all three of the garages, he has failed in his driving test, and the next one has a try. (You will need to draw a fresh diagram for each player, of course.)

You will be surprised to discover how few pass the test the first time.

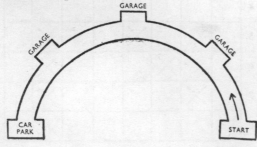

QUESTIONS AND ANSWERS

Each player needs only a small slip of paper, on which he writes a question, such as " Do you ever have a bath?" He then folds over the paper to cover the question and passes the slip to the left.

When all the slips have been passed on, each player writes an answer to the question he has just written and passed to his left. The papers are then collected and read out.

For instance the answer to " Do you ever have a bath?" might be " Once in four years," this answer being written by the player who asked " How often do we get a Leap Year?"

ALPHABETICAL WORDS

This is one of the most simple word games. A letter of the alphabet is given to the players on the word " go " and they have to write down as many words beginning with this letter as they can in ten minutes.

In this game the winner is the one with the most words, but there is a slightly more difficult form which is an interesting variation; each player reads out his list of words in turn and all the words which appear on more than one list must be crossed out on every list that has them. The winner is the one who has the most words left on his list after it has been " censored."

WORD-MAKING

A long word is chosen, such as " international," and when all the players are ready and armed with pencil and paper, you tell them what the word is.

Then you give them fifteen minutes to write down as many words as they can, using only the letters of this word. For example, in "international" there are the words in, tin, tan, intention, nation, lantern, treat, late, not, later, and many others. The words must all be in an ordinary dictionary, but they can be as short or long as the players like. One-letter words are counted.

Here are one or two examples of long words which are a good choice for this purpose: entertainment, concentration, registration, reinforcement, conversation, complimentary, perseverance, simultaneous, extraordinary.

AUTOGRAPH HUNT

This is a good beginning for a party, especially when not all of the players know each other to begin with, for they will have to talk to each other and will find out each other's names. Each player is given a pencil and a piece of paper and then on the word " Go " they must collect as many autographs as possible from the other members of the party. Allow them five or ten minutes to do this, according to the number of players. They need only write one initial and the surname, but all the names must be readable. The one with the largest collection of names when the time is up is the winner.

SERIAL STORIES

This is rather like Consequences. All the players are provided with long strips of paper, rather wider than for Consequences. Each one begins by writing two or three sentences of a story, making it up as he goes along. It doesn't matter how silly it sounds. Then all the papers are folded over to hide the writing and passed to the left. The next one continues the story he began on the new piece of paper

he has just received. After all have written another two or three sentences the papers are passed on again, and so on round the circle, until everyone has added something to each of the serial stories. When it comes to the last turn the players must finish off the story as best they can.

When the serials are read out there will be some very amusing and peculiar efforts.

MIXED PORTRAITS

A long, narrow strip of paper is required for each player, and the game begins by everyone drawing a head and neck at the top of the paper. The head may be any sort of head. It may be of a person, an animal, a fish, a bird, or a reptile, or even an imaginary one!

When each one is satisfied with his artistic effort, he folds over the paper, leaving a tiny piece of the neck showing, and passes it on to his neighbour on the left. Now everyone draws a body on to the neck, and this too can be the body of any person or creature. The tops of the legs should be begun, so that the next " artist " can finish them in the right place.

The paper is then folded over to cover the body and passed on again to the left for the legs and feet to be added. All the masterpieces are now unfolded and passed round the room, for everyone to see and admire!

write their own lists. Then tell them to add a letter to each of these words to form a new word. They may add the letter in any place they like, but they are not allowed to add an "s" at the end and simply make all the words plural without changing them. The first to complete his list is the winner providing, of course, that all his words are correct dictionary words.

Here is a list as an example, showing how the words may be changed. You will not, of course, include words in the list which cannot be changed in this way.

PLANE may be changed to PLANET.

LEAN may be changed to CLEAN or LEARN.

CURE may be changed to CURVE.

RAIN may be changed to TRAIN or GRAIN.

SEAL may be changed to STEAL or SEPAL.

SOIL may be changed to SPOIL.

CANE may be changed to CRANE or CANOE.

WORD CHANGING

The players are all given two words of the same length and they are told that they must change the first word into the second by changing one letter at a time. Every time they change a letter they must make a word and they must go on changing letters until they can form the second word.

For example, if they were given the words sand and hill, they might change sand into hill as follows: Sand to hand, hand to hind, hind to mind, mind to mild, mild to mill, mill to hill. The player who has used the fewest number of words in changing one word to the other will be the winner.

CELEBRITIES

Collect beforehand about twenty photographs of well-known people from the newspapers or magazines. When cutting them out make sure that the name is not left underneath or anywhere else on the photographs.

When you are ready for this game, place all the photographs around the room so that they can easily be seen by everyone. Then give the players about fifteen minutes to look at them and write down all those they can recognize. They must not mention any of the names aloud during this time, thus helping other players. The winner is the one with the largest number of correct names.

ADD A LETTER

Give each player a list of words, which you have made beforehand. You can either give each of them a copy or read out the words so they can

TRAY GAME

This is a good memory test. Put on a tray about twenty small articles, for instance, a thimble, a button, a penknife, a reel of cotton.

Having seen that all the players are provided with a paper and pencil, you bring in the tray and let them look at all the things on it for three minutes. They are not allowed to write anything down during these three minutes, of course.

The tray is now taken out again and the players then write down as many of the articles as they can remember. You will find that it is very rare for anyone to remember all the articles on the tray, but the winner usually gets down all but one or two.

CHANGE A LETTER

This game is very like Add a Letter. All the players are given a list of words as before, but this time instead of adding a letter to make other words they must change a letter of each word. They may change any letter they like, but they are only allowed to change one letter in each word. The first to complete the list is the winner.

Here again you must choose words which can be changed in this way when compiling your list. Below is a suggested list, but you will be able to think of many other words.

CREW may be changed to CROW.
BIRD may be changed to BIND.
SHARE may be changed to SCARE.
CHAIR may be changed to CHAIN.
SALE may be changed to SALT.
CLASS may be changed to GLASS.
STARS may be changed to STAGS.

BOXES

This game for two players requires a square of dots, ten dots to each side being a good number.

The game begins by the first player drawing a line from one dot to another, either across or down. He must not draw a line diagonally from one dot to another. His opponent now draws another line, and so on in turn. In drawing these lines each one must avoid giving a box to the other. In other words, if one draws a third line to a square where two of the lines are already drawn, the other player can draw in the fourth side of the box and put his initial inside it. He is then allowed to have another turn.

It is easy enough not to give away boxes at the beginning of the game, but later it becomes very difficult and each player must be " on his toes " and see that he gives as little away as possible, particularly as one careless stroke may give away several boxes. The winner, of course, is the one with the most boxes at the end of the game.

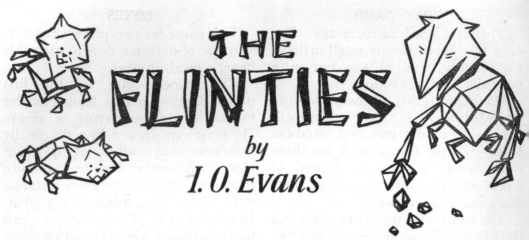

THE FLINTIES

by I. O. Evans

THE two men regarded each other with approval as they shook hands. The elderly professor was pleased to see the stalwart build of his new assistant, his firm jaw and keen grey eyes. The younger man was equally pleased to see his new employer, with his lofty brow and kindly face. They exchanged the usual polite greetings, then got down to business.

"Mr. Jarvis, you are a geologist with some experience of volcanoes, I believe?"

"Yes, Professor Thornhill—just back from a research on the lavas of Vesuvius."

"Vesuvius, eh? Then you will be accustomed to hot work, no doubt!" Though not quite seeing the joke, Jarvis laughed politely in answer to the professor's smile.

"Now let me explain," the Professor continued. "I am engaged in the synthesis of new materials for an industrial combine. Already I have prepared several which are said to be extremely useful, and so they have given me a free hand, with all the apparatus I need. I now wish to expose a number of minerals to an intense heat. Let me show you my electric furnace; please notice the range of temperatures on the thermostat."

Jarvis noticed them, and was impressed. He began to forget his dislike of being assigned to indoor work. The researches which went on here would certainly be worth his while.

"Now this is how you can help me," continued the professor. "I have been given several tons of minerals to work on—they are in the cellars here. But unfortunately the list of their names was accidentally destroyed in the central office, and I have no idea what they may be."

"And you want me to name them for you?" Jarvis was disappointed. He had hoped for something more exciting than that.

"Yes, and to tell me of what they consist. Then we shall expose them to extremely high temperatures in this furnace, and note the results."

So the work began. Jarvis sorted out the minerals, named them and fed them into the furnace. A few were queerly changed, and had to be elaborately examined and tested to

Jarvis put on his goggles and peered eagerly into the leaping flames

see if they were likely to be useful.

"Some of these are colloidal." The professor seemed amazed, though Jarvis was not far enough advanced in chemistry to know why.

One day the professor gave a shout of surprise. "Here, Jarvis, this is something new!"

A tiny peephole could be opened into the furnace. The flames were too dazzling to look at with the naked eye, and their heat too intense to face, so that goggles of heat-resisting purple glass had first to be donned.

Wondering what all the excitement was about, Jarvis put on his goggles and peered eagerly into the leaping, roaring flames.

"That thing," Thornhill told him, "like a group of crystals down in the corner. Watch it carefully, and tell me what you see."

This was certainly new. Crystal in that blazing heat! Jarvis peered more intently than ever.

"Yes, I see it!" he exclaimed. "There's a large knobbly sort of crystal, with smaller ones along its margin like a fringe. You're right, Professor, this *is* something new!"

Then he stared, blinked his eyes, began to push aside his goggles to get a clearer view, remembered the blazing heat, and checked himself in time.

"Why, it's moving," he shouted.

Movements, of course, were always happening in that mass of seething flame. But not like this.

The smaller crystals on the edge of the large one were slowly swaying to and fro. Jarvis was reminded of the time he had looked through a microscope at a drop of pond-water, and seen tiny creatures propelling themselves about by moving a fringe of hairs. This was clumsier, and moved more like a machine, or like some sort of robot, but the results were the same. The crystal, too, was moving about.

It rose in the furnace, now making use of the swirling currents of flame, now evading them by a sudden jerk. It looked like a skilful swimmer in a rough sea. Yes, swimming was the word, swimming here and there as though the crystal were exploring its glowing home. It seemed to be searching for something.

The crystals rose in the furnace, like agile swimmers in a rough sea

Then, with a sudden jerk like the pounce of an animal, it rushed at a smaller crystal which was drifting aimlessly about.

The small crystal vanished—and did not reappear.

Jarvis said slowly: "That crystal's—alive."

Thornhill, no less amazed, agreed.

They returned to their laboratory in the next room to talk things over.

"I suppose it's not to be wondered at." Thornhill summed the matter up, "Ordinary living things, as we know, flourish in the strangest places. Their bodies consist of different compounds of carbon, united in complicated ways. Silicon belongs to the same class of elements as carbon, and we find that when in fierce heat, it too, can form complicated compounds. And now it seems that some of these can live."

"The suggestion has been made," Jarvis agreed, "that the different crystals in the rocks are the remains of animals, formed of silicon, which lived long ago. But, of course, most geologists laugh at the notion. Now it looks as if the idea is right."

"It reminds me of a queer story," replied Thornhill, "that last century a scientist was carrying out some experiments. He let a shower of weak sulphuric acid fall on an iron plate

progressed. The crystal was motionless, and they feared it had died, like the unfortunate iron insects drowned in the acid. Apparently it was only resting, however, for soon it stirred its fringes, seemed to shake itself, and began to forage about.

"That fellow's hungry," said Jarvis, and the suggestion seemed reasonable enough.

They fed pieces of mineral into the furnace, in the hope of giving this strange creature some suitable food. "Ah, that seems to be what it likes," Jarvis again remarked, as it pounced on a melting fragment of pink felspar.

Next day they had another surprise. The crystal had grown.

That was nothing to the surprise they received a week later. Small crystal buds sprouted from the creature's back, grew fringes, and turned into tiny copies of itself. Presently they dropped off and began to move independently. Instead of one living crystal, there were half a dozen!

"It moves, it eats, it grows, it increases in number," murmured the professor. "We cannot doubt that it is alive."

"Let's have one of them out," Jarvis suggested. "Now that we've got a few to spare."

He put on an asbestos face-plate and gloves, and fished about with an infusible ladle in the seething glow.

"Got it!" he shouted. "Stand clear." Shaking off drops of molten liquid by a dexterous jerk of his wrist, he managed to bring out one of the crystals "dry."

The experimenters stooped over it, realized that it was no longer hot, and

while an electric current passed through it. He was surprised to see tiny projections forming on the surface of the plate. They grew into things like images of insects, with heads and feelers and legs. Finally they broke loose from the plate and began to crawl about. They were real insects, made of iron."

"What became of them?" asked Jarvis with interest.

"It was the greatest pity. While he wasn't looking, they fell into the acid and were drowned!"

The two scientists laughed, then returned to see how their experiment took off their masks to see it more clearly.

It was plainly alive, and did not seem to suffer from its contact with the cool air. Yet it was strangely different from ordinary living things. Instead of the graceful curves of animal or plant, this creature—it was only a few inches long—was all flat surfaces, straight edges and blunt points. Its body was made of a translucent crystal which apparently did not conduct heat, for inside it a glowing liquid could be seen swirling slowly round.

The fringe round its body had shrunk in the open air to three pairs of angular crystalline legs which jerked clumsily to and fro. The creature clicked noisily about on the floor, looking amusingly like a model tank. Jarvis dropped a few scraps of felspar in front of it; it ate them, two of the crystals in its forward end opening and closing on them like a mouth.

"We must find a name for these things," Jarvis decided.

"*Pseudoprotoplasma silicoënsis?*" murmured the professor.

Trust a scientist to find a proper jaw breaker! Jarvis thought, but aloud he merely remarked. "The first part's all right, but not the second. Sounds too much like an industrial disease! '*Pseudoprotoplasma Thornhillii*'— we'll name them after you."

The professor looked honoured.

"But we'll call 'em flinties for short."

They played with these weird pets for some days, the professor meantime compiling a sheaf of copious notes. They tried them with different foods and recorded all their habits. They observed that the flinties seemed quite happy in the open air, but that only when placed in the furnace did they "bud off" smaller flinties from their backs and so increase in number.

"What was that last mineral you fed a flinty on?" asked Professor Thornhill anxiously.

"A lump of amphibole—why? It hasn't done the little beast any harm, has it?"

"Well, I don't know. Just look for yourself."

Glancing into the furnace, Jarvis had a nasty shock. One of the flinties had grown! Already it was the size of a large dog, and next day when he looked at it, it was bigger still.

"Lucky we tried it on only one of them," was his comment.

So far the flinties had seemed quite harmless, and the two experimenters handled them freely. Suddenly, however, Jarvis, who had been carrying one out into the yard, dropped it with a startled yell.

"It *bit* me!" he wailed.

Really it was not an ordinary bite, but something between a deep graze and a burn.

"It seems to have done the thing good," Thornhill meditated, as he bandaged the wound. "Look, its colours are brighter than the others, and it's more lively. I think a plain diet of rock isn't enough to keep them healthy; no doubt it lacks vitamins. Perhaps they need a little carbon occasionally, just as a cat needs grass."

"Then you keep that big fellow away from me," grumbled Jarvis, as he nursed his smarting hand. "I don't want to finish up as a flinty's vitamin B!"

Mention of the "big fellow" reminded Thornhill that he had not looked in the furnace recently. As he went off, Jarvis fed the smaller flinties with scraps of meat, cheese, or wood, and found that any of these was enough, as he told the professor later, to buck the little fellows up.

The professor did not smile at the phrase or even seem to hear him. "That big one," he replied, "it's bigger than ever now."

Jarvis whistled as he peered into the furnace. The "big fellow" was about the size of a bear. "And I don't much like the look of it," he told the professor. "Looks as if it would be a nasty customer if anything annoyed it!"

"I, too, thought it looked pugnacious," the professor replied. "I wonder what we ought to do?"

"There's one thing we certainly mustn't do."

"What's that?"

"We mustn't feed amphibole to a flinty."

After some discussion, they decided, with regret—for they were getting fond of the little things—that the only thing to do was to kill one of the smaller flinties as a guide to dealing with the "big fellow."

But this, they found, was easier said than done. The flinties were impervious to hammer blows, acids and poison gas. They could not be drowned. They were not affected by liquid air. The heat of the furnace only increased their number. They could eat any sort of rock and get their vitamins from a blade of grass, a wood floor. (Only as a last resort did they bite anybody who touched them.)

Then Jarvis had an idea. He put a flinty in a tin box, stuffed it into his pocket, and cycled off to a country

Jarvis, who had been carrying a flinty, dropped it with a startled yell

road which was being repaired. Feeling a despicable quisling, he waited till a steam-roller came round the bend towards him, then put the flinty on the roadway just where it was likely to pass.

He felt more treacherous than ever as the little thing clicked into a patch of sunshine and began to eat its way through a piece of stone. The steam-roller came rumbling round the corner straight towards it.

Suddenly there was a terrific crash, a burst of flame and a puff of heated air. The steam-roller lurched, then came to a standstill with a hiss of escaping steam. Its crew tumbled out of its cab, swearing in English and Welsh. They stared for a few seconds,

looked intently at the sky, and dashed off down the road. Evidently they found a telephone box and told a convincing story, for some minutes later a police-car came dashing up.

Meantime Jarvis was examining the great roller which alone could overcome a flinty's crystal " hide." A hole had been blown through the thick metal, some of which had been melted by the fierce heat stored in the creature's body. A few scraps of rock-crystal and other minerals lay about —all that was left of the flinty itself. Jarvis put them in his pocket and cycled back.

When he heard the results of the experiment, Thornhill looked worried, said " Tchah," and perplexedly scratched his chin. Then he announced that the " big fellow " in the furnace had sprouted half a dozen buds, and that these had come off, turned into flinties the size of footballs, and started to grow.

" I am reminded," he said, half seriously, half with a smile, " of the old legends of magicians who raised evil spirits by means of spells, and then could neither control nor get rid of them."

"It reminds me," Jarvis replied, "of science-fiction stories of inventors who produced new animals which ended by devastating the earth."

"It can't be as bad as that. But if the only way to kill these creatures is to crush them, and if that makes them explode like a bomb then——" he paused.

"Then it's going to be no joke!"

"I think, at any rate, we had better discontinue the experiment."

They accordingly threw over the great master-switch that controlled the electric furnace. There came a crackle of sparks; several indicators swung back to zero, the pointer of the thermostat moved down the scale. It would be some time, however, before the furnace would completely cool down.

Next day Jarvis, who had a way with animals, was amusing Thornhill by

Jarvis opened his tin box and put the flinty on the roadway, just where the steam-roller was likely to pass

*Jarvis grasped the astonished scientist
round the waist, and rushed out*

making all the flinties sit up and beg, when suddenly there came a terrific crash. The furnace wall collapsed, and through the opening came a great crystalline bulk. Deprived of the heat in which they revelled, and of their supplies of food and "vitamins," the large flinties were coming out to look for them.

With a warning shout, Jarvis grasped the astonished scientist round the waist, and rushed him out of the building and down the street. Turning, they saw the building collapse. Then a line of flinties, six large and one enormous, emerged from the ruins and started to browse on the fallen masonry and the road surface, picking up some wayside trees by way of "vitamins," and seeming to enjoy the sunshine.

There came a frantic rush of the workmen from the buildings around, and a coming and going of police.

Professor Thornhill seemed anxious to explain, but Jarvis hustled him away. " You don't want to be lynched, do you? Well, we should be, if those fellows knew we were at the bottom of this. We'll get out of it while the going's good. All the workshops have been evacuated, and there's no danger of any loss of life."

" People are very unreasonable," Thornhill agreed. " They don't realize the value of scientific research.

But our notes, Jarvis!—the notes of all our experiments! Think of the irreparable loss to science if they are destroyed." He tried to turn back, but Jarvis restrained him.

"Your notes will be all right, professor. They're in a steel safe, aren't they? And metal's the one thing the flinties don't touch."

So Thornhill was comforted. " But Jarvis—what are we to do?"

" Report to the works manager, I suppose."

This was an unpleasant duty. The works manager was already boiling with indignation at the damage to his buildings and the interruption to the work, and now he saw the two culprits, his rage knew no bounds.

"Now that's quite enough of that, Mr. Manager," Jarvis interrupted him brusquely, seeing how distressed the professor was at being threatened and abused. "We're answerable to the board of directors and not to you. The instructions they gave the professor were specific, and all we've done is to carry them out. We were told to ascertain the effects of high temperatures on minerals with the idea of making new materials with unheard-of properties—and you can't say we haven't done it. So please keep a civil tongue in your head."

Jarvis looked so menacing as he spoke that the manager started back.

" Oh, very good, very good. I'll go and report it to the chairman of the board. But if I know anything of him, it's the last time you'll ever be employed by this concern."

" Thank you for silencing that fellow," said Thornhill quietly. " There is much to be said for his point of view, but I do hate any sort of argument. You seem to thrive on them."

" Geologists always do!" Jarvis replied, proudly. " There was a famous engineer who always used to attend meetings of a leading geological society. Somebody asked him why he was so very much interested in the science.

" ' No,' he told them, ' I don't care about geology at all. But I do like to listen to a good row!' "

With such talk he tried to cheer the professor. But when they were both summoned before a meeting of the full board, he began to feel uneasy. As a uniformed messenger ushered them into the impressive board room, in which a number of still more impressive gentlemen were seated, he felt just like a schoolboy in disgrace and ordered to appear before the Head; and he felt that Professor Thornhill was no more at ease than he was himself.

The reception they met with surprised them. As soon as they entered the room, the chairman himself rose politely and came forward with outstretched hands and a welcoming smile.

" Congratulations, my dear professor! An excellent achievement—the finest piece of work you have done."

" It—it is indeed a great gain to knowledge," replied the astonished professor. " But——"

" No doubt, no doubt. But I was not thinking of that. I have something more practical in mind. You, as a geologist will understand, Jarvis—you know that the Romans used to mine for gold in the mountains of Wales?"

" Yes, sir." Jarvis grinned. " I have a record in my field-book. ' Spent a week prospecting in the old Roman gold-workings, but no specimens forthcoming!' Worse luck!' "

" You understand, professor? Those workings are owned by the combine, and we know there is still gold in them, but only in such tiny traces that it does not pay for being worked. Now these—these creatures—of yours, I understand that they live on rock?"

" I see the idea," interrupted Jarvis, too excited to remember his manners. " We dump the big fellows on the hillside and leave them to nibble away at the cliffs!"

" Exactly — and as I understand from your report that they do not eat metals, they will leave the gold untouched. You agree, gentlemen?" He threw an inquiring glance round the board.

" Before we commit ourselves," somebody objected, " I think we ought to see one of these creatures eating rock."

None of the board, however, seemed to be anxious to visit the factory where the great flinties were still consuming the lorry-loads of broken concrete sent to feed them. The works manager was accordingly dispatched to the ruined building to fetch one of the " little fellows." Shortly afterwards he returned, his

As soon as they entered the room, the chairman rose with a welcoming smile

fingers bandaged and a deeply reproachful expression on his face.

The board meeting adjourned and its members broke into delighted laughter, as the little flinty clicked across the room and settled down contentedly to nibble at the hearth.

"They seem to be effective enough," someone remarked. "But those large ones—how are we going to get them to Wales?"

"We'll drug them with fluor-spar," Jarvis replied. "It seems to put the little fellows to sleep. Then we can carry them across in a cargo-plane."

This took a little arranging, and a few days passed before Jarvis, accompanied by two grinning workmen wheeling barrows full of fluor-spar, strode to the damaged factory.

"Go it, Jack the Giant Killer!" he heard one of the men whisper. He felt rather like that himself as he took a great lump of the mineral and walked up to the largest flinty, which loomed over him like an elephant. He felt that

*Jarvis was squatting on the largest
flinty, directing it with a chain harness*

it was regarding him balefully, but its mood seemed to change as he threw the spar in front of it.

"Look at it!" commented the workman, "putting the stuff away. Reminds me of a quick one at the local on a hot day."

To complete the resemblance, the monster lurched drunkenly across the road, smashed into a house, and seemed to go to sleep among the ruins.

The other flinties having also been drugged, all the monsters were with some difficulty lifted by cranes on to lorries, rushed to the airfield, and loaded on to the cargo-planes.

As they neared Plynlimmon, the plane in which Jarvis was travelling gave a sudden lurch. He yelled at the pilot, who yelled back at him, "Nothing to do with me!"

"It must be that flinty!" exclaimed Jarvis, as the plane lurched again. "The drug's wearing off and it wants a feed."

By a terrific effort, the pilot managed to succeed in mastering his erratic plane.

"I only hope," he remarked bitterly, "that next time they want stone whales carried, they'll choose another pilot."

It was a great relief to all when the landing was made and the released flinty waddled off sulkily and started chewing its way into the rocks.

Some months later, the professor flew over to see how the mining operations were going on. He was amused to find Jarvis squatting on the back of the largest flinty and directing its movements by a harness made of chain. The monster was followed by a machine mounted on tractor-treads, from which a suction tube, supported by a crane, projected over its head.

Jarvis explained the meaning of this appliance.

"The flinties breathe, professor, only they breathe silicon dioxide instead of carbon dioxide as we do. Their breath is a very fine sand, and we suck it up by a vacuum cleaner and send it to the factories—it's one of our best by-products and makes a special telescope glass."

"How is the gold-mining?" asked the professor.

"Going on well! If you'll take me back to London with you, I'll ask the Board to let us grow a dozen more big fellows and get them to work."

When they had reported to the board, the two scientists went off to visit the zoo. They made straight for a metal paddock, in which a number of the smaller flinties were methodically clicking about.

A keeper was talking to a visitor from the country.

"No, no, mum," he explained. "These little ones don't grow. Yes, mum, you can buy them in the pet shop outside. When we want more of them we just put one in the retort at the gas-works and shovel out half-a-dozen with the coke."

"But aren't they dangerous? Don't they bite?"

The keeper looked at her with professional scorn. "Bite? Not they, mum. Not if you give them some sawdust with their rock chippings. And the kiddies like them—a flinty makes a lovely pet."

Jarvis threw a fragment of amphibole in front of a flinty.

"When they put that fellow in the gas-works," he told the professor, "they'll certainly get a big surprise."

ZOO ESCAPES

By David Seth-Smith, F.Z.S.

CONSIDERING the large stock of animals kept in the London Zoo, the number that have escaped from their cages is really very low. Except for various small birds that have found their way out from time to time, not more than about a dozen cases have occurred in the last thirty-five years.

Some people seem to have the idea that to be in the Zoo after dark, or to live there for many years, must be a nerve-racking experience. In actual fact, one never dreams of the possibility of meeting an escaped animal, unless, perhaps, one happens to be of a particularly nervy disposition as was apparently the case with a certain night watchman. This man imagined he was seeing things as he went his rounds in the dark, and one night he had the fright of his life; for as he walked along he heard a distinct pit-a-pat, pit-a-pat, coming towards him,

and by the feeble light of his lamp, he beheld a shape approaching. That was enough for him. He took to his heels and ran to find his mate! The second watchman, not being so nervous, proceeded to investigate and was met by the old donkey that was used to draw the food cart. He had slipped his halter and was taking a midnight stroll.

On another occasion, a boy, newly employed at the Zoo, had been working late one night in the superintendent's office and so started home after dark. Now *he* was rather nervous because he had just been reading a murder story. Suddenly he thought he heard a sound, so he stood quite still and listened. Now he heard it

In the faint light the form of a large kangaroo came hopping past

more plainly, a steady pat-pat-pat, which noise, he was convinced, came from the rubber boots of some terrible man. All he could do was to fling himself into the bushes, where he lay, half dead with fright. The sound came nearer and nearer until, in the faint light, the form of a large kangaroo came hopping past. Well, there wasn't much in those two incidents, but there have been escapes of a more serious nature, though mercifully, they have ended happily.

One night a watchman, passing the old Ape House,* heard the sound of breaking branches coming from a tree alongside the house and, looking up, made out a shape, something like that of a man with very long arms, climb from the tree to the roof of the house. Watching with bated breath, he saw the shape reappear, climb back into the tree and proceed to break off branches to make itself a platform, or nest. It was Jacob, the large orangoutang, who had, with his very strong fingers, managed to unlace some of the stout wire netting of which his cage was formed, broken a window and

*This House has since been pulled down.

Jacob proceeded to break off branches to make himself a platform

Jack picked up the chain and handed it back to the keeper

walked out. Finding a tree within reach of his house, his instinct awoke, telling him to build a platform to sleep on—all this despite the fact that he had been in the Zoo for years. Thus he set to work to build, just as his ancestors in the East had always done. Watch was kept on him through the night, but he did not attempt to leave the tree, and in the morning, with some difficulty, he was persuaded to return to his cage.

Another escapade of one of the Great Apes, was that of an adult chimpanzee whose name was Jack. He had come to the Zoo when about four years old. Jack was a playful and very lively fellow, rather on the rough side, for chimpanzees differ in disposition as human beings do. He took part in the first of the Chimp's Tea Parties, and was always highly pleased when some particularly droll action on his part resulted in a burst of laughter from his human audience. As he grew up, however, his temper became uncertain towards both his own kind and human beings, and as he became a very powerful animal, it was found necessary to keep him in a cage by himself. Even his keepers decided that it was unsafe to go into the cage with him.

Well, it was about two years since anybody had been inside the cage with Jack when, one evening in the winter, a young keeper went to give him his supper and accidentally let him escape. Jack promptly decided to have a run before his supper. His own keeper, who had known him for years, was summoned and, equipped with a collar and chain, and accompanied by a second keeper, he followed in the direction Jack had taken.

Away went Jack, over lawns and flower-beds, until he came to the boundary fence which he climbed and found himself in the open park, his keepers following leisurely so as not to frighten him. When called by the one he knew best he looked round but declined to return. Thinking that it might be on account of the chain he was carrying, his keeper threw it away, whereupon Jack came and picked it up and handed it to him; but he refused to allow himself to be led back as his keeper had hoped he would.

There were still a few people in the park which was just about to close. A nurse, wheeling a perambulator with a small baby, was right in the line Jack was taking, but although he was interested in it he did not touch the occupant. Passing on, he gave a tramp the fright of his life by pulling his coat-tail while he was looking the other way. By now it was getting dark and a mist was rising, and the keepers noticed that Jack did not care to be far away from them, so it occurred to them that if they turned and walked towards the Zoo he would probably follow them and, sure enough, he did. He was evidently afraid of being out alone after dark. The writer unlocked the gate to let them in, and was greeted with a friendly grunt of recognition. The party proceeded towards Jack's cage which he entered with every sign of pleasure at finding his supper awaiting him. It was a satisfactory ending to what might have been a most awkward situation.

One foggy winter morning some thirty-five years ago, a carpenter who had just come to work was passing the cage in which the two large polar bears, Sam and Barbara, lived for many years. Suddenly he came face to face with the huge form of Sam right in the middle of the footpath. The carpenter happened to be carrying a piece of wood and, being a plucky fellow, instead of taking to his heels, he used it to give Sam a whack on the nose, so startling that gentleman that he turned tail and bolted back into his cage, the door of which the carpenter at once fastened. When the bear's keeper appeared on the scene, the carpenter told him what had happened and he was delighted to find Sam safe in his cage and none the worse for his adventure; but then he suddenly realized that Sam's mate, Barbara, was nowhere to be seen. There was no doubt about it, she was out and gone. The superintendent was at once summoned and he promptly called together as many of the staff as possible, including keepers, helpers, gardeners and stokers, to join in the search for the missing bear. The search did not last long for, as the mist cleared, she was seen sitting upon the steps of the restaurant.*

The question now arose as to how to get Barbara back into her cage on the other side of the big lawn. It is impossible to drive a polar bear; any attempt to do so would lead to a charge with, no doubt, serious injury to some-one. The whole party of perhaps a hundred men surrounded the bear, though taking care to keep at a respect-ful distance, while she looked at them with savage and scornful eyes and an expression which clearly meant, " You dare come a step nearer and I will charge!" The head-keeper clutched his rifle, expecting an order from his superior officer to shoot, when a young keeper who prided himself on his ability to out-distance any bear in running, volunteered to invite a charge and then to trust to his own speed to out-distance her in the race towards her cage. The superintendent agreed, but warned the man that he would have to run very fast and be careful not to trip or she would have him for certain! So while the others all stood at a distance, this plucky fellow approached the great white animal who eyed him with savage looks and evidently regarded him as easy prey. Then, with a roar, she charged, but the man was too quick for her and, turning, ran at full speed towards her cage while she followed close on his heels. As Sam was now safely confined in the *inner* den of the cage, the door of the *outer* part was thrown open, and near to this was another door leading in a different direction, and it was through this that our hero intended to escape if he beat his rival runner. Fortunately he did so, although he said afterwards that he had quite under-estimated the speed of a polar bear. Barbara pulled up just in front of the door of her cage won-dering, no doubt, where her intended victim had disappeared. In the end it took the combined efforts of all the other men to persuade her to admit her defeat and pass through the iron gate of her cage.

The use of a man to act as bait to capture an escaped animal happened in another case, told by the late A. D. Bartlett, in which a large rhinoceros had broken down his fence and walked out to freedom. The attraction of a bunch of carrots on the end of a stick was useless and the huge beast, weigh-ing three tons or more, wandered

*This restaurant has since been made into a Parrot House.

With a roar, the polar bear charged at the keeper

unhindered, prepared to hurl his weight against any opposition. Now there was one man towards whom he had, for no apparent reason, developed a great dislike. The sight of this person was always enough to cause him to charge the bars of his cage, so he was obviously the one to lure the great beast back if only he could do so without being overtaken. The appearance of the man had the immediate and desired effect, for the animal charged full tilt at him as he dashed for the rhino's house, squeezing out to safety between the bars and leaving the animal inside, a captive once more.

When young, some of the smaller bears are expert climbers, and are clever at squeezing their bodies through narrow spaces. When the extensive bear enclosure at Whipsnade Park was completed, a number of young bears were sent there from Regent's Park. Now, the high fence of iron bars curves in at the top, and for any animal to get out seemed quite impossible. During the night following the arrival of the young

Snugly curled up in the nest box was the raccoon, fast asleep

bears, the head-keeper, living in a cottage in the park, heard strange sounds outside his window as of somebody climbing a nearby tree; this was followed by a sort of mumbling, purring sound. Taking a lantern, he went out and discovered a small black bear high up in the branches. As soon as daylight came it was easily captured and returned to the enclosure, but only after a careful inspection of the fence had been made, and one or two possibly weak places strengthened. However, that little bear, having tasted the delights of freedom and exploration, was not to be easily defeated. The following night a lady living by herself in another house in the park, was awakened by the clatter of crockery in the kitchen, and although somewhat alarmed, sallied forth, poker in hand, to face the intruder. On entering the kitchen and switching on the light, she discovered a small black bear devouring the breakfast set for the morning. Being a resourceful lady, she took a saucer of milk with which she enticed the animal into a cupboard, and then turned the key.

It was now clear that this bear would get out of the Whipsnade enclosure every time it was replaced there, so the only thing was to return it to Regent's Park. There it was placed in a somewhat similar, though smaller, enclosure, from which no bear had ever escaped; but it had not been in there for more than half an hour before it was out of that, too! In the end it had to be housed in a cage which was covered at the top, until it grew too big and heavy to squeeze its body between the bars.

The American raccoon is an animal requiring a very strong cage as it is very quick to discover any weakness in the structure. One morning a large raccoon was missing from its cage, having forced the door in the night. Later in the day in another part of the gardens, a keeper went to feed some hens that were kept for hatching the eggs of pheasants and other game birds. He was surprised to find none of the hens out in their run, so opened the door of their roosting house. A scene of desolation met him! The place was covered with feathers and dead birds, some of which were half-eaten, while, snugly curled up in a nest box, the raccoon, cause of the trouble, was fast asleep. It had just managed to force its body through the small opening used by the hens, but having eaten so much was too fat to get out the same way, and so was trapped.

These nocturnal animals—raccoons, genets and others—are very difficult to find if they happen to escape, owing to their habit of sleeping in some obscure hiding place and not venturing out until after dark. The raccoon just mentioned was recovered unusually quickly, but another couple were loose for many months without ever leaving a trace of their whereabouts, though search was made in all likely places. It was after these two had been almost forgotten that there came a thunderstorm with deluges of rain, following a long dry spell, and as the rain ceased, a man walking past the Parrot House, saw a raccoon climb out of a ventilator in the roof and proceed to quench its thirst from the rain water in the gutter. How long it had lived in that hollow roof no one could say. It had probably fed sumptuously upon rats, though drink must have been scarce, and the sound of the water trickling down the gutter was too good to resist. No one had ventured inside that roof for many years, but now a careful search was made. The one animal was boxed without difficulty, but there was no sign of its companion.

Weeks passed and no one had seen the missing raccoon. Then, one night, a watchman in the aquarium heard strange sounds as though something was moving in the special service passage behind the tanks. The sound was not repeated and he decided that he must have been mistaken. A few nights later, however, something brushed past him as he opened the door in the darkness. Switching on the electric lights, he followed in the direction it had taken and distinctly saw something grey rush into a large empty box which was more or less hidden by other boxes and old junk. The watchman had heard of the escape of the raccoon and, realizing that this must be the same creature, determined to catch it. Blocking the entrance to the box, he quickly collected any weights he could find to ensure that the animal could not push its way out, and then ran to awaken the curator from his bed in another part of the gardens. Incidentally, it was two o'clock in the morning! The box was large and heavy but not too strong, and it was obviously desirable to place this elusive animal in a more secure place before it had time to work its way out. A car was brought from the garage, and the raccoon placed on board and motored to the raccoons' enclosure at the other side of the gardens, where it was restored to its mate by the light of the car's headlights.

African genets are small, cat-like animals with big eyes denoting their nocturnal habits, sharp fox-like faces, long tails and short legs. They are great climbers. The usual colour is buff or grey, with dark spots and blotches; but occasionally black specimens are found and these are regarded as rarities. One such lived for some time in the Zoo Cat House,* but, as it spent most of the day sleeping, was rarely seen by visitors. One morning, as the keeper opened its cage door, it suddenly sprang out and, although the doors of the house were closed, quickly climbed to the skylight and was gone, and by the time the keeper reached the outside of the house it had completely vanished. Although all the members of the staff were warned to keep a sharp look-out, no trace of it was seen, and after a full twelve months had passed, it was officially regarded as finally lost. It was well after a year from the escape of the black genet that the writer, having set a cage-trap near his house for rats, and going to inspect it one morning, was surprised to see in it a black object which he at first took to be a small cat. Closer inspection, however, showed it to be the long lost black genet looking considerably larger and fatter than before. It had been noticed that the Zoo rats had become scarcer than usual and no doubt the genet was responsible for this satisfactory state of affairs though where it had managed to hide by day always remained a mystery. It was restored to its cage in the Cat House, but later contrived to escape again and has never been seen or heard of since. Let us hope it is continuing the good work of rat destruction!

At one time a very active sea lion made a regular practice of climbing

* The Cat House is where the smaller cats and their near relations live.

the fence of its enclosure and waiting for its keeper to arrive and let it in again. On more than one occasion it was met wandering round after closing time, but it would always follow any one and allow itself to be shut into the shed below the rocks for the reward of a fish. Fortunately it never found its way to the Regent's Canal or it might have travelled a long way before being recaptured. This once happened in Rotterdam, where a sea lion escaped from the Zoo and went for miles along the intricate system of canals there.

A walrus at the London Zoo loved human society so much that when some workmen were digging a trench in its vicinity, it smashed down the temporary fence surrounding it in order to keep them company. It was a harmless, affectionate creature and no very strong fence was thought necessary to confine it. It did not, as a rule, make any attempt to get out; but one morning, feeling rather lonely perhaps, it broke out and made its way to the time-keeper's gate to meet its friends, the keepers, as they signed on for duty !

One morning, feeling lonely perhaps, the walrus broke out and went to meet his friends, the keepers

A PLACE IN THE TEAM

By Christine Chaundler

"ANYONE here seen Beth Green?" Gillian Bartrum, Games Captain and one of the Senior School Prefects of St. Agatha's, put her head round the door of the Lower Fifth sitting-room to ask the question. Josie Arnold, one of the half-dozen occupants of the room, looked up from the book she was reading.

"No. I haven't seen her since tea. But Jean Macgregor's classroom monitress this week," she said.

Gillian chuckled at the apparent irrelevance of the reply.

"Have you the parasol of my aunt? No, but I have the pen of my great-grandmother," she remarked in an amused voice. But the answer had satisfied her, and she strode off in the direction of Five B's classroom in search of her quarry.

Beth was, as Gillian had expected, in the classroom helping Jean to get it ready for the hour and a half of preparation which would begin when the bell rang in a few more minutes. Gillian smiled at the two girls amiably.

"Ah, here you are! The pen of my grandmother and the parasol of my aunt," she remarked, a cryptic utterance which made the two fifth-formers stare at her in such bewilderment that Gillian laughed aloud. She did not, however, stop to explain the joke, but merely said briskly:

"You're the person I want to see, Beth. You played a very good game of tennis the other day in the Second Team match against Petfield High School. There's a vacancy in the First Team this term. Moira Swan's not coming back after all. I rather think we are going to put you in to fill it. Are you doing anything special after prep this evening? If not, will you come along up to the courts and we'll try you out for it?"

"Yes, no, yes—I mean I'm not doing anything I can't put off and of course I'll come," Beth said, a little incoherently. "But, Gillian, it wasn't only me in the match. It was Jean, too. We were playing together."

"I know you were, and if there were two vacancies I should probably put you both in, for you make a jolly good pair. But I think you're the better really. I was watching your last set rather closely, and I noticed that Jean was making rather a lot of double faults. If you'd been playing against Petfield First Six, which is our next match, instead of their rather feeble Second, you'd have been knocked flat."

"Yes, but there was a reason for it," Beth protested, eagerly. "She'd run a beastly splinter into her hand just before that last set and we couldn't get it out. It took Sister half an hour with probes and things in the surgery afterwards to do it. It was hurting her

voline Sweet

"Ah, here you are, the pen of my grandmother and the parasol of my aunt," she remarked cryptically

horribly every time she gripped her racket. You mustn't judge her play from just watching that one set, Gillian, truly you mustn't. She's as good as I am when she's all right. In fact, she's miles better. Her service is so awfully good when it does come off."

"Oh, no. Beth's the best! *Ever* so much the steadier," Jean said firmly, and Gillian laughed again.

"Damon and Pythias!" she said

lightly. "Well, if it was the splinter that was responsible for the faults, perhaps we'd better try Jean out, too. Her service *is* rather good when it comes off, I must admit. Whoever the new member is she'll have to partner Phyllis Pratt, and Phyllis's strong point is her net play. A really smashing service is just what she needs in her partner to bring off some of her best shots. You'd better both come up to the courts this evening, then, and we'll put you to play against each other. Singles—then perhaps we really shall find out who is the better. Seven-ten, shall we say? That ought to give you time enough to get your shoes and rackets and be up on the court."

"We'll be there," promised the two Lower Fifth girls, and Gillian went on her way, leaving them to finish Jean's monitorial duties, neither of them

*The members of Form Five B were
thrilled when they heard the news*

quite knowing whether to be pleased
or not at the glittering prospect before
her. To play in St. Agatha's First Tennis Six was breathtaking glory for a
member of Form Five B. The Sixth
and the Upper Fifth Forms usually
supplied all the players for the school
tennis team. In all the years they had
been there, neither Jean nor Beth
could remember a member of the
Lower Fifth's having represented the
school in a first tennis match. But the
thought that they would have to com-
pete against one another for the honour
was agonizing to both of them. Each
of them would have preferred her
friend to be chosen to play.

"You shouldn't have said that about
my splinter! I'm not so good as you
are, really, you know I'm not," Jean
said, reproachfully. "You are so much
steadier than I am, and they'd practically chosen you. You should have said
nothing and just have gone along to be
tested the way Gillian told you to at
first. You know I shouldn't have
minded!"

"No, but *I* should," Beth responded.
"On the days when your service comes
off you can beat me to a frazzle. And
most other people as well. Look at
the way you mopped the floor with
Hilary West the other day. Two years
older than you and Five A, and yet you

licked her 6-4, 6-1. I don't believe there's a girl in the school, not even Gillian herself, who could easily stand up against that swerving service of yours when it really comes off."

"But it so seldom *does* come off," Jean sighed. "And when it doesn't I'm just as likely as not to make a double fault, as Gillian said."

"Rats! You only make a double when you try to send down another smasher for your second. If only you'd remember always to play safe when it comes to your second serve, you'd be as steady a player as I am."

"If I live to be a hundred I shall never play as steady a game as you do," Jean declared. "You're as safe as a rock, and you know it, too. You're the one of us who ought to be in the Six, and you will be, too, if the Selection Committee knows its job."

That, Beth reflected, was probably true. She *was* steady. She never seemed to suffer from nervousness as did her more volatile friend. It must be Jean's Highland blood. Highlanders were notoriously excitable. Unless Jean was in a calm and equable mood tonight, it was she, herself, who would probably be chosen. And yet Jean could play such a brilliant game at times!

"I wish there were two vacancies in the team so that we could both be in it," she sighed.

"So do I! But there aren't, so I suppose we shall just have to leave it to the Selection Commitee to decide."

"Well, I hope they'll decide upon you," Beth said.

"I don't. I hope it will be you," Jean responded. "But come on. Let's go and tell the others. There's still five minutes before prep."

The others—the remaining members of Form Five B—were thrilled when they heard the great news. To have one of their number playing in a First Tennis Six was not merely an honour for the form—there were advantages attached to it as well. When outside matches were played against schools in the neighbourhood, the girls in those forms which had a member playing in the team were allowed to accompany it to away fixtures, if they wished, to cheer the players and give them encouragement, and afterwards either to have tea with the teams, if the school visited was hospitable, or else, to find some tea-shop in the vicinity which could serve them with refreshments. To be allowed to accompany the team for an away match was a highly-esteemed privilege at St. Agatha's, while even the milder excitement of joining the meal provided at home for the players on match days was greatly sought after.

So the members of Five B were enthusiastic when they learned of the possible glory—and teas—in store for them, and when prep was over that evening and Beth and Jean went up to the tennis courts, half the members of the Lower Fifth went with them to cheer them on.

As far as the latter object was concerned, however, they might, as Lorna Deane said afterwards disgustedly, just as well have stayed away. There was nothing to cheer. Absolutely nothing! Never had either Beth or Jean been known to play so badly, and surely never before had two such feeble players taken so long to finish so poor a set. The only excitement the spectators had at all was in hunting for the balls that went out of court, and hunting for lost balls, as anyone who has

ever done it will agree, is an excitement that very soon palls. The scoring was dreadfully monotonous. One-love. One-all. Two-one. Two-all. Three-two. Three-all. Four-three. Four-all. Five-four. Five-all. If one player *did* manage to get ahead for the moment by more than one point, she invariably lost the next two to level things up again. Five B, thrilled and excited when the game began, very soon grew thoroughly bored.

"Is it tennis we're watching or a game of patball?" Rita James inquired loudly as the set wound its weary way through the eleventh game. Muriel Graham, in an equally loud voice, complained with would-be sarcasm:

"Patball! Nothing half so exciting. Pat-a-cake, pat-a-cake, baker's man, I should think it is."

While Josie Arnold, not to be outdone, resting her head on her neighbour's shoulder, shut her eyes and said with an ostentatiously noisy yawn:

"I think I'll have a snooze while we're waiting. Wake me up if either of them gets a ball over the net, so that I can join in the cheering."

This little witticism did arouse one of the players to action. Throwing up the ball she had been about to serve to Beth, Jean gave it a terrific swipe and sent it in Josie's direction with such

Jean gave the ball a terrific swipe and sent it in Josie's direction with unerring aim

unerring aim that it hit the would-be slumberer plumb in the middle of her waistband, causing her to shriek and jump up in such haste that she upset the bench on which several of the members of Five B were sitting, bringing them all in confusion to the ground. Laughing and giggling, they sorted themselves out, though with rather apprehensive glances towards the members of the Selection Committee, sitting in portentous silence on the other side of the court. The Selection Committee took its duties seriously, as Five B well knew, and would usually "have been down like a ton of bricks" on such an exhibition of "assing about" at an important test. But instead, they all suddenly rose to their feet, and Gillian called out calmly to Beth and Jean:

"That's enough, you two. No need to play it out. We have seen all we want." And without even a reproving glance at the raggers, she and her companions walked off.

"What a dramatic finish to a thr-r-rilling struggle," said Josie. Then she turned in reproach to the two players:

"Well, you've played a nice game, you have! Petfield High will have a walk-over if that's the sort of show you're going to put up. I don't know which was the worst of you. Honestly, I don't!"

"I was, if you want to know," Jean told her. "Beth would have won if we'd played it out."

"No, I'm afraid I was playing worse than you were," Beth hurried to say.

"You needn't sound so pleased about it," Muriel began, when she was suddenly interrupted by Josie who had been eyeing the two players shrewdly.

"I believe they did it on purpose! Each of them played as badly as she could hoping that the other would be chosen for the team," she remarked, and Beth's violent blush and the expression on Jean's face confirmed her suspicions.

"They did! Look at them! Look at their faces!" Muriel exclaimed.

"I believe they did! Oh, the silly chumps!" exclaimed Lorna Deane.

"But why? Why on earth should they do that?" Muriel demanded in bewilderment.

"Oh, because they love one another so dearly that each of them wants her beloved friend to have the honour and glory of playing in the team," Josie told her. "Talk about David and Jonathan, they simply aren't in it with Beth and Jean!"

"Well, I guess they've puzzled the Selection Committee," commented Muriel, a comment with which the other members of the form agreed as they made their way back to the school.

"I believe they did it on purpose," said Josie

valerie Sweet

"They'll have to toss up to decide which to put in, I should think," said Lorna. "There's no other way of finding out which was the worst."

The problem, however, was not quite so insoluble as Five B supposed. Just before prayers that night, when the members of the form were waiting in their sitting-room for the bell to summon them to Chapel, Lorna came dashing into their midst with bad news writ upon every feature.

"What do you think! Those asses, Beth and Jean! The committee hasn't chosen either of them. The vacancy's been filled by Hilary West."

"What!" shrieked Five B with one voice.

"The vacancy's been filled by Hilary West," Lorna repeated. "Gillian's just pinned up the team for Petfield away on the notice board, and she's put Hilary West to partner Phyllis Pratt as third string."

Wails of wrath and disappointment filled the Lower Fifth sitting-room.

"What a swindle! Five A's got two players in the Tennis Six already. They can all go and watch away matches whenever they like. And there's a tophole teahouse at Petfield, quite close to the High School where you can get the most gorgeous eats. And now, thanks to those two silly idiots, we shan't be able to go," lamented Five B, casting reproachful glances at Jean and Beth, who were staring at each other in horrified dismay. When, in her zeal that her friend should be chosen for the team, each girl had privately made up her mind to play badly in order that the other might be selected, neither had dreamed of such a result as this. Hilary West, too, of all people. Why, either of them could beat Hilary with

Valerie Sweet.

Gillian pinned up the team for the Petfield away

the greatest of ease if she really set her mind to it. Beth and Jean were both sure of that. In their anxiety to prove their friendship they had merely succeeded in letting down their form—if not their school.

"We couldn't help it——" Jean began to say in response to the reproaches with which they were being assailed, and then, luckily, the ringing of the Chapel bell enabled the pair of them to escape further revilement for the time being.

But only for the time being! Five B,

having had its hopes—or perhaps it would be truer to say its gluttony—aroused, could not quickly forget its disappointment. Beth and Jean found themselves the recipients of many reproachful looks during the next day or two, and both of them wished fervently that they had not attempted to act so quixotically at their test.

"But how could we guess that the Selection Committee had the least idea of putting in Hilary? Either of us can lick her to a frazzle if we want to," lamented Jean.

"Well, I suppose it's our own fault. We ought to have played up and not worried about each other. Only I *did* so want them to choose you," Beth said.

"And I wanted them to choose you," Jean confessed. "The others are quite right. We *did* play badly on purpose—at least, I did."

"And I did, too, so I suppose we are properly punished. Oh, well, it can't be helped now. I'm sorry about it, though, especially about the rest of the form. It's rough luck on them when they thought they were going to be able to go about with the team at last, to have the privilege snatched away from them."

"Oh, the form! You needn't waste your sympathy on those greedy pigs. Spell team without the m if you want to know what it was upon which they'd set their hearts! What I'm sorry about is letting the school down. I don't care what dozens of Selection Committees say—Hilary West isn't up to match play. Don't know whether we are ourselves, if it comes to that. But, anyhow, both of us are miles better than Hilary."

"Yes, I think we are," Beth agreed. "But, of course, we can't do anything about it now. We've made the committee think we're no good and they've selected Hilary. Even if we went and owned up that we were assing about on purpose, it probably wouldn't make any difference. And, anyway, we just couldn't do that. It would seem so—so—well, one just couldn't!"

"No, one couldn't," Jean sighed. "Well, we had our chance for one of us to play for St. Aggie's, and it was our own silly faults that we lost it. So we must just make up our minds not to be such blithering idiots if ever we get another chance to play in the team."

"We're not likely to get another chance! Fate doesn't usually give one second chances. Like that bit from Shakespeare we had in literature this morning. You know: 'There is a tide in the affairs of men . . .'"

"'Which, taken at the flood, leads on to fortune.'" Jean took up the quotation and declaimed with gusto:

"Omitted, all the voyage of their life
Is bound in shallows and in miseries.
On such a full sea are we now afloat;
And we must take the current when it serves
Or lose our ventures."

"And we *didn't* take the current when it served, and so now all our hopes of playing in the Tennis Six this summer, at any rate, are a washout! Shakespeare certainly knew what he was talking about."

But, for once in a way, it seemed that Shakespeare was not quite so right as usual. Perhaps the Selection Committee was not quite so obtuse as might have been supposed. Perhaps its members had guessed something of what lay

" Beth, Jean, we want you to come up to the tennis courts tonight for another test "

behind the shockingly bad play they had watched in the test game. For Hilary was really not quite up to match form. A few practices had convinced the Powers That Be of that, and two days before the Petfield match was due

to take place, Gillian once more came in quest of the two friends in the Lower Fifth sitting-room.

"Beth, Jean, oh, you are both here! Look here, we want you up on the tennis courts tonight for another test. Can you turn up again after prep, both of you?"

Could they? Couldn't they! Breath-

lessly Beth and Jean assured her that they could, hardly daring to think what such a request might mean and not venturing to ask any questions. The other members of the form, however, were troubled with no scruples on that point, and in reply to the clamour of queries that assailed her from all sides, Gillian nodded her head.

"Yes, if you want to know, it *is*," she told them.

"Isn't Hilary——"

"No, she isn't. At least, I don't think so if we can find anybody better. She's not shaping well, and so we've decided to give Beth and Jean another chance to see if either of them can put up a better show this time. No! Don't go and run away with the idea that either of them is certain to be chosen! If one of them is, she'll have to play a jolly sight better than she did the other night. There are one or two people in the Sixth and Upper Fifth we could fall back upon if the worst came to the worst."

"The worst *shan't* come to the worst, though, this time!" Jean muttered grimly under her breath in her friend's ear, and Beth nodded her head in determined agreement.

"No, indeed! I'm going to put everything I've got into my play tonight, even if I do have to lick you."

Gillian turned to her companions with a look of comical perplexity

"So am I," said Jean. And that night, certainly none of the spectators could complain of a poor show. Jean's brilliant service came off nearly every time. Beth played a fine, steady game, placing her balls with skill and intelligence. Stroke after stroke from both ends of the court met with approving comments from the members of the Selection Committee, who, however, seemed very little happier than they had been on the previous occasion—though this time for a different reason. Last time both the Fifth Form girls had played so badly that there had not been a pin to choose between them. This time they were both so good that it was impossible to say which was the better. The last game of the set was still in progress, five all with deuce points mounting up to an enormous number, when Gillian turned to her companions with a look of comical perplexity on her face.

"Which on earth of them shall we choose? If they'd only play like this on the day, they'd both of them be good enough for the team in their different ways. With Jean's service and Beth's steadiness they'd make a first-rate couple."

"Put them both in then, and drop me." Phyllis Pratt, a Sixth Form member of the team said suddenly. "I'd be just as well pleased *not* to have to play on Saturday. My brother's home on leave from India, and I've got an exeat for the weekend. I was going on from Petfield station after the match, but I'd really rather get away earlier if I could. Honestly, those two kids would play a better game together

"All right, you two," she said, " you're both selected for the team"

than either of them would with any-one else."

"I believe they would," agreed Gillian. "We'd be sorry to drop you, though, Phyl. Are you really serious when you say you'd rather not play?"

"Absolutely serious," Phyllis assured her. "I wouldn't let you down if you really needed me, but I don't think you do when you've got those two. And I *would* like to get home early to see as much as possible of John."

"What do you others say?" Gillian turned to the rest of the committee. And when they all agreed with Phyllis's opinion, the Games Captain jumped to

her feet and stopped the trial set just as deuce had been declared for the twenty-second time.

"All right, you two. You needn't play any more. We've decided. You're both selected for the team for the match on Saturday, and will partner each other as third string. And, if anybody from Five B wants to go with the team to Petfield, they'd better give in their names to Miss Vernon as soon as they get down to school tonight."

But she might have saved her breath over that last order.

The members of Five B were already on their feet scurrying off at top speed in the direction of St. Agatha's.

HOW TO TAKE PHOTOGRAPHS

By Gwyneth Pennethorne

NEARLY everyone loves pictures. Most of you like to draw and paint them yourselves and get a great deal of pleasure out of them, even if they are not quite perfect. Then one day someone gives you a camera.

Now a camera is an instrument for taking pictures. It can do so beautifully and accurately. Whether it does or not depends on how this wonderful machine is used. To make really good pictures with it you must understand how it works.

The most important part of a camera is the lens. This is the eye of the camera and the part that actually produces the picture on the film. It is also the most expensive part and the better the lens, the better the photographs will be. Take care of the lens and never touch it with your fingers.

Next comes the shutter. A photograph is taken by allowing light to come through the lens on to the film. The shutter opens and shuts—like your eyelid—and so allows light to pass through the lens to the film, while preventing it from going through except at the moment of taking a photograph. You will probably notice a small wheel or pointer on the front of your camera—the method differs on

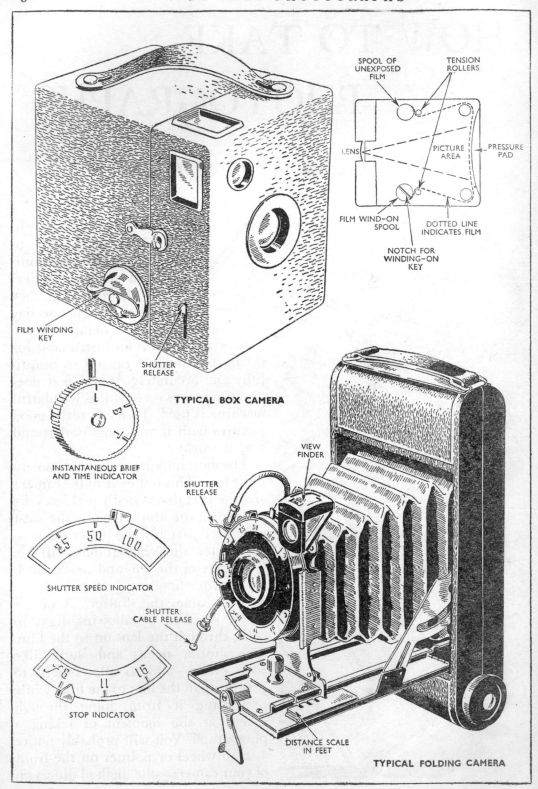

SPOOL OF
UNEXPOSED
FILM

TENSION
ROLLERS

LENS

PICTURE
AREA

PRESSURE
PAD

FILM WIND-ON
SPOOL

DOTTED LINE
INDICATES FILM

NOTCH FOR
WINDING-ON
KEY

FILM WINDING
KEY

SHUTTER
RELEASE

TYPICAL BOX CAMERA

INSTANTANEOUS BRIEF
AND TIME INDICATOR

SHUTTER SPEED INDICATOR

STOP INDICATOR

VIEW
FINDER

SHUTTER
RELEASE

SHUTTER
CABLE RELEASE

DISTANCE SCALE
IN FEET

TYPICAL FOLDING CAMERA

different cameras. Very likely it will be marked I, B and T. These letters stand for Instantaneous, Brief and Time. Instantaneous is what is generally called a snapshot. Set the wheel or pointer to I, open the back of the camera (with no film inside, of course) and, holding up the camera with the lens pointing to light, look through the camera from the back. Now press the lever or trigger and you will see a flash of light. The shutter has opened and shut. That is what happens when you take a snapshot. In some cameras there is only one snapshot speed, but in others you may see figures, such as 100, 50, 25. These stand for 1/100, 1/50 and 1/25 of a second. Set the pointer to each in turn and notice how much more slowly the shutter opens and shuts at 1/25 compared with 1/100.

Try now with the pointer at B. Press the trigger and hold it down. The shutter will stay open until you release the trigger. This is for taking photographs when the light is not good enough for snapshots. You can give a quarter of a second by opening and closing the shutter as quickly as you can, or even two or more seconds. *But you cannot do this with the camera held in your hand.* You must have it on a firm support to keep it steady.

Again set the pointer to T. You will find that when you press the trigger the shutter will open and stay open until you press it again.

Take another look at the front of your camera. You may see a pointer and several numbers, possibly F8, F11, F16. These are called stops. Again look through your camera from the back with the pointer set to the smallest number. You will see, if you

open the lens, that it looks very large. Now move the pointer along all the numbers and the lens opening will become smaller and smaller. So you see the higher the number of the stop the less light comes through the lens.

There are two reasons for these stops. On a very bright day in summer you might use your fastest snapshot and yet your photograph would be over-exposed—that is, too much light would have come through the lens if you used a large stop. So you " stop down " as we say, that is, use a smaller stop and let in less light. The other reason is not quite so easy to understand, and it will be explained when we get to focusing.

If your camera is a very simple one it may have no extra stops and only one snapshot speed; it may also be what is called a fixed focus· That means that you must always stand at a given distance—say, for example, eight feet—from the subject you are taking. If you do this, your pictures will be in focus —that is, sharp, or clear. But if your camera is more elaborate, it may have a scale marked in feet. With this type of camera you can go closer to your subject, for whatever distance you are from it, it will be in focus if you have set the scale correctly. Now supposing you were taking a photograph of a garden, for instance—you might have a flower bed about four feet away, with the rest of the garden stretching out behind for a long distance. Now, if you set the scale at four feet, the flower bed would be in focus but the rest of the garden would not. And if you set the scale to twenty feet that would be all right for the distant part, but the flower bed would appear as a mess. So here is where your stops come in. With a

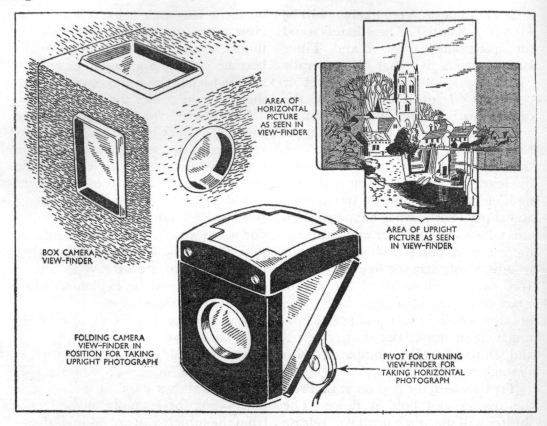

AREA OF HORIZONTAL PICTURE AS SEEN IN VIEW-FINDER

AREA OF UPRIGHT PICTURE AS SEEN IN VIEW-FINDER

BOX CAMERA VIEW-FINDER

FOLDING CAMERA VIEW-FINDER IN POSITION FOR TAKING UPRIGHT PHOTOGRAPH

PIVOT FOR TURNING VIEW-FINDER FOR TAKING HORIZONTAL PHOTOGRAPH

large stop, the exact place you focus on will be in focus, but, with a smaller one, other distances—both far and near—will also be sharp. Always remember, though, that the smaller the stop the less light comes through the lens and the more exposure you must give.

Lastly, the view-finder. This shows you on a small scale what you are going to get on your film. Unless your camera takes square pictures you will have two finders, one for upright and the other for horizontal pictures.

Check each direction in your book of instructions with the camera, so that you really understand what each knob and gadget is for. Then, before putting in a film, handle the camera, so that you become accustomed to it. First,

decide what you will take. Look at it first with your naked eye, and then in the view-finder. See how near you need go to take in all you want. Try which way up suits the subject. Someone standing will need the upright shape, but if you take four or five people standing in a row, the horizontal shape will be required.

Next, focus the subject. Step or measure the distance and set the scale to the correct figure. Decide which stop you will use. Now set the pointer to I and to the snapshot speed you want. You need a steady hand, so stand with your feet slightly apart, take a gentle breath, hold it, and very, very gently *squeeze* the trigger. Don't jerk it, or the camera will move and then you will get a blurred image.

When you have taken your photograph, wind the film. Always make a habit of doing this immediately after taking a picture, and then you will not have the disappointment of finding two pictures on the same film!

Now try a B or brief exposure. You will need a real support for this—either a tripod or a table. It is quite impossible to take a Brief or Time with the camera held in your hand.

Go through all the motions as before and then wind the film. Then take a Time. In a short while, you will feel you have got to know your camera, and you are now ready to load it.

Always load your camera in a shaded place, and to begin with, choose a medium speed film. Open the back

WRONG POSITION   RIGHT POSITION

of the camera and put the empty spool you find there in the take-up hollow. Now drop your new (unopened) spool into the opposite space and then, not before, break the seal and pull out a few inches of backing paper. Carry this across to the empty spool and push the end into the *wider* slot, being very careful to keep the paper even with the sides of the camera. Wind on a little way, then shut the camera back. Now continue winding until the figure 1 appears at the little red window. You are at last ready to take a photograph.

You should now be able to set out with confidence. You will probably begin by taking outdoor photographs: landscapes, garden scenes, people or animals. Suppose you want to take a photograph of your own house. Choose a sunny day. You can take photographs on dull days but photographs of houses or landscapes come out much brighter when the sun is shining. But sunshine is not enough. You must have it in the right place, shining on the house from the right direction. So notice where the sun is at different times of the day. Never take a picture, if you can possibly avoid it, with the sun exactly behind the camera. It will be most disappointing, a dull grey, with no shadows showing, altogether uninteresting. And don't take it with the sun shining on your lens, for that will cause fog on the film. As a general rule, you will find that for landscapes and houses the best place for the sun is to one side and slightly behind you.

Choose your position carefully. You will find a house taken from straight in front will be rather stiff. You will find the picture much more attractive if taken at an angle where part of the end can be seen as well as the front. If you can't get the chimneys in without tilting the camera, go further back or find something to stand on. If you tilt the camera, the house will look as if it is falling over backwards.

Pictures of gardens can be pretty, but they are often disappointing as photographers can be misled by colour. You may see in your view-finder a lovely bed of scarlet tulips. Hoping for a perfect picture, you snap them, but the print is dull as the riot of colour appears in print only as dull grey. So beware of being caught by colour. You want form as well. A birdbath, sundial, pergola, or a child will make a picture, when a flower bed is no good at all.

Of all subjects, people are the most popular, and also the most difficult. That is not to say you cannot in a first attempt take a photograph of Aunt Dorothy which everyone will be able to recognize. But that is quite different from taking a photograph of Aunt Dorothy that Aunt Dorothy herself will like. If you take her with a bright sun shining on her face and making her screw her eyes, she will say you have made her look hideous.

If you take her in that way one half of her face may be black and every wrinkle—if she has any—will look like a furrow. You must realize that portraiture is quite different from houses and landscapes. Forget about brilliant sunshine and find a soft light for your subject. You can do this by taking it on a dull day or in a shady spot. But be sure it is real shade, not that speckly kind you get under trees. Then see that the light comes partly from the side and partly in front. You will need a plain or dark background. Possibly the

SUBJECT

CAMERA

SUN

RIGHT

WRONG

Photograph them with the sun hidden behind a light cloud

porch, with the front door open, so that she is against the dark hall, or photograph her in the shaded angle of a wall. Use your largest stop, and always focus on the face.

If you want to take a picture of children remember that children have no lines in their faces so you can often take most attractive pictures of them in full sunlight, although even child-ren appear better if the sun is behind a light cloud. Try to take them naturally, not staring at the camera.

Animals are much the same as children. If you have a family of puppies, put them on the lawn to play, or on a garden chair. You will not be able to measure the distance so set the scale to the distance you think will be correct and try hard to keep it.

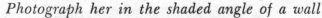

Photograph her in the shaded angle of a wall

Don't be afraid to try some interiors. They are not a bit difficult. If you can take outdoor photographs, you can take indoor ones. The great difference is in the exposure, which will need to be very much longer. In some cases you may need to give a minute or more. In a dark hall or church, the exposure might be a quarter of an hour. You need your smallest stop, so that things close as well as distant are all in focus.

Lastly, a few tips and reminders to prevent failure. Before taking a photograph, check your stop, focusing and snapshot speed. If in doubt what exposure to give, give more rather than less.

Look at your subject and be quite certain from which direction you want to take it. Hold the camera steady, and use a support if you give a slow snapshot speed. Don't tilt the camera to include the chimneys. Wind the film *directly* you have snapped the shutter. Never have the sun immediately in front or behind you. Load and unload your camera indoors or in a shady place. Read your book of instructions carefully.

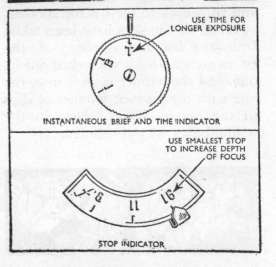

USE TIME FOR LONGER EXPOSURE

INSTANTANEOUS BRIEF AND TIME INDICATOR

USE SMALLEST STOP TO INCREASE DEPTH OF FOCUS

STOP INDICATOR

Party Games

By David Rodney

FLOWER BOXES

Six small boxes—any kind will do—are needed for this game. Place these boxes round the room and beside each box put a list of flowers, say about twelve. The lists must all be different, so that you will need about seventy-two flowers in all. Each of these flowers must be written on separate small slips of paper as well as on the lists, the slips being put in a hat.

When the word "Go" is given, each player takes a slip from the hat, writes his name on the back, and then rushes to find which list has the flower written on his slip. As soon as he finds it he puts the slip in the box beside it and runs back to the hat for another.

When all the slips have been taken from the hat and disposed of, the boxes are emptied and checked one by one, and the winner is, of course, the one with the greatest number of slips in the *correct* boxes. Slips in the wrong boxes are not counted.

Flower Boxes

BRAYING DONKEY

For this little catch, pick as a victim someone who doesn't mind a joke against himself. Begin by announcing to the party that you are going to play a farmyard game, in which every one is given the name of an animal. You then go round pretending to give each one an animal name, but instead of doing so you tell all except the victim to do nothing but listen. When you come to the victim you tell him that he is to be a donkey.

You now inform the players that you are about to tell them a story about a farm, and every time you mention the word "farmyard" they must all imitate the noise of the animal they represent. You proceed to tell them a story, bringing in the word "farmyard" fairly soon. Immediately a loud bray rings out in the silence, to the confusion of the poor donkey and the amusement of everybody else!

NURSERY RHYMES

This is most suitable for a big party in a hall or large room. The players are divided into five or six equal groups, which are spaced round the room, each group seated in a small circle. One player is left out and he stands by himself in the middle of the room.

The groups are given a minute or two to think of as many nursery rhymes as they can. Now the game starts by the one in the centre pointing to any one of the groups. This group must immediately sing or recite a nursery rhyme (the first verse is enough). As soon as they have finished, the leader points to another group, who must carry on with another nursery rhyme. The leader points in turn to all the groups, seeing that each one has its fair share of turns.

No nursery rhyme must be repeated, and if a group begins to sing a nursery rhyme which has already been used, that group is "out." As the game goes on ideas begin to flag, and any group which cannot think of a fresh nursery rhyme within a reasonable time (say until the leader has counted ten slowly) must be counted out. The winning group, of course, is the one that survives after all rivals have had to retire from the game.

WHO AM I?

This is a good game for starting off a party, as it makes the players talk and get to know one another. First write on slips of paper the names of famous people, alive or dead, or in stories, such as Nelson, Alice in Wonderland or Robin Hood.

One of these slips is pinned on each player's back, then all the players are turned loose and told to find out who

Nursery Rhymes

Who Am I?

TINY
TIM

they are. This they must do by asking
questions of anyone they can find to
listen to them—for every one wants to
do the asking! The sort of questions
to ask are: "Am I a man?" "Am
I alive?" " Do I live in England?"
etc., and the only answers that may be
given are " yes " or " no."

The first one to guess is, of course,
the winner, but all must finally guess
who they are or pay a forfeit.

Another way of playing this game
is to use it to pair up the party for
supper, or perhaps some other game
that requires couples. In this case the
slips are written in twos and the names
might be Jack and Jill, Romeo and
Juliet, William and Mary, etc. The
men's names are, of course, pinned on
the boys' backs and the women's names
on the girls' backs. They must all find
out who they are by asking questions,
and then, each one having guessed,
they hunt round for the right partner.

PASSING THE RING

Thread a ring on a piece of string
long enough to go round a circle of
seated players, tying the ends of the
string together in a neat small knot.
Each of the players takes the string in
both hands (palms facing downwards)
and one player is chosen to stand in
the centre.

He must cover his eyes while the
ring is concealed in the hand of one
of the players.

When he is allowed to look, the
players must all start moving their
hands backwards and forwards along
the string, each pretending to be
passing the ring along. While all these
movements are going on, the ring is
actually passed from one player to
another, care being taken that the one
in the centre does not see. His job is
to discover where the ring is and he
may challenge any one whom he
suspects of having it. That player
must immediately show both his
hands, and if he is caught with the ring
he must go into the centre, while the
guesser takes his place.

If the players who have not got the
ring act very suspiciously, there is
more scope for a great deal of fun in
their efforts to baffle the guesser.

MUSICAL CUSHION

This is a variation of musical chairs
which can be played very happily by
a number of people at a large party,
where not enough suitable chairs can
be found for the original version to be
played.

The players stand in a wide circle,
with as much space between them as
possible, and when the music com-
mences they pass a cushion quickly
from one to another around the circle.

The unfortunate person who is caught with the cushion in his or her hands when the music stops has to fall out of the game, while the circle closes in to fill up the gap.

KITCHEN UTENSILS

To begin this jolly game all the players except one choose the name of a kitchen utensil, such as cup, fork, saucer, frying-pan, etc. The one without a utensil listens to all these names carefully so that he will be able to remember them, asking the players to repeat them if necessary.

He now stands in the centre of the circle of players and calls out three times the name of one of the utensils chosen. He does this as quickly as possible and, before he has finished, the player whose utensil it is must call it out. He has only to say the word once, but he must get the whole word out before the caller has said it three times. If he fails to do so he must change places with the caller, who takes his utensil.

The caller need not look at the player whose utensil he names, and he

Poor Pussy

will soon find a victim to take his place if he jumps swiftly from one utensil to another.

POOR PUSSY

This is a game in which those who are good at keeping a straight face score. One of the players is chosen to be pussy, and the rest sit in a circle.

The pussy goes over on all fours to any one he chooses and gives a loud and pitiful miaow, and he may at the same time perform any cat-like antics he can think of to make his victim smile. The latter must stroke his head and say: "Poor pussy," keeping a perfectly straight face all the time.

Pussy is allowed to repeat his performance twice more if his victim does not break down the first time, and if he still does not succeed in getting a smile he must then try someone else. But the player is very strong-minded indeed who can hold out against three attempts, and a smile will mean changing places with the pussy.

Musical Cushion

MURDER

This is as exciting as it sounds. To begin with, folded slips are picked by all the players. On one of these slips the letter " D " is written, and whoever picks it is the detective and at once announces himself. On another slip is the letter " M " for murderer, and the one who picks this must give no sign that he has picked the fatal slip. All the slips are now refolded and collected, so that there is no possible chance of the murderer being spotted in advance.

Everything is now ready for the " dark deed " to be committed. The lights are turned out in the rest of the house and all the players except the detective go out into the darkness. They roam about the house, keeping an eye open for anything that looks suspicious. The murderer also roams about, looking for a victim. When he finds one in a convenient spot he commits the murder by giving a gentle pinch on the arm. The victim immediately gives a scream and falls down " dead " exactly where he is at the time.

On hearing the scream, every one must stand still (except the murderer, who gets as far away from the scene of the crime as he can without being noticed) and the detective comes out and switches on all the lights. He then examines the " corpse " and notes its position, and also the position of the other members of the party, particularly those near the " corpse."

The players then go back to the room from where they started and the cross-examination begins. The detective questions every one—except the corpse—asking such questions as: " Where were you when the crime was committed?" " Did you see any one behaving suspiciously?" and so on.

Every one must give evidence truthfully except the murderer, though he must use skill in his lies if he is not to be trapped. No one, however, must say who they think the murderer is—they may only give evidence that may lead to his arrest.

When the detective thinks he has a strong clue to the identity of the murderer, he accuses the " suspect."

Murder

If he has made a false deduction and accused an innocent person, he may ask further questions and make one more accusation. If he fails a second time to find the guilty one he must give up the case. The murderer then confesses his crime.

AIR, SEA OR LAND

The players sit round in a circle and one stands in the middle with a soft ball or handkerchief in his hand. He throws the ball into the lap of any one he chooses and calls out one of the three words: "Air," "Sea" or "Land." This player must quickly name an inhabitant of whichever is called before the thrower counts ten. For instance, if "Air" is called he might say "Eagle." If he manages to say this before ten has been counted, the thrower tries someone else, but if he is too late he must change places with the thrower.

The same name must not be used twice and if any one calls out an inhabitant which has been already mentioned he must take the thrower's place. Occasionally the word "Fire" may be called out when the ball is thrown, and in that case the one who receives it must keep silent.

GHOSTS

A quiet spelling game is good fun as a "breather" after more riotous games at a party. One player begins with a letter, say B. The next one adds a letter, but it must be one that makes it possible for a word to be built up, so that a letter such as D or C would not do. Suppose he chooses R. The next one might add E and the next A.

The object of the game is to avoid completing a word, so that if the next

Air, Sea or Land

player is clever he will avoid the pitfall of adding a D, which would form the word "bread," and will add instead a T, so that the player after him has to complete the word "breath." This player loses a life and the next player begins a new word.

Words of two and three letters do not count and all words must be in an ordinary dictionary—it is a good plan to have a dictionary at hand to check any doubtful words. Any player may challenge another if he thinks there is no word possible after this player has added his letter. The challenged player must then give the word he had in mind, or forfeit a life if he is unable to do so. As many words often seem very strange in their half-spelt form, this often leads to a mistaken challenge, which means a life lost by the challenger.

As soon as any one loses three lives, he becomes a " ghost " and drops out of the game, though he tries to get the other players to speak to him. If they are so incautious as to answer him they lose a life each time they do so.

COFFEE-POTS

One player is sent out while the rest choose a word, preferably with more than one meaning, such as row, roe, or bear, bare. This makes it more difficult for the guesser, who now comes in and asks questions round the circle of players. Each player must introduce the chosen word into his answer, but instead of saying the actual word he must use the word " coffee-pot."

For instance, the questioner might ask, " What is your favourite sport?" and the answer might be: " I like coffee-potting on the river," if the word were " row." The next question might be " What do you do on Saturdays?" to which the player might reply: " I help dig the garden and plant things in coffee-pots." " What do you have for breakfast?" " Bread and butter and herrings with coffee-pots." And so on until he guesses the word. The questioner is allowed two guesses and if he fails he must go out again, but if he guesses, the player who gave the word away must go out.

THE PARSON'S CAT

The players sit in a circle and the first begins by saying: " The Parson's Cat is an artful cat," or any other word he may think of beginning with the letter "A" and describing the cat. The next player may say: " The Parson's Cat is an angry cat," and so on round the circle. Each player must think of a different word beginning with "A" and if any player repeats a word already used, he has to pay a forfeit.

After the letter "A" has gone round the circle several times, the game starts afresh with the letter " B," and so on through the alphabet as long as you wish.

THE MOON IS ROUND

This is a simple little catch, which usually keeps everybody guessing. Provide yourself with a walking-stick, or any other long stick, and then seat yourself and the players in a circle.

You now draw an imaginary circle with the stick on the floor in front of you, saying, " The moon is round. It has two eyes a nose and a mouth," drawing in these imaginary features as you mention them. (Two dots for the eyes and two dashes for the nose and mouth.) You then pass the stick

The Parson's Cat

My Aunt Went to Town

MY AUNT WENT TO TOWN

The players first choose a letter of the alphabet, say the letter P, and then one of the players says " My Aunt went to town and bought a poodle," or some other word beginning with P.

The next one says " My Aunt went to town and bought a poodle and a parachute," and the next, " My Aunt went to town and bought a poodle, a parachute and a pumpkin." This goes on all round the circle, each player in turn having to go through all the names in order and add a new one of his own beginning with the chosen letter. Every time a player makes a mistake he has to pay a forfeit.

When the letter has been round the circle two or three times, a new one is chosen. This time the last player begins and the letter goes the other way round the circle, so that those who had the most names to remember in the first game will now have their turn to start off the game.

PUSS-IN-THE-CORNER

This game for five players may be played indoors or out-of-doors, in the latter case the corners can be marked with chalk squares.

Four of the players stand one in each corner of the room, and the fifth one stands in the middle. The object of the four players in the corners is to change places without being caught by the one in the middle. When one of them thinks it is safe to do so, he beckons to one of the others and says " Puss, puss." Each then dashes across to the opposite corner and the one in the middle tries to catch one of them before they have changed.

In the meantime two others are taking advantage of the chance to

to the player on your left and say: " Can you do this?"

He tries to imitate you exactly, even passing the stick to the player on his left, as you have done. To his surprise you say, " Wrong," and the next player tries, and so on round the circle, the players getting more and more mystified. You show them again once or twice, and still they don't get it right.

The secret is that as you pass on the stick, which you have been holding in your right hand, you transfer it to your left hand and pass it on with your left hand. This is very rarely spotted, and even if someone does so you merely say " Right," and the other players are just as puzzled as ever!

Conversations

change while he is trying to catch the others, and so the game goes on. If a puss-in-the-corner is caught he must change places with the catcher.

ADVERBS

This is another favourite guessing game, which causes a great deal of fun as a rule. One of the party having been sent out, the players choose an adverb which describes something that is said or done, such as playfully, seriously, etc. The player outside now comes in and he is invited to find out what the chosen adverb is. This he does by asking each one of the players in turn to perform some action in the manner of the adverb. For instance, he might ask someone to cross the room, shake hands with another player and ask him the time. If the word chosen is "seriously," the performer of the action will try to look very solemn.

Three guesses are allowed, and if the guesser succeeds in naming the adverb correctly, the last one who acted the adverb must go out for the next turn. Otherwise, the guesser himself goes out for another turn.

CONVERSATIONS

Two talkative players should be picked out and sent outside, as this game will give them a good chance to use their "talent." The rest choose two short sentences, which may be as silly as they like. For instance, the sentences might be, "He always eats a water-melon before breakfast," and "She likes to paint her pictures upside down."

The players outside are given separately one of these sentences, and they are then called in and told they must carry on an ordinary conversation and lead up gradually to the given sentence. This must be brought in naturally during the conversation and must not be forced in. The conversation might run as follows.

A: "Good morning. I hope you are well."

B: "I'm very well, thank you. It's a long time since I've seen you."

A: "Yes, it must be several weeks. What bad weather we have had lately."

B: "Yes, I wish I were in some warm climate such as South Africa. I have an uncle out there whom I should like to visit when I'm older."

A: "How funny! I have an aunt who is also in South Africa. She is an artist, but rather an unusual one."

B: "My uncle is also a little unusual in his habits. He finds the hot weather makes him so thirsty that he always eats a water-melon before breakfast!"

That is B's triumph, as he has managed to get in his sentence before A, who was leading up to her sentence with her artistic aunt.

PROVERBS

The art in playing this game is to choose a proverb which will not be given away by a very obvious word. For instance, "Where there's a will there's a way," is a better choice than "People who live in glasshouses shouldn't throw stones."

When the proverb has been chosen (the one who is to do the guessing having been sent outside), each player is given a word of the proverb in sequence round the circle. If the proverb is not long enough to provide a word for all, start from the beginning again. It does not matter if the proverb is not completed a second time, as long as it is completed once.

The guesser now comes in and is told at what point in the circle the proverb starts, so that he begins his questions there. The answers should not be too short, so that it is easy to bring in the given word of the proverb without making it obvious. The first question might be "Do you like walking?" and the answer, "I like it very much if I may walk where I want to go." The second question might be "What is your favourite flower?" and the answer, "I don't think there's

anything to choose between the rose and the carnation."

The questioner has three guesses after he has been all round the circle.

HOW, WHEN AND WHERE

One player is first sent out of the room and the remaining players choose an object, for instance, an apple. The player outside now comes in and asks questions of each player in turn.

First he goes all round the circle saying: "How do you like it?" and the players must give an answer such as " I like it very juicy." Next he asks all the players, "When do you like it?" and each player must give an answer such as: "I like it after dinner."

Finally he asks the question, "Where do you like it?" to which one answer might be, "I like it in the garden." It is very unusual if he is not able to guess the word before he has finished asking all these questions, but if he is not able to guess it after three tries he must go out and try again with another word.

If he guesses correctly, then the player whose answer finally gave him the clue is the next to go outside.

Proverbs

SARDINES

This is a popular form of hide-and-seek, and it may be played indoors or out-of-doors.

One player goes off and hides, choosing his hiding-place carefully so that it will hold a number of people —even if not comfortably! The other players give him three minutes to hide and then they scatter and begin the search. When a player finds the hiding-place, he says nothing to the others but waits his opportunity until no one is looking and then creeps in and hides beside the first hider.

This continues until the players are crowded together like the sardines which give the game its name. By this time the last few seekers should have no difficulty in finding the hiding-place from the scufflings and subdued giggles that will be heard from even the quietest party! The first player to find the hiding-place is the next one to hide.

FORFEITS

There is always an accumulation of forfeits from various games during the party and here is a list to help you when giving them out:—

BITE AN INCH OFF THE POKER. You hold a poker an inch from your mouth and take an imaginary bite.

SIT UPON THE FIRE. Write the words "the fire" upon a piece of paper and then sit on it.

PUT ONE HAND WHERE THE OTHER CANNOT TOUCH IT. Put your right hand under your left elbow.

GO OUT WITH TWO LEGS AND COME BACK WITH SIX. Walk out of the room and then come back carrying a chair.

PUT FOUR CHAIRS IN A ROW, TAKE OFF YOUR SHOES, AND JUMP OVER THEM. The catch in this is that you jump over your shoes and not the chairs.

ASK A QUESTION TO WHICH THE ANSWER "NO" CANNOT BE GIVEN. You ask "What does y—e—s spell?"

LAUGH IN ONE CORNER, CRY IN ANOTHER, AND SING IN ANOTHER.

PLACE A BOOK ON THE FLOOR WHERE NO ONE CAN JUMP OVER IT. The book is placed by the wall corner.

SING A NURSERY RHYME BACKWARDS.

STAND ON YOUR HEAD IN A CORNER. This is like sitting on the fire. You write the words "My head" on a piece of paper, then put it in a corner of the room, and proceed to stand on it.

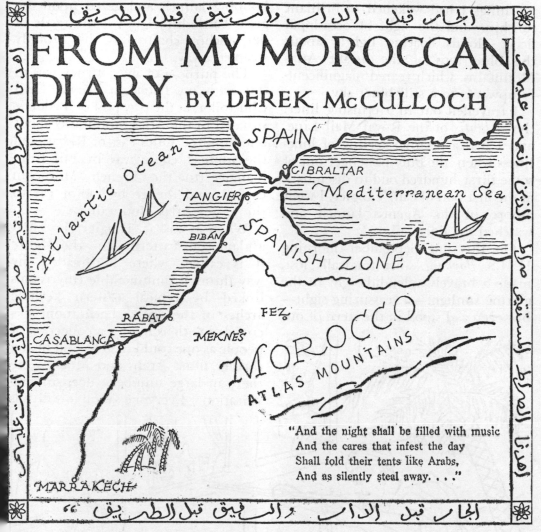

FROM MY MOROCCAN DIARY BY DEREK McCULLOCH

"And the night shall be filled with music
And the cares that infest the day
Shall fold their tents like Arabs,
And as silently steal away. . . ."

I THINK that now I appreciate a little more what must have been in the mind of Longfellow when he wrote the above lines. For a short while I lived with the Arabs, staying for the most part with a tribe called the Berbers, who are a fine upstanding people. I have eaten their native foods in native fashion; I drank, and learned to like, the mint-brewed tea peculiar to the country; I have seen a great deal of the vast, magnificent, only partially developed French Morocco, and I was privileged to observe closely and at first hand French Colonial administration. Yet I had never visualized any of the adventures which befell me, and about some of which I will tell you. The most exciting, perhaps, was how I became a corporal in the 4th Regiment of the famous French Foreign Legion.

I left England in September, 1937, arriving back on a cold, grey November morning. Only a week or so before, I had been dipping my sheet into a pitcher of cold water to keep myself cool during the nights, while in the mornings I had wakened to brilliant sunshine and the sight of occasional fleecy clouds floating lightly about the blue tops of the distant Atlas Mountains, which reared magnificently upwards to a still bluer sky.

I travelled out in a cruising liner, the *Atlantis* of the Royal Mail Line, and I had a peculiar feeling of loneliness when, the only passenger out of some three hundred odd to disembark at the first port of call, Tangier, I went ashore in the Agent's launch and watched the liner sail.

On this fine September morning H.M.S. *Barham*, since tragically lost, made a bravely splendid sight in the glaring sunlight—a reassuring sight— but even as I stood in the stern of our

bobbing launch and gazed upon the great battleship, I heard the rattle of her anchor chain and she proudly steamed away.

The purpose of my journey was to stay with my friend, a French Civil Controller, at the tiny post of Tedders, situated in the Atlas Mountains about one hundred miles east of Rabat, and the route I chose was by rail from Tangier to the French Moroccan capital, and thence by motor car to the Lesser Atlas Mountains.

When I was at Tangier, I visited a glamorous eastern café—the *Maure* it is called—where I threaded my way through innumerable tiny rooms linked by typical eastern keyhole arches in the walls. Each room was crowded with as motley a collection of people as one could wish to find in any thriller film. Arabs and Moors were there in large numbers, deep in conversation. Everyone sat on low divans

One of the guards seized his rifle and came swiftly towards me

or hassocks, some even on the lovely mosaic stone floors. Everyone was talking, and in a variety of languages.

The Royal Mail Agent at Tangier, who was also Norwegian Consul, turned out to be a tower of strength and a most influential person with police and customs authorities, but nevertheless I was thankful that before leaving London I had obtained a special visa to pass through the Spanish zone. You see, the Spanish Civil War was raging. My luggage, including a cabin-trunk, was slung in nets across the flanks of a fairly obliging mule, and carried to the station, but there, even the Agent's influence was of no avail: no one would concern himself about my luggage until that night, an hour before the train was due to leave at nine o'clock. In the end, I passed through the customs quite easily, and for that I had to thank the Agent. There were many travellers for the small train drawn up at the platform, and I noticed that practically every-one's luggage was opened before it was put into the luggage van.

The train was rather late in leaving, and the little station was thronged with sightseers, clad in many different costumes. The train was very full, and we had not been travelling very long before it stopped with a most frightful jolt. At first there was that curious silence which can be heard when you are in a train and it suddenly stops. Then there came the sound of voices speaking in Spanish and in French. The station was called Biban, and it was in complete darkness, for when travelling from Tangier to Rabat one had to go through the Spanish zone. Suddenly, armed guards in native clothes appeared as if from nowhere.

They were Spanish Moors—Franco's men—and with them were a bunch of civilian officials who boarded the train.

I must tell you about one amusing episode which occurred while the train was halted. I let down the big window in the corridor with a bit of a bang, whereupon one of several guards on the other line seized his rifle, which was lying on the platform, and came swiftly towards me. There was light enough showing from the train for me to see what went on. Reassured by my greeting, he replied: " *Bon soir, mossuo,*" and climbed into the train. He was dressed in a most picturesque blue and white *burnous,* or Arab gown, with marvellous green and white facings. In texture it looked rather like bath-towelling. On his feet were leather slippers, and on his head a white turban which completed his costume. The man spoke only a few words of French, laughed all the time, and seemed very proud of his rifle, which he let me examine. It was very antiquated, and he admitted he had no idea how it worked. We smoked a couple of cigarettes. On leaving me, he opened the door into the corridor, and seemed quite scared when he found his way barred by a gigantic figure. It was only after they had pointed their rifles at each other that they found they were both guards belonging to Franco. At last the train rattled off again and I settled down for some sleep until we arrived at Rabat at five o'clock in the morning.

Rabat, the capital of French Morocco, standing at the mouth of the River Bou Agreb, has a very fine modern railway station, with wide mosaic stone staircases. The platforms and walls are made from the same

*So modern are the stations, that the Arabs, in their traditional costumes,
look very strange squatting on the platforms waiting for the trains*

material, and the interwoven colours are very beautiful. Some fast French electric trains run along the coast from Rabat to the sea port of Casablanca. So modern is it all, that you cannot help but notice how strange the Arabs look squatting on the platforms waiting for a train. Men and women—the dark, bright-eyed women are veiled—are nearly all dressed in white. They seem to like waiting, somehow, and have endless patience.

At this point in my story, instead of taking you with me on the romantic journey to Tedders, I am switching straight to Marrakech which, with Meknes and Fez, is one of the most famous cities in French Morocco. Meknes and Fez lie due east from Rabat, and I visited these two places before taking the long journey by autobus to Marrakech, which is due south from Casablanca.

I stayed in Marrakech at the Hotel El Maghres which spells its name in Arabic like this:

HOTEL EL MAGHRES
Sur le Tour des Remparts
MARRAKECH

From Fez I had travelled back to Casablanca, and from there by autobus to Marrakech, a journey of some 150 miles. I left early in the morning. The sun rose gorgeously beneath a mass of thundercloud, and for a long way we drove through sheets of rain alternating with brilliant sunshine. Along the wayside was an everchanging stream of Arabs bound for my destination. It would take them a long time. Some were on foot, while the more fortunate rode donkeys or mules. Some wealthier ones had camels or horses but these were few and far between. Some of them were hurrying, others dawdling, while even more squatted by the roadside giving the impression that for them time was no object. The weather cleared when the road began to climb a little, and soon the sun was very hot. Sometimes we passed orange groves and other patches of cultivated land, but in the main the journey was not very exciting and the scenery rather dull.

It was almost noon before we got to Marrakech, and I went straight to my hotel, which was a most picturesque building designed in the Moorish style. Next day I spent sightseeing and going through the *souk* or market, where I made some amusing purchases. I was greatly helped by a *mohazni,* or civil policeman, who was detailed to look after me. Then there was the Arab boy who came along to carry my goods. He was most amusing and spoke a droll mixture of Arabic and French. He had all the assurance and cheek of a real London Cockney lad. I took a lot of cinematograph pictures, and over these he behaved like the child he was. At every place at which I stopped to take pictures he would appear from no-

where—usually in time to spoil the sequences, though occasionally it was so funny that it improved things. For instance, we went into the date market, where you never saw such a gigantic mass of fat, succulent dates in all your life. When picked they are as fat as figs and very sticky. For a few pennies you could buy as much as you could eat. I had just got my camera in focus and was filming my pile of dates when —*voilà*—there was the boy grinning at my camera and holding up a luscious date to drop into his own mouth. He was firmly under the impression that

The boy was grinning at me, holding up a date to drop into his mouth

my films would be shown in all the big cinemas in the world. He gave my camera an elaborate eastern salaam, exclaiming: " Thus the world will see how I, Ahmed, greet and salute the world."

There were at the time of my visit two French Resident Generals in Morocco. General Nogues gave me a letter of introduction to the general at Marrakech, upon whom I made an official call. Unluckily the general was away on a tour, but I was received by his aide-de-camp, a captain dressed in a picturesque red and blue uniform. He had fought in the First World War and was most excited when he found we had several times been fighting in the same sectors in France. I had dinner with the captain, who there and then made arrangements for me to visit the headquarters of the 4th Regiment of the Foreign Legion. This was fixed for the next day and I considered myself very lucky, as few foreigners are allowed such an opportunity.

Next morning I woke early to find it was sheeting with rain. The lovely snow-capped Atlas Mountains were blotted out completely, and for the moment Marrakech had lost all its charm and beauty, all its sunshine and blue sky. After a breakfast of coffee, rolls, butter and honey I tried to get a car, but succeeded only in raising an old one-horse cab or *fiacre,* as it is called. In this, dressed in a lounge suit and with a raincoat over my shoulders, I set out for the barracks which are some way from the town itself.

The drive seemed endless, through long streets which would have been thick with clouds of dust had it not been for the rain which was lashing down. Dripping palm trees lined the route, and there was nothing to be seen except a few unhappy-looking dogs. Worse still, the roof of the cab leaked badly and I was getting thoroughly wet just sitting there. It was a slow journey, but at last we reached the military quarter of Marrakech. We drove first past the camp which housed the Spahis, who wear dark blue cloaks over their uniforms and who are such wonderful horsemen. They are native Algerian cavalry in the service of the French. Next came the camp of the dark-skinned Senegalese — the men who come from Senegal, in French West Africa. At last we reached the lines of the Foreign Legion and the cab stopped at the main gates where a sentry was standing guard.

I paid off my cab and turned towards the sentry, who seemed surprised to see a dripping wet Englishman approach and ask to see the colonel of the regiment. However, he called out the guard and a captain hurried from the guard room and saluted me. I followed him inside and inspected the guard. To my embarrassment I found the regimental band also paraded, and I stood to attention while they played " God Save the King." Next the adjutant appeared, followed by Colonel Lorillard, in command of the regiment. He greeted me warmly and led the way to the adjutant's office, where he gave me a brief history of the regiment.

From the office we started off on a complete tour of the camp, and, thank goodness, the rain suddenly ceased and the sun came out. Soon everything was steaming in the heat, including myself. We visited and inspected the sergeants' quarters, those of the corporals, the pioneers, quartermaster's stores, kitchens, messrooms, and barracks. At every place a member of the Legion was waiting, stood to attention and told me his name and duty. It was a most impressive show. I inspected the men drawn up on parade, and I shall not easily forget those fine soldiers. It is generally believed that the men who enlist in the Foreign Legion are fugitives from justice, or are those who have committed grave crimes which they want

I turned towards the sentry, who seemed surprised to see a dripping wet Englishman approach and ask to see the colonel of the regiment

In the Corporals' Mess there was a tray set with roast beef, mayonnaise, potatoes, pudding and a glass of wine

to forget. This is not the case at all. The majority of the legionnaires are there because they want adventure and because the romantic traditions of the Foreign Legion appeal to them. One thing which is said about the Legion, however, is quite true. No one ever asks a man *why* he is there. I believe the majority of them serve for five years.

On the occasion of my visit an English doctor, a major, had completed his service and had left the Regiment. Some want to stay on and serve. Men of all nationalities, including Germans, enlist in the Legion and all submit to the very severe discipline which is expected of them. They have to take French nationality. The result is wonderful, and very few men are not proud to be legionnaires and to uphold the great traditions of the regiment.

At the Officers' Mess, or *Salle d'Honneur*, I found most of the officers of the regiment already assembled. I was introduced to as many as possible and then we sat down to champagne, sandwiches and biscuits. Above my head hung the precious colours of the regiment while other flags and battle honours decorated the walls. There were Frenchmen, Poles, Germans, Danes, Italians and many other nationalities, but all seemed to speak French fluently, while just a few spoke a little English.

At eleven o'clock exactly, the colonel stood up and read a long speech in French. I became redder and redder in the face. The speech was in my honour. It spoke of the First World War, my service, and how proud the colonel was to receive me. At any rate, if somewhat embarrassing, it was very exciting and a little amusing, but I did not laugh when I suddenly discovered the colonel's speech was coming to an end and that I was expected to give a suitable reply—in French. I rose and did the best I could and, thank goodness, it seemed to please them.

It was now nearly lunch-time and we went across to the Corporals' Mess. It was with obvious pleasure that the colonel told me there was an English dish on the menu that day. In the mess I found a tray set ready for me. There was a plate of roast beef, mayonnaise, potatoes, pudding and a glass of wine. This was exactly the same food that would be served at lunch-time. Colonel Lorillard whispered that the corporals would be most upset if I did not taste their food. I took up my knife and fork and then, just as I had poised in mid-air a choice mouthful, the band, which had been following us round, struck up " The Roast Beef of Old England."

Now it was time for me to leave, as I was lunching with His Majesty's Consul in Marrakech. Before leaving, however, the colonel presented me with the green chevrons of the rank of corporal in the regiment. With these went the gaudy dress épaulettes and the wine bottle or tin in a khaki cover which is part of the equipment. Finally, I was given the insignia, or badge, of the regiment. This is diamond in shape, with a grenade on which the figure four is superimposed. Two bars, one green and one red, slant from bottom left to top right, and left middle is a Moorish tower. I kept up correspondence with Colonel Lorillard, but after some time our letters fell off and I had good reason to believe he was serving in the North African Campaign. If I am any judge of him and the officers and men who serve under him, then the 4th Regiment of the Foreign Legion will have fought with great distinction and bravery.

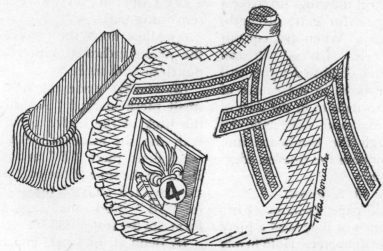

RACING CAR

THAT WILL WORK

THE plan on the opposite page is on a smaller scale than the model which you will make. Follow the instructions carefully, and you will find this model racing car can be made quite easily.

Materials Required.

A tube of seccotine, a strong rubber band, a pin, a piece of cardboard, a wooden skewer $\frac{3}{16}$ in. in diameter by $2\frac{1}{2}$ in. long, and a piece of stiff paper 4 in. by $2\frac{5}{8}$ in.

Instructions for Making.

1. Draw the outlines of the various parts on your card.

2. Stick another piece of cardboard behind the wheel drawings (to make a double thickness for extra strength) and leave to dry. When dry, cut out the four wheels. Unless you can borrow punches of the sizes you will require, make holes in the centre of the wheels with nails to fit the sizes of the motor tube and rear axle, by nailing through the cardboard into soft wood. Smooth the uneven edges with sandpaper.

3. *To Make the "Motor."*
Take the stiff paper (4 in. by $2\frac{5}{8}$ in.) and roll one inch of it around a piece of wood $\frac{1}{4}$ in. in diameter. Hold firmly

and glue the remaining 3 in. of paper as you roll it round the wood. When this is dry, you will have a strong little tube.

Pass a short length of cotton through the rubber band and thread it through the tube until the band just shows at the end. Push the pin carefully through the tube, about $\frac{3}{4}$ in. from the end, so that it pierces the rubber band inside the tube.

4. *To Make the Body of the Car.*
(a) The score lines are marked on the diagram by the heavy dotted lines *without* arrows on the ends of them. Mark these score lines and then cut along them to the depth of about one-third of the thickness of the cardboard.

(b) Cut out the body and the remaining parts.

(c) Make holes the correct sizes at the places indicated, either with the punch or with nails.

(d) Having made the hole in the small piece marked " A," stick it to the back of the body, to correspond with the slit made at " AA."

(e) Bend piece " B " at the scores. Bend up the sides of the body and stick the inverted ends of the piece " B " to " BB " inside the body, so as to form the flat seat raised from the floor.

(f) Bend at the scores and raise the

windscreen " C " and the back of the seat " D " to the vertical.

5. *To Insert the Wheels and the Motor, and Complete the Body.*

(*a*) Fix the rear wheels over the motor tube, one on the outside edge of the pin and the other to balance at the other side of the car.

Push the " pin end " up through slot " Y," so that the wheel fits between the pin and the side of the car. Pass the end of cotton through the slot " AA," pulling the end of the elastic after it. Under the loop of elastic, slip a ½ in. length of match. Gently release the cotton and the match will " lock " it into " AA." Remove cotton.

(*b*) Fit the front wheels tightly over the wooden axle about ¾ in. from each end. Insert the axle through the holes " X " in the body.

(*c*) Bend the front and rear sections of the body at scores " E," and the sections " F " bend downwards at right angles.

(*d*) Stick the fronts of sections " F " to the back of sections " C " and " D " respectively. As you do this, sections " G " will become slightly rounded.

Now paint the racing car a brilliant colour. Wind the motor, anti-clockwise about forty or fifty turns, and you will find the car will run for several yards on a non-slippery surface.

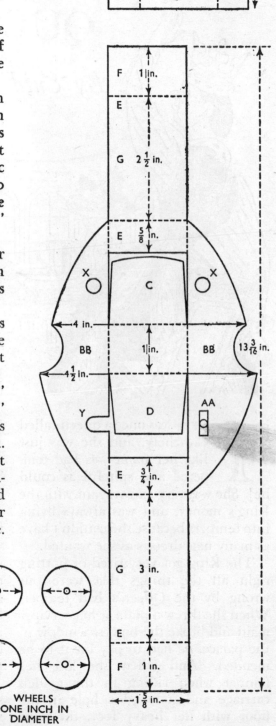

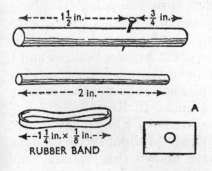

RUBBER BAND

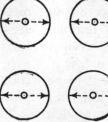

A

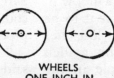

WHEELS
ONE INCH IN
DIAMETER

THE BAD TEMPERED QUEEN

By Enid Blyton

She threw a plate at her serving-maid, and broke the biggest window

THERE was once a queen called Crotchety, and she was just like her name—as bad tempered and spiteful as could be! She was very extravagant with the King's money, and was always flying into tempers because she couldn't have as many new dresses as she wanted.

The King got very tired of putting right all the things that were put wrong by the Queen's bad temper. When she threw a plate at her serving-maid and broke the biggest window in the palace, *he* had to pay for it to be mended. And when she lost her temper when riding in the golden carriage and stamped a hole in the floor with her heavy foot, the poor King had to pay for a new carriage. It was very upsetting.

Ah, but one day she went too far! You shall hear what happened.

The King was expecting some visitors from a Prince in a far-off land. The Queen was in a bad temper when he told her that they were coming, and she wouldn't have them to stay in the palace.

" It's just like you to ask visitors when the spring cleaning is going on!" she cried. " The six spare rooms are all upside down, and my cook is leaving to get married. I cannot and I *will* not have visitors from a foreign country just now. So put that in your pipe and smoke it, King Bollo!"

" I don't smoke a pipe, my dear," said the King. " I should have thought you'd have known that by now."

"Oh, go away!" said the Queen, stamping her foot crossly. "Go away! GO AWAY!"

The King fled. The Queen had a big needle in her hand and he didn't want her to prick him with it. She didn't care *what* she did when she was in a temper.

He wondered what to do about his visitors. Then he suddenly thought of his cousin, Prince Gladsome, who lived in a small castle next door, and who could put up his visitors quite easily. So he went across to ask him.

"Certainly, certainly," said the Prince, kindly. "I've plenty of room. They can all come and stay here. The only thing is, that as you know, I'm keeping pigs in my garden, so my grounds don't smell very nice. Could they use *your* garden, do you think?"

"Of course," said King Bollo at once. "They can come through the gate that leads from your garden to mine and can spend all their time there, if they want to. It's lovely now that all the tulips and lupins are out. Well, that's settled then—they can stay with you and have meals in your castle, so that Queen Crotchety won't be upset—and they can use my garden whenever they want to. Of course, they will come to meetings in the palace, but I'll see that they all wipe their feet, and I don't think they will make much mess."

So it was all very nicely arranged. King Bollo didn't tell the Queen anything about it. He was afraid she might fly into a temper again over something, and be rude to his visitors when they came to meetings in his palace.

The King gave careful orders to his gardeners to get the garden looking as bright and attractive as possible.

"And you'd better paint all the garden seats," he said. "They look a bit faded. Paint them a nice bright green."

So the gardeners were soon very busy. They hadn't quite finished their work when the visitors arrived, but the garden was looking lovely in the sunshine. There were only three garden seats left to paint, and these the gardeners packed away in a little hidden spot by the round lily pond, hoping to finish them the next day.

The visitors didn't at all mind staying with the Prince instead of with the King. They had heard of Queen Crotchety's bad temper, and hadn't very much looked forward to staying in her palace.

"But pray use the palace gardens to sit in and walk in," said the King to the visitors, when he welcomed them. "The pigs are not very pleasant company in my cousin's garden, and the flowers are really lovely in mine."

The twelve little foreigners bowed low. They had come to make an important treaty with King Bollo, and they thought him a charming man.

The next day was a sunny, warm day. The twelve visitors had a splendid breakfast with the Prince, and then they thought they would go and sit in the palace gardens next door. So off they went, and were soon looking at all the rows of red and yellow tulips, the blue and white lupins and the little button-daisies trimming the edge of each border.

Soon they found themselves by the round lily pond. The gardeners had just finished painting the three seats there, and had left them in the sun to dry. The visitors had no idea that the paint was wet, and they sat down on the seats to rest and look at the lilies on the water.

Now it so happened that just at that moment the Queen came by, on her way to pick some gooseberries from the bushes at the bottom of the garden. She saw the twelve little men sitting by the pond and stared at them in surprise.

She had her crown on, so the visitors knew that she was the Queen. They all tried to stand up and bow—but, alas for them, they had stuck to the wet paint on the seats, and they could not move!

"Where are your manners?" cried the Queen, angrily. "Get up and bow! And what are you doing here, I should like to know! I don't know you! You are not staying at my palace! Therefore you must be trespassing in my gardens. How dare you! How dare you, I say!"

The poor little visitors were frightened and dismayed. The chief of them tried to get up once more, but he could feel his trousers being torn, so he gave up trying. He opened his mouth to explain matters to the Queen, but as he spoke in his own language, which the Queen couldn't understand at all, it didn't make things much better!

"Oojatillynomkejopupillaterona!" said the little man politely.

"What nonsense are you talking!" said the Queen stamping her foot. "Say something I can understand, or I'll have you put in prison."

"Tippyun nyretudanalilliponotoff!" cried all the visitors in horror.

"All right, all right," said the Queen, a fearful frown on her face. "Hey! Gardeners! Where are you?

"Where are your manners?" cried the Queen angrily. "Get up and bow"

Come and lock up these nasty little people at once!"

Up ran all the gardeners, and to the visitors' great horror they found themselves roughly seized. The Queen stalked off in fury, and left them.

The gardeners soon discovered that the twelve little foreigners were stuck fast to the three garden seats. So they carried them off and locked them up in a big barn at the end of the grounds and left them there until they got further orders from the Queen.

Queen Crotchety went to pick her

very puzzled. He had been expecting his twelve visitors to come to a meeting at the palace at twelve o'clock and none of them had arrived! So he thought he would go to his cousin the Prince's castle after lunch and see what had happened to them. Perhaps they had mistaken the time!

But when he got to the castle he found the Prince even more puzzled than he was—for though the Prince had prepared a perfectly magnificent lunch for his visitors, not one of them had turned up! He had thought that maybe the meeting at the palace had gone on a long time—but when he heard from the King that there had been no meeting, he was more surprised than ever.

"Wherever can they be?" he asked. "Do you suppose they've gone back to their own country?"

"I hope not," said the King, looking worried. "We haven't done anything at all about that treaty yet, and if they go back without signing it, I'm afraid my country will lose a lot of money."

"Well, we must hope they'll turn up," said the Prince. "You'd better go back to the palace to see if they are there."

So back went the King, only to find no visitors at all, of course. Instead, he found the Queen waiting for him, with a frown on her forehead. She had just remembered the twelve little men she had seen sitting on the seats, and who, she thought, had been so rude to her. She wanted to have them punished.

"Some nasty little men were very rude to me this morning," she began. "They must be punished."

"Dear me, what did they do?" asked the King, quite interested to hear that

gooseberries and they were so ripe and juicy that she began to feel happy again, and soon she forgot all about the little men she had sent to be locked up. She filled her basket and went back to the palace to see that the new cook was cooking the lunch properly.

Meanwhile, the King was feeling

anyone had been brave enough to be rude to Queen Crotchety.

"They wouldn't bow to me, and they talked a lot of rubbish when I asked them what they were doing in my garden," said the Queen. "So they are all locked up."

"Quite right," said the King. "I'll give orders to have them brought before me, and I dare say I'll have their heads chopped off."

So his servants were sent to bring the prisoners, and the King sat on his throne, looking very important indeed. He didn't *really* mean to have anyone's head chopped off, but it sounded very fierce. So just as his servants were coming back, he cried out in a loud voice: "Yes, I'll have all their heads chopped off!"

The poor little visitors were terrified when they heard this. They were still stuck tightly to the garden seats, and the footmen had to carry them in, seats and all. They put them down in front of the King.

"What's all this, what's all this!" he cried, jumping up from his throne. "Why, dear me, these are my visitors, the little men from Far-Off Land, come to sign a most important treaty! What are they doing on those seats? Surely, surely, these are not the people you have been complaining of, my dear Queen?"

"Well, that's just what they are then!" snapped the Queen. "Off with their heads!"

The twelve little men shrieked with fear and tried to leap off the seats. But they couldn't.

"Gently, now, gently," said the King to the Queen. "I want to get to the bottom of this. First of all, why are these men brought in on garden seats?

Why are they not allowed to walk in on their own legs?"

"It's wet paint, Your Highness," said one of the footmen, showing his fingers all stained with green where he had carried the garden seat. "The poor creatures can't get up!"

"So *that's* why they didn't get up and bow to you this morning!" said the King to Queen Crotchety. "They were stuck to the wet paint and couldn't. Oh, what a mess and a muddle you've made, my dear! These are twelve important visitors of mine, and they are staying with the Prince next door, because of the spring-cleaning in the palace. And you go and have them locked up!"

"R i l l t o b a baranurituberfida!" shouted the biggest visitor in an angry voice. The King understood the language perfectly, but the Queen didn't.

"Quite, quite!" he said. But the Queen snorted.

"Pooh! That's the sort of silly nonsense they spoke to me this morning!" she cried.

"Well, I am sorry to say that you have offended these poor men," said King Bollo to the Queen. "They are honoured visitors of mine, and you've had them locked up and they heard me say I'd have their heads cut off. Now we're in a pretty pickle, I expect their country will go to war with us. And you know what *that* means, don't you? No money for any dresses or hats or necklaces! That will teach you not to lose your temper and interfere in things that don't concern you!"

The King looked so fierce that for once the Queen turned pale.

"W-w-w-w-w-what can we do?" she said. "I don't want war. Ask them

BOWYER

" What's all this, what's all this?" cried the King, jumping up from his throne. "Why, dear me, these are my visitors from Far-Off Land!"

The Queen had to go to prison

what we can do to make up for my mistake."

The King spoke to the twelve little men, and they answered him.

"What did they say?" asked the Queen.

"They said that if I gave orders for you to be put into prison and kept there for as long as you lost your temper, they would forgive the way they had been treated," said the King.

"Oh!" screamed the Queen, in a rage. "Me, put into prison! Oh, I never heard of such a thing!"

"Now, there you go, losing your temper again," said the King. "I'm sorry, my dear, but I can't afford to go to war just at present—so I'm afraid you'll have to go to prison for a bit at any rate—just while my visitors are here. Then they can stay in the palace instead of next door, and I can treat them as grandly as I like without having to listen to your complaints. Footmen, take the Queen away!"

And off she went! Then what a fine time the King and his visitors had! He gave them grand new clothes, em-broidered in gold and silver, and the best of meals. The new cook did her best, and the footmen fell over themselves in their hurry to wait on the twelve visitors.

The treaty was signed and the visitors returned to their own country, without even saying good-bye to the Queen.

"You pop her into prison every time she loses her temper!" said the chief visitor. And the King really thought he would. But, you know, he never needed to again—for Queen Crotchety had had such a shock that she never once scolded or grumbled after that but grew into the kindest, nicest old lady you ever saw.

As for the garden seats, they were put back by the round pond—but the Queen could never bear to sit there, and I'm not surprised, are you?

BIRD MIGRATION

By Seton Gordon, C.B.E.

To migrate is to travel from one part of the land, or the ocean, to another. Many living creatures migrate. Salmon are associated in our minds with Highland rivers, yet most of their actual growth takes place in the deepest waters of the Atlantic Ocean. A crab caught and marked in the waters off the Isle of Skye, one of the Hebrides, was caught shortly afterwards off Wick, on the north-east coast of Scotland. Butterflies migrate across the English Channel to us from the Continent. Those small rat-like creatures, the lemmings, migrate in great swarms in the Arctic, and when they reach the edge of the coast, they plunge as though mad into the sea and are lost.

But it is in birds that migration is seen in its most highly developed form. That is only natural, for the flight of birds is a thing apart. If they give us a thought except, alas, in fear, how slow and laboured must our walking, and even our running, be to birds! You and I are quite pleased if we walk three miles in an hour. How far will a bird fly during that time? A gannet flying home to its distant nestling on lonely St. Kilda will cover about forty-five miles in an hour on a calm day; if the wind is favourable, it may cover sixty or seventy miles in that time. But some birds fly very much faster than a gannet. In the earlier days of flying when aircraft were slower, an airman was cruising at a speed of about ninety miles an hour. A golden eagle on the same course overtook him, and as the eagle passed ahead it looked calmly at the aircraft without fear.

Few birds travel as fast as the eagle, yet they can all (except the few species which have lost the power of flight) move fast enough to migrate hundreds of miles.

Before you are told more of these great flights, it may be well to pause for a minute and ask the question: "Why do birds migrate?"

In some instances the reply is simple: they migrate because they are hungry, or know that they soon will be hungry if they stay where they are. That is the reason why the birds that nest in the Arctic fly south at the approach of autumn, for autumn in the Arctic is not the pleasant season of golden leaves and blackberries as it is in Britain, but of frost and snow and blizzards. The birds *must* fly south if they are to live. That is migration in its simplest and clearest form. But there are much more puzzling migrations. Why, for instance, should the stonechat live in its territory all the year round and move scarcely half a mile during that time, while the whinchat, a bird similar in size and habits, feeding on the same food, flies away to Africa at the close of the summer and does not return until the early days of May? Why should the blackbird stay with us all the year round and the ring ousel or mountain

blackbird come to Britain only in spring, leaving again when summer is over? There are many problems for which no answer has yet been found.

We all know the swallow, and most of us know that it flies south over land and ocean to Africa in autumn. We all take its long flight for granted nowadays. But in former times naturalists did not think the swallow migrated, they thought it hibernated, that is, went into a very deep sleep like the dormouse during the winter months. More remarkable still, they thought swallows dived beneath the water to hibernate in the muddy bottom!

Former naturalists of repute firmly believed that swallows in autumn assembled on the reed beds of some lake, then after much excited twittering dived beneath the water and burrowed into the mud. They said that fishermen sometimes dragged them up in their nets in winter; that when at first exposed to the air they seemed lifeless, but when taken to a fire and placed beside it they gradually returned to life. But now we know that swallows in winter are not in Europe at all, but are catching flies in the warm sunshine of South Africa.

When chilly mornings warn them in September that summer is on the wane, the swallows may be seen to gather on telegraph wires preparatory to the migration towards the south.

But swallows do not always migrate in large flocks. They may often be seen moving south in pairs or in little family parties. So long as the weather remains fine they are not weary, for they travel slowly, feeding as they go.

Swallows gathering to begin their journey

But strong contrary winds sometimes bring the migration over the land to a standstill, while storms over the ocean may exact a heavy toll.

There is a belief that swallows travel by night but their journey is usually in daylight. One of the most impressive migrations of the swallow the writer recalls, was seen by him just after sunrise one morning at the end of August, on a pass in the Cairngorm Hills of Scotland. It was a beautiful morning, clear, sunny and without wind, and the swallows were travelling in single file only a foot or two above the ground. Flying in this curious formation, their speed seemed very fast.

Lighthouses claim many bird victims during migration, but the swallow suffers less than the thrush or blackbird, skylark, or redwing. Nor does the swallow stay so late in Britain as its relative, the house martin, which sometimes is rearing its third brood in the nest in October, when a sudden cold spell may cut off its food supply and force it to leave its young to their fate.

The spring migration north is done in leisurely fashion, and the swallows nesting in the north of Norway do not arrive there until almost eight weeks after their English-nesting relatives have reached this country. They are wise to be certain that summer has preceded them; there are few sadder sights than swallows hawking for an occasional insect in the lee of a wood, while snow squalls whiten, as they too often do, the April landscape. Sometimes great flocks of swallows arrive on

Swallow

and by its long, deeply forked tail. It does not nest under the eaves of the houses, as many people will tell you: it is the house martin that nests under the eaves, and the swallow nests in out-buildings, where it cannot often be seen. The house martin makes those neat nests of mud under your eaves, and it may be news to you that it hates modern tarred roads, because it used to take mud from the old-fashioned roads for its nest, and it cannot find any mud on the tarred roads. There was an inn when the writer was a boy, where many house martins made their nests. On passing the inn recently, he looked up to the eaves to see whether his old friends—or their children— were still there. But there was not one nest, and suddenly he realized why.

lonely Scottish isles long after the resident population of birds have taken their departure. These late-comers have probably nested in Scandinavia.

A great immigration of swallows descended in October a few years ago on the far northern Shetland Islands.

We all know the swallow, but do we also know the swift, the house martin, or the sand martin? These are all swallow-like birds, and all of them are migrants. But they each have their own special time of arrival, and as they are found almost everywhere in the British Isles it may be a good thing to give a short description of each of them, so that they can be recognized when in flight.

The swallow can be recognized by its chestnut-red throat and forehead,

House martin

The old road had been replaced by a tarred highway, and the poor martins, no longer able to find mud for their nests, had been obliged to leave the ancestral home. The house martin can always be recognized by its white breast, and by the white rump—that is the base of the tail. The rest of its plumage is of an inky blue-black shade.

While writing of the house martin, something must be said about the horrible way that the house sparrow tries to use the house martin's beautiful home for its own untidy nest. A sparrow will allow a pair of martins almost to finish their nest and then will fly in and take possession! Martins are gentle birds, but one pair got more than even with a pair of sparrows

Swift

which did this. That great naturalist, the late W. H. Hudson, records the incident in one of his books.

It was noticed that, after the hen sparrow had laid her eggs in the martin's nest and begun to sit on them, nothing more was seen of her, and that there was no appearance of any young. The matter was forgotten, but next year someone went up to the nest on a ladder, and found that the martins had walled up the small opening and imprisoned the sparrow and there was her mummified body still sitting on the eggs. It seems that the moral of this story is: "Don't take what doesn't belong to you."

The sand martin is rather smaller than either the swallow or the house martin and is usually the first of the three to arrive. It is a brownish

Sand martin

LITTLE TERN
3rd. Week April

COMMON TERN
4th. Week April

ARCTIC TERN
End April

SUMMEI

SANDWICH TERN
2nd. Week April

SAND MARTIN
End of April

RING-OUZEL
2nd. Week March

SWALLOW
1st. Week April

BLACKCAP
2nd. Week April

WHINCHAT
3rd. Week April

HOUSE MARTIN
End of March

WILLOW-WARBLER
2nd. Week April

REED-WARBLER
End of April

SWIFT
End of April

CHIFFCHAFF
3rd. Week March

REDSTART
3rd. Week April

GARGANEY
3rd. Week March

WHEATEAR
3rd. Week March

WHITETHROAT
3rd. Week April

SPOTTED FLYCATCHER
1st. Week May

NIGHTINGALE
3rd. Week April

WOOD-WARBLER
3rd. Week April

WRYNECK
1st. Week April

NIGHT JAR
1st. Week May

GRASSHOPPER-
WARBLER
4th. Week April

WINTE

CUCKOO
2nd. Week April

HOBBY
End of April

ESIDENTS

BRENT GOOSE
Sept. to April

BARNACLE GOOSE
Oct. to May

GREY PLOVER
Aug. to May

PINK-FOOTED GOOSE
Sept. to April

REDWING
Mid-Sept. to Mid-April

KNOT
Aug. to May

GREYLAG-GOOSE
Sept. to April

WHOOPER SWAN
Oct. to April

LONG-TAILED DUCK
Sept. to May

BAR-TAILED GODWIT
Aug. to May

SNOW-BUNTING
Sept. to May

WIGEON
Sept. to April

BEWICK'S SWAN
Nov. to March

RAMBLING
ept. to May

WOODCOCK
Sept. to May

FIELDFARE
Sept. to May

PINTAIL
Sept. to April

SCAUP-DUCK
Sept. to May

POCHARD
Oct. to April

ISITORS

COMMON SCOTER
Sept. to April

SMEW
Mid-Sept. to Mid-March

Goldcrest

coloured bird and tunnels out small round holes in a sandbank, nesting sometimes at arm's length, sometimes farther down these holes.

The last of the swallow-like birds is the swift. It is a dark bird with long, sickle-shaped wings. Some people think the swift is the fastest bird that flies, and that it sleeps on the wing, floating at a great height far above the earth. The swift certainly does nearly everything on the wing. It feeds on the wing, it drinks on the wing, it gathers nesting materials on the wing. Indeed, if for some reason it *does* find itself on the ground it cannot rise again if the ground is level, because of the shortness of its legs and the length of its wings.

It is of course very seldom that the swift is on the ground, but the writer saw one instance of this. When he lived at Aviemore, beneath the Cairngorm Hills, swifts nested in his house, entering it through small holes below the eaves. One day a swift, on flying low towards the house, struck a wire fence near by. It must have fallen to the ground, and there it was found lying resting quite uninjured on the grass. It was cold, for it had been out all night, but when it was warmed before the fire, it soon revived. It was taken out, tossed into the air, and away it flew. But had it not been found, there it would have remained with no chance of being able to rise again into the air. It would probably have fallen a victim to a wandering cat or a stoat.

Swifts are interesting birds; for one thing they are almost the only birds to be seen any day of summer flying backwards and forwards above the great cities. Glasgow has a population of over a million people, and yet, flying high over the streets and the great ship-building yards, are the swifts. In Edinburgh, too, they can be seen, and in almost every British city, except London. To see the swifts in London the bird lover must go a few miles outside the city boundaries, and over Kew Gardens they may be seen in numbers. The swift, although mistaken by many people for the swallow, is really the first cousin of the nightjar, and no relation of the swallow.

But swift and swallow, house martin and sand martin, all winter in South Africa. The sand martin is the first to come back; he is sometimes seen in Britain at the end of March; the swallow in April, the house martin and the swift not until early May.

Think of the swallows flying all the way from South Africa to nest in the barn or cowshed near your house. They have come hundreds, maybe thousands of miles to their old home. By marking the birds (a very light aluminium ring with a number on it is placed round one leg) it has been found that they come back year after year to the same place and the secret of their great flight is now well known, for they have been caught (and set free again) in their winter quarters in South Africa, and the number on their rings has been noted.

They take a considerable time over their great flight towards the north, reaching Spain and Portugal several weeks before they fly on to Britain. They may be said to follow the spring—a very delightful thing to do, and I am sure that we human beings must envy them.

The swallow is well known, but I wonder how many people know the goldcrest, the tiniest of all British birds? It has a high piping cry, so high and shrill and thin that some people cannot hear it. This wee bird is fond of fir and spruce plantations, and builds a lovely nest, very small, and hung to the lower part of a spruce branch high up in the tree. One might

imagine that this little bird was so delicate that it could not fly far, yet each autumn it crosses the stormy waters of the North Sea from Scandinavia to this country on migration.

You may think that the old birds, when migrating, lead the way, but that is not so. The young cuckoo migrates to Africa after the old birds leave this country, so that on its great flight it has only instinct to guide it.

How do these migrating birds find their way? They are out of sight of land for hours, the sun may be hidden in mist, and indeed the birds travel usually during the night hours. How do they know which way to fly? If a man is lost, he usually finds himself going round in circles, for without knowing it he takes a rather longer step with the right foot than with the left. A bird's right wing may not be stronger than its left, but there may be a strong side wind blowing, and unless it knew exactly how to steer it would be blown to leeward of its destination. Has it a sixth sense which keeps its course right? It seems as if migrating birds have this sixth sense; if so it is a very wonderful sense and, with all our knowledge, we know nothing about it

Cuckoo

TEAM RACES
TO PLAY AT PARTIES

By David Rodney

CHOPSTICKS RACE

FOR this race you will need twenty-four dried peas—or any other small round objects of similar size will do—four small bowls and four used matches.

Place two bowls on the table in front of each team leader and arm him with two match-sticks. Put twelve of the dried peas in one of the two bowls in front of each leader. At the word " Go " he must pick up the peas as quickly as he can with the match-

sticks and transfer them to the other bowl. He is not allowed to touch the peas with his hand, and if he drops one of them on the way to the other bowl he must pick it up from the table with the match-sticks.

As soon as he has dropped the last of the twelve into the other bowl he gives the match-sticks to the next member of the team, who proceeds to transfer the peas back to the empty bowl in the same way, and so on until every member has had a turn.

*Short, quick strokes
of the fan are best*

FANNING THE FEATHER

For this team race you need two small feathers—such as those that come out of pillows—and two fans. If you haven't any fans, a folded newspaper will do.

The party is divided into two teams and a chalk line is drawn at each end of the room. Half of each team now stands behind the lines, so that they are opposite the other half of their own team. Sufficient space should be left between the two teams so that they do not get in each other's way.

The leader of each team is now given a fan, and a feather is placed on the line in front of him. At the word " Go," the leaders fan the feathers as quickly as they can across the room and across the line at the other end. They will find they do better with short quick strokes of the fan than by waving it wildly and furiously.

As soon as the feather has crossed the line the next member swiftly takes the fan and begins fanning it back across the room to the line from where it started, and then the next one on that side of the room takes his turn, and so on until the whole team has changed sides, the first team to do so being the winners.

MATCH-BOX RACE

The party is divided into two teams, which form a line down each side of the room. The leader of each is provided with the outside of a match-box, which he has to push on to his nose.

At the word " Go," he tries to transfer the box from his nose to that of the next one in the line. Neither must touch the box with anything but his nose. If the box should fall to the floor, the leader must pick it up and put it back on his own nose.

When the second player has managed to get the box on to his nose, he turns round and transfers it in the same way to the nose of the third player, and so on all down the line. The winning team is usually the one with the biggest noses, a thing to remember when choosing sides!

BACK AND FRONT RACE

The teams are seated in two lines and by the leader of each team you place a bowl of about ten small objects, such as marbles or acorns. At the word " Go," he picks up the objects one at a time, passing each one on to his neighbour, who in turn passes it on, and so on down the line.

When the end of the line is reached the objects have to be passed back *behind* the team until they are safely in the bowl once more. This is not so easy as it sounds, as there is a lot of confusion when players are trying to

pass the objects in front and behind at the same time. Anyone dropping one must pick it up and the rest of the team have to stop and wait for him before passing along any more.

ANIMAL TREASURE HUNT

This is a very good game for a large party, about twenty players being an ideal number. To prepare it you need about two or three hundred brightly-coloured beads, or other such small objects which are easy to pick up. These you put in groups of about five or six in nooks and corners all over the house where they are not too easily seen—for example, between the railings of the stairs, or behind chairs.

To start the game, the party is divided up evenly into teams of four or five and you choose one member of each team to be captain. Each team is

When the captains hear members of their teams calling them, they rush to the spot as quickly as possible

then given the name of an animal, such as cat, dog, sheep, cow. When this has been done you give them the signal "Go" and all the members of the teams rush off singly and try to find the hidden treasure, the captains remaining behind. As soon as a member of a team finds a heap of beads he stands near it and makes the noise of his animal (a cat would miaow and a dog would bark, for instance) until his captain comes along to retrieve the treasure. He is not allowed to go and find his captain or to tell him where the treasure is, but must wait until his captain comes to him. No one but the captain is allowed to pick up the treasure and he must wait until he hears one of his team barking or mooing, or whatever his noise is, before he can go and find it.

Then, having picked up one pile, he dashes off to the next one of his team, who will surely be calling for him by this time. And the fun reaches its height when the same piles of beads are found by members of various teams and the sound of frantic animal cries is heard, each member trying to make his own captain hear and bring him on the spot before the others arrive!

The game continues until all the treasure is found and the winners are, of course, those with the largest haul.

Front of the house

FIND THE

DINKY BATES was not very good at games, though he tried hard and did not slack while others played; but he just was not built that way, and there were some chaps who looked down on him in consequence, for they often forgot that he was always keen to get into a football or cricket match and was only left out because he hadn't the knack.

You may remember Dinky. He was that lanky chap who stayed with us one time. His hair was always untidy, and he wore glasses, and his trousers were always about two inches too short for him, and he used to swot at the most frightfully deep books.

In fact, he was about the cleverest chap I've ever known, and if he could not play games, there was one thing he could do, and that was solve puzzles. You know those puzzles they set you over the radio and in the newspapers. Dinky could bat them off like lightning while we chaps were all worrying our brains without getting a start, and it was because of this gift of his that he performed that perfectly amazing feat. . . .

But I'm running away with myself. This is really a detective story and it doesn't do to tell you how it all finished until you have had a chance to try and solve the mystery.

Dinky and I got to know a Mr. Marchant. He was a jolly, decent old boy with white hair, very feeble on his legs, and we often went to his place to tea. I must tell you about his place

Back of the house

ANSWER *By John Hunter*

because it has a most important bearing, as they say, on what happened, and I want you to remember these details just as you would if you were listening to one of those wireless detective problems.

Mr. Marchant lived in a little house right in the middle of the main street of the village. The house was not detached, but was wedged between two other houses. That is to say there were no side windows—only windows back and front.

At the back was a small garden, and at the bottom of this garden was a high brick wall that was very old and weathered. I'm supposed to be pretty good at climbing, but to have reached the top of that wall I'd have had to take a running jump and then have

scrambled up by digging my toes into the crevices between the bricks.

There was a back door leading into the garden and, of course, a front door leading into the street. These were the only outer doors in the house. On the ground floor there was one window at the back and one at the front. And now I'll tell you what happened.

Dinky and I had been to tea with Mr. Marchant quite a number of times and had become very friendly with him. On this particular afternoon, we walked right in without knocking. He never locked his front door in the daytime and he had told us that all friends of his were not expected to knock, but to come straight in. A Mr. Stebbins used to do the same. Mr. Stebbins lived at the far end of the village, and he was

He opened the case, and Dinky and I gasped with surprise

a short, fat man, very wheezy in his breathing and, like Mr. Marchant, he lived alone.

"And what are you two boys going to be when you grow up?" asked Mr. Marchant, as we sat drinking tea in his little sitting-room.

"Well, sir," I said, "I want to be a pilot and fly a big passenger plane, but father says I'm to be a doctor, then I can take over his practice. I don't fancy that very much, though. No chap would, would he? Not if he could fly an aeroplane."

Mr. Marchant smiled and said something about doctoring being a fine profession and turned to Dinky.

"And you?" he said.

Dinky went red and wriggled his long, lanky legs as he always did when somebody questioned him; then he said: "I think I shall be a policeman."

Now he had never told me what he wanted to be. I, naturally, had always imagined he'd set himself on driving an express train, or being a sea-captain, or a pilot, or something really exciting and worth while, and when he said he intended to be a copper, you could have floored me.

Before either of us could answer he went on hurriedly: "I'm studying languages and—and things, Mr. Marchant. What I thought was . . . you see . . . I mean . . . if I could manage it. The special branch, or something like that."

This was different, and I looked at Dinky with admiration and said: "That's a good wheeze, Dinky. I wouldn't mind it myself. I've a good mind to have a go at it. You mean trailing crooks all over Europe!"

Mr. Marchant chuckled: "It isn't quite like that. Dinky knows he would have to serve in the uniformed police first. So you want to become a flying man and will probably become a doctor instead, and Dinky wants to be a detective. Now what would you think I did when I worked for my living?"

Of course, we had no idea. He was frightfully old, and I doubt if really exciting jobs were going when he was young, so I said I couldn't tell.

Dinky said: "You didn't do any hard manual work, did you, Mr. Marchant?"

"Why—no." He stared at Dinky, then glanced at his own hands. They were very small and neat and well-kept. "Oh, I see. My hands would have become big-knuckled and strong. Quite good. No, I didn't do any hard manual work. As a matter of

fact, I was a dealer in precious stones."

Before either of us could reply, he went on: "Sit here a moment. I'll show you something."

We waited while he went upstairs, and when he came down he was carrying a little gem-case covered with fine black leather. He put this case on the table, opened it, and Dinky and I gasped with surprise.

I don't know anything about diamonds except that they shine like anything, but I did know I was looking at something right out of the ordinary. It lay on its velvet bed like a spot of white fire shot with water-blue, and when Mr. Marchant picked it up it sent little rays of light in different directions.

Mr. Marchant's manner had changed. My father knows a man who collects old glass, and when he manages to get some particularly beautiful or unusual piece he looks exactly like Mr. Marchant looked when he picked up that diamond.

"I am not a rich man," said Mr. Marchant, "save for the value of this wonderful stone. But I have enough to live on in the way I like to live, modestly, with good friends around me, so I have never sold this—the finest gem that ever came into my hands. You see, I loved precious stones, not for their value but for their beauty; and this is a beautiful thing. I have willed it, with my other possessions, to my granddaughter. It is worth a great deal of money—many thousands of pounds, in fact."

I have told you that his intimate friends always walked right into his house, and as he spoke there was a movement at the partly open door of the room and we saw Mr. Stebbins who, as I have already said, was a short and very fat man, with a dreadfully wheezy way of breathing. I believe if he had tried to run a hundred yards he would have dropped dead.

His eyes were on the great diamond, and Mr. Marchant naturally had to tell him all about it and let him examine it.

" You ought to keep a thing like this in your bank's strong-room," said Mr. Stebbins huskily. " You're asking for trouble, Marchant, having it here, in this house."

Mr. Marchant smiled and said : " I'd never see it if I put it into the bank's keeping. It's perfectly safe. I lock it up in my bedroom, and when I go out I carry it with me. By the way, I am relying on you three not to mention its existence."

Naturally, we promised, and a little later Dinky and I left the house.

As we went, I said : " Mr. Marchant's eccentric, isn't he? Keeping that diamond in his house. Mr. Stebbins was right about putting it into the bank."

" He certainly was," agreed Dinky. " But when you've got collector's mania, you want your collection where you can have a look at it when the fancy takes you. And that diamond is the whole of the old boy's collection, if you follow me."

We went on, past Mr. Stebbins's house, which was a nice little place, standing alone in its garden, and we were just in time to shoo off his big tabby cat from creeping up behind an unsuspecting bird, and this reminded us again of Mr. Stebbins.

" I've an idea," said Dinky, " that Mr. Marchant regretted bringing the diamond out when he saw old Stebbins. It was really a silly thing to do, wasn't it? You don't want too many people to know you've got a diamond worth a fortune."

Of course, this was Dinky doing detective stuff and pretending to see suspicious characters and all the rest of it, so I pulled his leg until we reached the school.

It was a week later that it happened, and by one of those bits of luck which rarely come to you in life, Dinky and I were right in the middle of it.

.   .   .   .   .   .

We had got permission to go to a party given by some people I know in the neighbourhood, and we were walking back through the village at about eleven o'clock at night. It was dark and still, and we were staggered to find two or three folk outside Mr. Marchant's house, the door of which was open. We heard somebody say something about the police, and ask if Mr. Marchant were badly hurt, and before I could grasp all this Dinky made a bee-line for the open door and went inside. Of course, I followed him.

In the house were the village doctor, the village policeman, Mr. Marchant and Mr. Stebbins—all in the little downstairs room where Mr. Marchant had shown us the diamond. Mr. Marchant's head had been tied up by the doctor, and he looked pretty sick and ill; which gave Dinky and me a lot of pain, because he was as decent an old boy as you could ever wish to meet.

The policeman started to order us out, but Mr. Marchant stopped him.

" These boys are friends of mine," he said, and then he looked at us and added in a queer broken sort of voice : " My diamond has been stolen."

I knew that he was grieved not only

The policeman started to order us out, but Mr. Marchant stopped him, saying, " These boys are friends of mine "

The constable was passing by and saw the open door

for the value of the thing, but also because he had lost something very beautiful in his sight; perhaps more for that than for what the stone was worth; and my sorrow for him increased.

Dinky's eyes lit up.

" How did it happen?" he asked.

We got the story in bits—from Mr. Marchant, the policeman and Mr. Stebbins, and this is how it went.

Somebody got into the house and hit Mr. Marchant on the head while he was asleep, so that he did not see the robber. The diamond was kept in a little cupboard in his bedroom, and this had been forced. You can say—as the policeman said—that it was the craziest place in which to keep a stone like that, but there you are.

Mr. Stebbins had been for a walk, and he saw the house door open. Naturally, he wondered why it should be open at that time at night, for he knew Mr. Marchant invariably went to bed at half past nine; so he started to go in. He said a man rushed past him and bolted up the street.

This alarmed him, and he went right up to Mr. Marchant's bedroom, where he found the old chap lying unconscious in bed with a nasty crack over the head.

Now by chance the constable was coming by on his bicycle and he, too, saw the open door and like Mr. Stebbins, he came inside. He shouted to know if anything was wrong and, seeing a light upstairs, started to climb to the upper storey. Thus he met Mr.

Stebbins coming out of Mr. Marchant's bedroom, and heard what had happened. Mr. Marchant's house had a telephone and the policeman rang for the doctor.

The policeman looked round the room after we had been told all this. He was a keen young chap, as I very well knew.

He said slowly: "I understand from Mr. Marchant that only three other people knew he had this stone—you two boys and you, Mr. Stebbins."

This was a shock to me, for I hadn't thought of it, but Dinky didn't seem shocked at all. His eyes only gleamed behind his glasses.

And now you must read this carefully, because it's where the real puzzle starts. I think it is only fair to tell you I have already given you a clue before this point was reached.

When the policeman said that we three were the only ones who knew of the stone's existence, Mr. Stebbins wheezed up.

"I've already realized that," he said. "And as I was on the spot when the constable came in, I insist on being searched."

Mr. Marchant said: "My dear Stebbins. . . ."

"I insist," wheezed Mr. Stebbins. "I expect the police officer is an expert, and I'll go into the next room with him. Please. . . ."

There was no getting over this, so they went into the next room, and when they had gone, Dinky spoke.

"Do you know how long you were unconscious, Mr. Marchant?"

The doctor answered this, and said: "Not more than five minutes, the head injury isn't very bad. But why?"

Mr. Marchant broke in: "Dinky has detective ambitions, doctor. Any other questions, my boy?"

"Would you mind if I went up to your bedroom?" asked Dinky.

You can bet I was feeling a little excited, for I knew old Dinky was on to something though what it was I couldn't see for the life of me, and when he went upstairs I followed him. I'll use his own words to tell you what we saw.

"See?" said Dinky. "The room is at the back, on the top floor. Lend me your torch a moment."

I handed it to him and he stood for a moment looking round again.

"*I insist on being searched,*" said
Mr. Stebbins

" No real window," he muttered, " he had it bricked up "

"No real window," he muttered. " He had it bricked up. I suppose it was in case somebody might get in and nab his diamond. Only that small ventilator high up in the wall. It's open, but not even a small boy could squeeze through it."

" Then the thief couldn't get in that way," I said, trying to be bright.

" No. The thief came in the front door. Let's go to the kitchen."

I trailed after him, and he looked at the old-fashioned dresser.

" The key's there," he said, and pointed to a spare key of the front door which we had often seen hanging on one of the dresser hooks.

" It's always there," I said. " The woman who comes in daily and does for Mr. Marchant has her own key."

" I know. Only—that front door wasn't forced open. It was unlocked by means of a key. Now the daily woman could have done it, but she didn't know Mr. Marchant owned a valuable diamond, so why should she? Besides, she's in the house day after day, often when he's out, so if she wanted to steal anything she has had plenty of chances. But——"

" But what?" I asked.

" If somebody knew this key was always here, and came in, say, during the day and lifted it, used it to get in tonight, and replaced it on its hook directly he entered the house . . . well . . . that's just that, isn't it?"

" I say! That's jolly clever, Dinky!" I exclaimed. " But who'd do it?"

He shut the door and spoke quietly.

" The key's there," said Dinky

" Stebbins," he said, and while I goggled at him, he went on : " He's the only person, apart from you and me, who knows about that diamond. He has the free run of this house. He knew the key's kept here. He must have known about it, just as we knew."

" But," I gasped, " he saw the front door open and came inside, and the policeman met him as he left Mr. Marchant's bedroom, and he's insisted on being searched. And as Mr. Marchant, on the doctor's evidence, was only unconscious for a few minutes, Stebbins wouldn't have had time to steal the thing, go and plant it somewhere, and then come back and meet the policeman. He couldn't run ten yards."

" That's just it," said Dinky. " He has insisted on being searched because he knows he'll be suspected, just as you and I may be suspected, and he wants to clear himself. For only we three knew about the stone. I tell you, Stebbins got all this worked out cleverly during the week, since the day

he unluckily came in and saw Mr. Marchant showing us the diamond."

" But if he hasn't got it on him, how can he have stolen it?" I protested.

" Don't talk so loudly. I've got to think," hissed Dinky. " He's been clever, as I've said. I've got to be clever, too. And we haven't much time, either."

" Did he have somebody to help him?" I asked. " He could have thrown the stone through that ventilator to a confederate down in the yard."

I think this was pretty good, don't you, and I was feeling quite proud of myself.

Dinky opened the kitchen door and went into the yard with my torch. I followed close behind him, and pointed to a lean-to shed against the house wall and directly under the ventilator.

" The confederate might have stood on that," I began rather helplessly.

" Give me a leg-up," replied Dinky, and I did so while he tested the roof of the shed with his hands.

" It's old and shaky," he announced. " It wouldn't bear the weight of a man, or even a boy."

The only way into and out of the yard, save through the house, was by getting over the high wall, and I ran the torchlight all over the brick-work carefully.

" Not a scratch anywhere," Dinky said. " That was a jolly good idea of yours, but this wall hasn't been climbed for years. Let's go inside."

He was very thoughtful when we got to the kitchen once more, and I stood and watched him, for by this time I was ditched completely. As far as I was concerned, this was a conjuring trick that had me beaten.

Has it got you beaten? Or can you see what must have happened? Think it out before you go any further. Think of the one way Stebbins could have done it, for Stebbins did it all right. I'll tell you that much.

Suddenly, in the kitchen, Dinky clapped his fist into his open palm.

" That shed!" he breathed. " Come on!"

I expected him to go to the yard again, but instead he made his way to the other room. By this time the searching was finished, and Stebbins and the policeman were with the doctor and Mr. Marchant. I gathered, from what they were saying when we came in, that the police officer had rung up the nearby town and a flying squad car was on its way over.

" It's old and shaky," he said. " It wouldn't bear the weight of a boy"

I ran the torchlight all over the brickwork very carefully

Dinky's eyes were positively brilliant now, and he said to the policeman: "Can I have a word alone with you, Mr. Jenkins?"

They went into the kitchen, and we waited in a sort of uncomfortable silence until they returned. The policeman was looking thoughtful and uncertain of himself, and a moment passed before he spoke.

Then he said: "I'd like to come home with you, Mr. Stebbins, if you don't mind."

I have never seen a man's face change so much as did the face of Stebbins, as the policeman said this. At first it went pale, then reddened with sudden anger.

"Do you realize what you're suggesting?" he demanded. "You've searched me, and——"

The policeman had seen the change in his face as well as I had, and his manner became more sure.

"I'd like to come home with you," he replied, and his tone was a bit heavy now.

We went—for Dinky and I made up the party—leaving the doctor with Mr. Marchant. The doctor was to tell the police car party where we had gone.

Stebbins was very quiet all the way to his house, and when he unlocked his door I saw that his hand was shaking, so that he had difficulty in fitting the key into place.

As we went inside, the policeman, after Dinky had whispered something to him, said: "Please leave the front door open, Mr. Stebbins."

I can see the man still—standing there with a face the colour of chalk as Mr. Jenkins said this.

What he would have done I don't know, for at that moment there was a

" mirroo " and his big tabby cat came slipping into the house. Dinky pounced on it before Mr. Stebbins could stop him and picked it up.

He cried: " There's only one living creature that could be dropped through that ventilator on to the roof of the shed below with the sure knowledge that it wouldn't hurt itself. One living creature, Mr. Stebbins, that can always find its way home from wherever it happens to be. Look ! "

Round the big cat's neck was a collar, and tied to that collar was a tiny pouch. Inside the pouch was the diamond.

It was a good job the policeman was there. I believe Stebbins would have killed Dinky.

Mr. Marchant doesn't keep his diamond in the house any more. In fact, he anticipated his will and had it made into a ring and gave it to his granddaughter when she was married soon afterwards.

As for Dinky, I shouldn't be surprised if one day he's the boss of Scotland Yard, would you? I hope I know him if he is, because he might let me go around with him when he's on a case.

One other point. Don't forget I mentioned the cat before the robbery took place. That was the clue.

There was a " mirroo" and his big tabby cat came slipping into the house

CAN YOU READ THE CLOUDS?

By G. A. Clarke

THE great writer, John Ruskin, once said that it was a strange thing how little we knew about the sky, even though it was in the sky that Nature had done her best to teach us to seek for beauty. When we are on holiday, we rejoice to see the sun shining in a cloudless blue sky, but let us think what it would mean if we always had blue unclouded weather. We should never know what it is to have a refreshing shower and all the land round about us would become a dreary desert, for nothing can live without water. Also we should never see the gold and crimson glories of the sunset, nor the towering majesty of the storm-cloud. The sky is always presenting us with ever-changing pictures which are well worth watching; let us see what we can learn by doing so.

The first thing we notice is that the forms—or types—of the clouds are not always the same. At times they appear to be thread-like and high, at others, heavy rounded masses and quite low. How high, do you think, are the clouds? In this part of the world even the highest of them are only about six miles above our heads, while by far the greater number are only a quarter of a mile to one mile high. In a district from which hills or mountains are easily seen, their crests are often hidden by low clouds. Every time a sea-fog spreads over the land and hides everything from our view, we are for all intents and purposes in the midst of a cloud lying on the ground, for that is what clouds really are, merely masses of vapour that float in streams of very damp air.

The highest clouds of all, called "mare's tails" by sailors because of their wispy shape, will be quite easy to pick out. Sometimes they lie in fairly straight lines; sometimes in sweeping curves like feathers, or in little tufts; they are of a soft, silky white colour, which at sunset turns to gold and then to a beautiful rose-pink. They are often seen before a spell of bad weather, but this is more likely when these clouds increase in quantity till the whole sky becomes covered with a milky white sheet of cloud. It is then that we see wide rings round the sun and the moon and these are usually looked upon as signs of rain to come.

The clouds of the middle heights, that is to say, those between two and five miles above the ground, are by far the most interesting and beautiful of all. They appear in sheets of waves very like the sand-ripples left on the

High clouds   *Medium*

shore by the ebb-tide; sometimes the waves are straight, but at other times they are curved or zigzagged. There are times, too, when the waves are broken up by another series of waves crossing the first, so that the whole sheet of cloud is divided into separate small pieces, giving the sky a chequered appearance. That is why we call the result a mackerel sky, a mottled sky, or a dappled sky. On these clouds, because they are more solid than the higher clouds, the colours of sunrise and sunset are more brilliant and fiery, and at times may spread over a large part of the sky.

There is, however, one kind of the middle clouds which is not beautiful; it spreads over the sky completely as a thin, grey sheet through which the sun may be seen dimly shining. We call this a watery or greasy sky, and it is almost sure to be followed by rain a few hours after it has been seen.

So far the clouds we have mentioned have been spread over the sky in sheets, either complete or broken; but now we come to the low clouds, less than a

mile in height. These are the heap clouds, so-called because they grow upwards till they reach a height of three or four miles at their tops, often passing through the middle clouds, though they begin at only half a mile or so above our heads. A rough idea of the way they grow can be obtained by watching the smoke coming from the funnel of a train.

These clouds are usually called the woolpack and thundercloud. The first named are very common on summer days, when you can see them forming in the early forenoon, then increasing in size and number till the middle of the afternoon, and thereafter slowly becoming smaller in size and number till by sunset-time they have disappeared from the sky. They are usually dome-shaped at the top with a more or less level surface underneath. As a rule they bring fine weather, but if by chance they continue to grow upwards and become thunderclouds, sharp rain or hail-showers are likely, or a thunderstorm may take place. These thunderclouds are very large and spread over

clouds   *Low clouds*

many miles of sky in all directions, so it may happen that all we can see of them is their undersurface which is dark grey and gloomy, but if we have the good fortune to see them in the distance they seem to be towering up like a range of mountains against the blue sky.

The remaining forms of low clouds require little to be said about them because they have no claims either to form or beauty. There is the rain-cloud, called flying scud by sailors, a dreary grey sheet with darker torn masses flying across it; and, lowest of all clouds, the lifted fog, a sheet of quite uniform grey colour, which often brings us drizzle.

If there should happen to be more than one type of cloud present in the sky, it is possible to see one kind travelling past much faster than the other; usually the lower appears to be faster than the higher, but sometimes it is the other way around. In reality the higher clouds are almost always the faster travellers, but their greater distance from the ground has the

effect of lessening their speed. Then, if there is a weathercock, or any other means of telling north, south, east and west, in your neighbourhood, you can soon learn that the clouds, especially the higher ones, nearly always move from some westerly point, either south-west, west, or north-west. Sometimes the higher and the lower clouds seem to be moving from quite different directions, and when this happens a change in the weather will soon take place.

If thunderclouds are present, heavy showers are likely to fall from time to time, and then the sun will break through and shine brightly. This is the time to see that most glorious of heavenly sights—the rainbow.

You can see rainbows only when the sun is shining and a shower falling at the same time. This means that the cloud-sheet must be broken where the sun is, and that is why they are so often seen when large thunderclouds are about, and heavy showers are frequent. Also they can be seen only when the sun is directly behind you,

The colours of the rainbow are due to the sun's rays falling on raindrops from a cloud, and reflected to the earth in prismatic colours

and the shower directly in front. Then again they are best seen when the sun is low, and if the sun is on the point of setting, the rainbow arch is a perfect half-circle and is displayed at its best. When the sun is higher the arch is of course lower, while if the sun is as high as forty-two degrees no rainbow is possible. That is why you see the rainbow most frequently in spring and autumn, when the sun is not often too high, the right kind of clouds are about and showers are fairly frequent.

Next time you see a rainbow, notice carefully that the colour red is on the outside of the bow, and violet on the inside, but if, as is often the case, a rainbow appears double, then the colours are the other way about in the outer bow, red on the inside and violet outside. The sky between the two bows appears dark, while inside the chief bow and outside the second bow it appears lighter.

In the old legends of the Norsemen, the rainbow was the bridge which joined the earth to Asgard—the home of the gods. Poets have sung in praise of the rainbow, but none so prettily as Longfellow in his masterpiece, *The Song of Hiawatha*:—

Saw the rainbow in the heaven,
In the eastern sky, the rainbow,
Whispered, "What is that, Nokomis?"
And the good Nokomis answered:
"Tis the heaven of flowers you see there;
All the wild-flowers of the forest,
All the lilies of the prairie,
When on earth they fade and perish,
Blossom in that heaven above us."

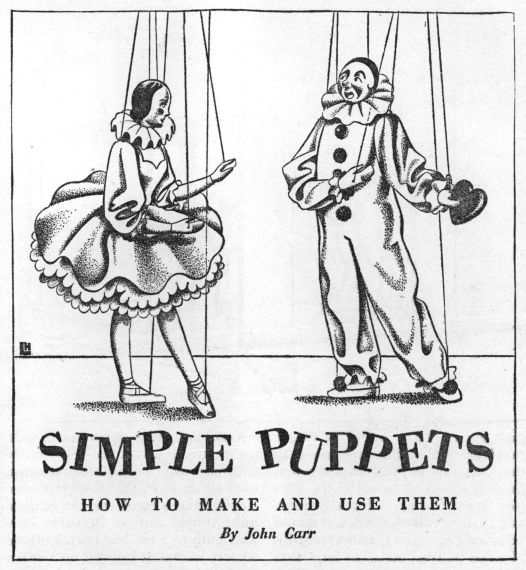

SIMPLE PUPPETS

HOW TO MAKE AND USE THEM

By John Carr

LET'S give a show! We all want to, at some time or other. But how? Shall it be in a toy theatre, made out of a wooden or cardboard box turned upside down, with actors and scenes cut out of cardboard; or shall we make some glove or hand puppets like Mr. Punch, or marionettes suspended on strings? All are fascinating and even the youngest boy or girl can take part.

The toy theatre requires very little room and is easily made. You should obtain, if possible, a box from about eighteen inches to two feet square and four or five inches deep, but it is better, if you can, to make one. The sides can be of pieces of wood three or four inches wide and the top (or floor) of the stage of three-ply wood or stout cardboard. The front of the stage, which is called the proscenium, can be made of this, and should be affixed at the sides to pieces of wood about one

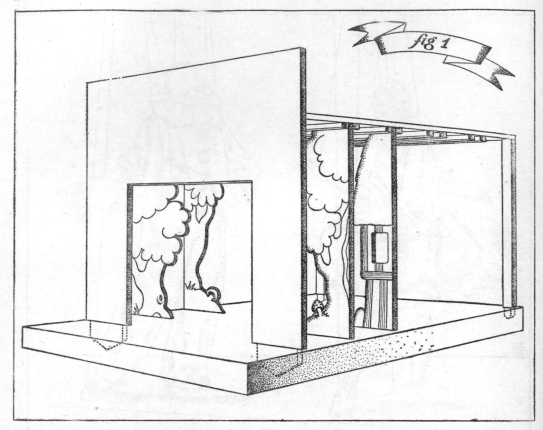

fig 1

inch square. They should be longer than the sides of the proscenium so that they can be put into sockets on the stage floor, or bolted to the sides (see Figs. 1 and 2). A frame is necessary to support the scenery and should be as wide as the stage and have strips of wood fastened across to form slots into which the scenery can slide. This frame can be either hinged on to the proscenium or clipped on (see Fig. 2). Two supports at the back can be either bolted to the stage or put in sockets. Next comes the curtain. This must be of thin material and you can either put this on a roller or draw it up from the sides through rings sewn diagonally. Wooden blind pulleys can easily be screwed firmly on to the back of the proscenium for this purpose.

Lighting is very important in your toy theatre. It may be done elaborately with miniature bulbs fitted on strips, used either as footlights or toplights. Toplighting is better and can be done quite simply with an ordinary sixty-watt bulb in a tin box resting on the scenery frame. It can rest on another removable frame made so that coloured gelatines can be slid along to give colour effects. These squares of coloured gelatine are placed between two pieces of glass about three inches wide and fifteen inches long, bound with gummed paper. A second light box can be fixed at the back of the stage so that if the back scene is just a plain paper tinted blue, various sky effects can be shewn.

It is as well not to fit the theatre

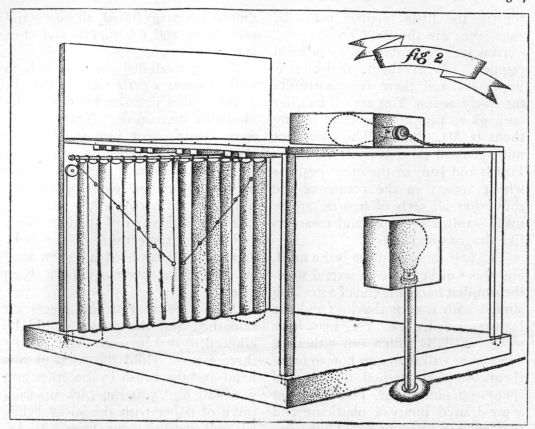

fig 2

together permanently but to make the parts fit in sockets or have them bolted together so that it can be packed away flat when not in use. I have not given in great detail the exact methods of making the parts, for a good deal of the delight of making is to design and develop ideas of your own.

Having built the stage, you will want to put on a play—a pantomime story is best, for it allows a variety of scene, and the more changes of scene in a toy theatre the better. Dick Whittington is a good example. You can have scenes of old London in the city, at the docks, and of Highgate Hill, the coast of Barbary and the sultan's palace, with processions and the Lord Mayor's Show as a grand finale. If you can draw and paint your own scenes

and characters it will give you a great deal of pleasure, but if you cannot—a good idea is to copy suitable scenes from your story books. You can even cut out your characters from books, post cards and old Christmas cards. Indeed, lots of things which are usually thrown away can be used both in the toy theatre and for puppets.

In painting the scenes, poster colour gives bright and clean effects. Scenes of coloured papers can be stuck on to cardboard, finishing with a few touches of water colour. It will help if you have a suitable picture or model on which you can build up a scene.

You need not have separate speakers for each part. A good idea is for someone to read a story which has lots of changes of scene, for in the toy theatre the little pictures made by each scene are the chief joy.

Now let's think about glove or hand puppets. With them, dialogue is important and there is opportunity for lively action. You are all familiar with glove puppets, for chief among them is Mr. Punch. This does not mean that all glove puppets are either Punch and Judy or the other puppets which appear in the course of the show, but all sorts of figures can be made—animals, people and creatures like dragons and insects.

The first thing to make is the head, and this can be made in several ways, the simplest being the end of a stocking stuffed with rags or shavings and the features painted on. You may have some rag dolls which can either be adapted or will show you how to make them. Another method is to model them in papier mâché. To do this, get a good sized lump of plasticine and push it on to a stick or rod. Then press it into the shape of an egg, with the widest end at the top. This done press in the eye sockets and put in and form balls for the eyes, the nose may be pinched up from the cheeks or a lump can be added and moulded into shape. Lips and eyebrows can be added. If you can get a modelling tool, it will make the modelling much easier, or an orange stick out of mother's manicure set will do almost as well. The eyes should be about half way down the face and need not be modelled in great detail. Sometimes a deep cut is sufficient, especially when an amused or laughing expression is wanted. It is also a good idea to model the face on one side with a miserable expression, while on the other side is a cheerful one (see Fig. 3). The features

should be exaggerated, the eyes and nose large and the mouth and chin very plain.

Having modelled the face, it is as well to smear a *little* vaseline over it, as this makes it easier to remove the plasticine afterwards. Next tear up some tissue paper into small pieces about the size of a shilling, with rough edges, and then paste them one by one on to the plasticine, overlapping them until you have covered it all. Now take pieces of paper of another colour and do the same thing. Then make another white covering and so on until at least nine coverings have been given.

Take care to put the pieces on smoothly, and the model should be allowed to dry between every two or three layers. Hold the stick in one hand and the brush in the other and you will find you can pick up each piece of paper with the sticky brush without getting your fingers sticky. You will have to be very patient when making a puppet and not try to finish it all in one day.

When the head is quite dry lift it carefully off the stick and gradually dig the plasticine out of the hole with the handle of a teaspoon. With practice it can be got out very cleanly, but you must be very careful not to push the spoon right through. The next thing is to get a cardboard tube to put into the head. This can be bought at the stationers, or if not can be made by rolling and gluing paper or thin cardboard round a stick. The tube should be long enough to fit into the head and leave enough for the neck (see Fig. 4). It should be glued in and may be packed with more tissue paper. This done, the whole should be

fig 4

fig 3

painted. Oil colour is best but poster or water colour will make a good job of it. This is where your school paint box will be useful. White, with a very little vermilion and yellow will make a good first coat and the features can be painted with vandyke brown.

The hair can be painted on, but it is better to make a wig of coloured wool, string, or theatrical crêpe hair stuck on with seccotine or glue.

Now you can dress your puppet. A glove puppet is really a three-fingered glove, the two arms being the thumb and the second finger, and the head the first finger—so you see how you have to make it. Really it is like a bag, shaped at the top like this (see Fig. 5).

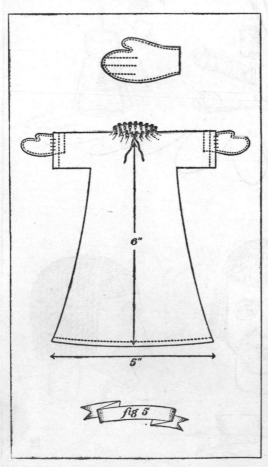

fig 5

It should be about ten inches round the bottom and about six inches from neck to hem. At the end of the sleeve pieces you can fit little pink bags stuffed with wool to make hands. They need not have real fingers. You will be able to get a lot of effect when your own thumb and second finger are inserted—such as clapping them, picking up a stick or other object, putting them round another doll's neck, etc. Put the neck of the doll over the middle finger, fastening on the glove either by sewing it to the cardboard neck, or sticking it with glue or seccotine. Then put on a dress that is suitable for the person it is supposed to be. You can, if you like, do without the three-fingered glove, and put on the dress just as it is, tying it around the neck by a tape. Very good effects can be obtained that way, but it will not be so strong.

Now for the theatre or booth, as it is usually called. You have all seen a Punch and Judy booth, but it is not necessary to have so big an affair as that. Indeed if you are not very big you can kneel on an arm-chair and use its back as a stage, a screen on either side would help a lot, or you could have a small booth which you could put on a table (Fig. 6 or Fig. 7).

It is an excellent idea for you to start like this, making do with whatever you have so that you can learn what sort of stage you like best. You can then set to and make a really good one. It should be one that can be taken to pieces or folded so that it can be stowed away, because you won't want to use it all the time and anyhow it would be in the way and get dirty. The main thing, however, is what sort of play or entertainment you are going to give—

a pantomime, fairy story, folk tale, or what? In your story books there are lots of stories you can use. The best are those where there are not many characters and in which they do something. You see, with a glove puppet you can pick up things, hold swords and move objects about. You've noticed how Mr. Punch holds a stick and hits everybody with it. Perhaps you've seen how St. George fights the Dragon and slays all his foes. It is a good plan to make several dolls which will do for all sorts of plays such as a king and queen, prince and princess, fairy, policeman, crocodile or dragon, teddy bear, monkey and so on. You can even make up little stories about them yourselves.

No doubt there will be some of you who cannot manage to make things. Well, here is a little play in which you

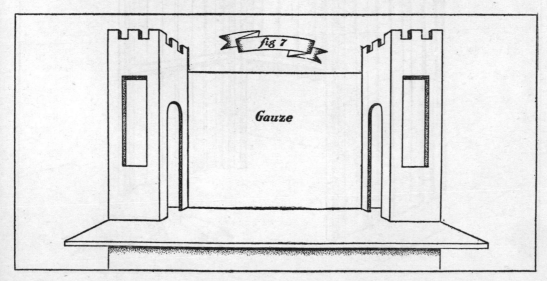

Gauze

could make your toys act with hardly any " making " to do at all, although of course, if you can make them, so much the better. Now what have you in your toy cupboard? Is there a stuffed duck? A Wilfred or other sort of rabbit, or a cat? A doll of any sort? If you are a family of boys there may be no lady dolls, but I expect you will be able to borrow one from somebody, or get mother to make one out of a stocking and a cardboard face bought at a toy shop. Here is my idea of the characters:

Derek Duck   Maid Molly
Robert Rabbit   Timmy Terrier

but if you haven't any of these, alter the names to fit the people you have.

Now to make the " acting place " or stage, a good thing to have is a tallish clothes horse draped with a table cloth or a curtain (Fig. 8). You can sit on a

hassock down behind it and pick up your dolls from the floor beside you as you want to use them.

Another easy way is to get behind a chesterfield or arm-chair, and let the top of the back be the stage. As each character speaks, seize it by the legs, if it has any, and hold it up above the stage, moving it, making it bow, sliding it along and back again. If it hasn't any legs, and you think your hand might show, tie a coloured duster very loosely over your hand, so that your fingers can move freely under it, and grasp the animal doll as low down as you can before putting it on the stage.

Now, are you down behind your stage, with something to sit on? If you like you can kneel, but it gets very tiring. Well, pick up the doll, boy or girl and, holding it up to face the

fig 8

Maid Molly · Robert Rabbit

Derek Duck

Timmy Terrier

audience, you say in a voice which you think will be suitable to it : —

" Good afternoon, ladies and gentlemen. You are now to see the Beverley Road puppets give their famous entertainment. The play is called *Trouble in the Toy Box*."

If you don't live in Beverley Road, you should say the name of the road where you *do* live instead. Then make your doll bow and bring her down again.

Then, picking her up in your left hand and Tim Terrier in your right, hold them both on the stage.

M. Tim Terrier, what was the meaning of all that noise in the toy box last night. I could hardly get a wink of sleep. I am thankful that I have a proper bed all to myself and do not have to sleep in the box with such a noisy lot of people.

T. It was all Derek Duck's fault. I was just thinking of all the lovely things I had been doing all day, and especially of the beautiful smell of the mud at the bottom of that big puddle in the garden, and wondering whether I dared chase one of the chickens, when Derek Duck gave a loud " Quack, quack " right in my ear.

(Take down Molly and pick up Duck.)

D. Who's mocking me? Don't you dare to do it. *I* am the only one who can say " Quack " properly. I have a cousin Donald who thinks he can do it, but you listen to me—Quark quark quark.

T. Don't do that. Your horrid voice gave me a nightmare last night, and now this morning I have got into trouble with Molly. It is a shame because I was expecting to be taken out with her when our mistress takes out the doll's pram. Now I shall get left behind.

D. Oh, that isn't fair. *You* weren't the only noisy one. What about Robert Rabbit? His squeak is deafening.

(Make a loud squeak and take down Dog and put up Rabbit.)

RAB. Squeak, squeak—no peace for a poor rabbit. Tim Terrier has chased me up here because he can't bear to hear me. I am *much* less noisy than that horrid dog, aren't I?

D. Yes, I suppose you are: but your squeak is *very* irritating. It makes me feel the same as when the pram wheels want oiling; and if you aren't careful someone will be oiling you one of these days.

RAB. Don't be rude. My voice is very nice for those who like it. I wouldn't be you for anything. Quarking all over the place. Wark, wark, wark, who ever heard anything so silly.

D. How dare you—I'll punch your nose in.

(Here make them both have a fight, making squeaks and quacks loudly all the while. When you think the fight has gone on long enough bring them both down and pick up Molly.)

M. Oh dear, oh dear. I don't seem to have done any good by scolding Tim. He has grumbled at the others so much that he has made Derek and Robert Rabbit have a terrible fight. I believe they are still at it—what shall I do?

(Pick up Tim in the other hand.)

TIM. How very naughty of Derek and Robert. Did you hear them fighting? I am ashamed of them. And you, Molly; fancy saying that *I* kept you awake. You can hear how noisy they are. Really I am very hurt to think you could be so unjust.

M. No Tim, you are being very silly. *You* made them fight, and kept out of it yourself, didn't you?

TIM. Well how about *you*, Miss smug-face. Who was it that started the grumbling? It is all very well for you. You have a lovely cot to sleep in, all trimmed up with lace and ribbons. Every night our mistress puts you cosily to bed and rocks you to sleep. Very often you sleep in her bedroom too.

M. Yes, of course, I know how lucky I am.

T. Just think of the rest of us. We get thrown into the toy box on top of the bricks and engines and all the other cornery things.

M. Yes, it *is* a shame.

T. And then we're expected to keep quiet.

(Take Tim down and bring up Rabbit.)

R. Oh, I *am* miserable. I really didn't mean to have a fight, but everything has gone wrong today. I think it is because I had such a bad night's sleep.

M. Poor Rabbit. Tim thinks it is because you are not put to bed properly, do you think that's it?

R. I shouldn't be surprised. Here Derek.

(Take down Rabbit and bring up Duck.)

D. Did Rabbit call me? Where is he?

M. He's gone to lie down, I think. But he says he's very sorry he fought you.

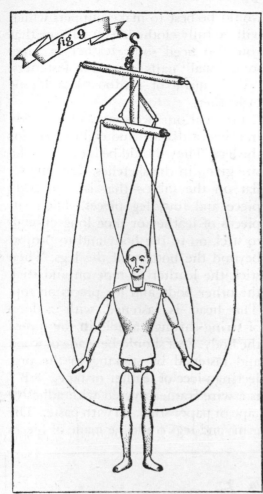

fig 9

D. I'm sorry I fought him, too. I can't think why I got so angry.

M. Tim thinks it is because you are sent to bed in such an uncomfortable way, all amongst the hard bricks and cars and engines. Do you think it might be that?

D. Yes, I do. Sometimes the corner of that tin ship digs into me like anything. I wonder I don't come unstuffed. I can't sleep at all.

(Take down D. Pick up Tim.)

M. Oh Tim, I have been talking to the others, and I am really sorry I grumbled at you about last night. I can see how uncomfortable you all

are. I am going to speak to our mistress about it, and suggest that she puts you away *properly* every night, and doesn't fling you all in higgledy-piggledy as she has been doing. Do you think you'll be quieter at night then, and feel more pleasant in the morning?

T. I'm sure we shall. Hooray! Bark bark.

(Take Tim down, bring up Rabbit.)

R. Squeak, squeak.

(Take R. down, bring up D.)

D. Quark quark.

M. So that's settled. Goodbye everybody. I'm so glad we're friends again.

If you are a boy you must say "master" instead of "mistress" and where it says the pram, say "go out with the tricycle."

MARIONETTES

MARIONETTES are puppets, although, as you will realize by now, all puppets are not marionettes. A marionette is a jointed doll and is made to move by strings from above. They are harder to make than glove puppets, because you have not only the head to make, but also the body and limbs. These may be quite simple, but you must be patient and take trouble. Here is a picture of a marionette (Fig. 9) shewing where the strings are usually fastened. The wooden thing at the top is called the control although some people call it the "perch," but "control" or "controller" is a better name. It seems difficult to make a marionette, but you can start by making quite simple ones which will give you a lot of fun. The heads can be made in the same way as glove puppet heads.

The bodies may be made in various

ways—effective ones have been made out of cotton reels, bits of bamboo rods, even of wire wrapped round with paper. Here are some examples (Fig. 10, A, B and C). If you are a boy and have some tools try and make one of wood. It should not be less than ten inches tall when finished. If made smaller, it is likely to be too light in weight to work properly. It is as well to make a rough sketch first, as otherwise you may get the legs too short or the arms too long. It is best to make the legs a little longer than ours are in comparison with our bodies and the head, hands and feet should be larger in proportion than a real person's. Until you've had some practice it would be best not to try and shape the whole body out of wood, but to cut out the shape and build it up with paper or cotton wool. The legs need not be shaped especially if the puppet is going to wear trousers or a long frock or costume. Indeed, at first it

would be best to make puppets which will be fully clothed. You will see that you also need some leather or tape, some small nails or paper fasteners. "A" is made of cardboard and tape or leather.

First cut out two shapes of the body in thick cardboard and eight pieces for the legs. They should be four times the size given in the sketches. Lay one set flat on the table—that is, one body piece and four leg pieces. Then cut pieces of leather or tape long enough to stick on to the body and to project beyond the bottom of the legs. Then stick the leather or tape on and stick the other body and leg pieces on top. The head is fastened with a loop of string through a hole in the top of the body. Feet should be made of wood and fastened by sticking to the projecting piece of leather or tape. "B" is a wire frame covered with adhesive tape or paper stuck on with paste. The arms and legs could be made of pieces

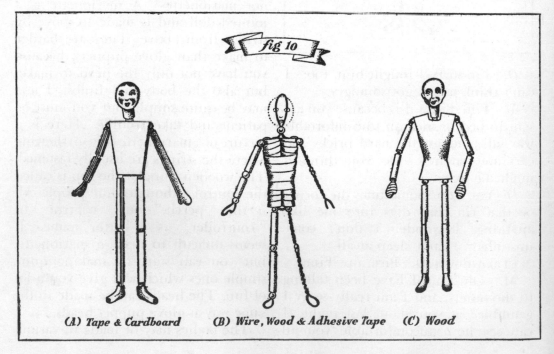

(A) Tape & Cardboard   (B) Wire, Wood & Adhesive Tape   (C) Wood

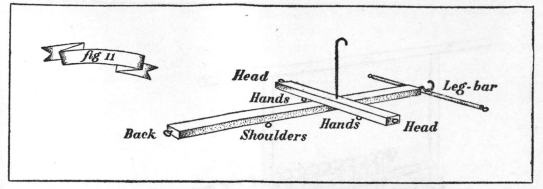

of bamboo with a bead at the joints. The bamboo must be cut to the right lengths very carefully and the wire threaded through before it is looped on to the body frame. "C" is all wood and the body cut out of a piece of board about an inch thick. Pieces of curtain rod will make good legs, or you may be able to get some tool handles, which will be shaped. The arms may be made of pieces of lead tubing—casing from electric cable is very suitable and this should be threaded on to a loop of string which can be fastened to the body and the wrists by screw eyes. Hands may be made out of wire covered with adhesive tape or cut out of sheet lead or wood. The legs should be hinged at the knees with leather inserted in saw cuts and stuck with seccotine.

The wooden puppets are the best, although they are more trouble to make and you need some tools. When you have made the marionette and its costume, it must be strung on to a control. This may either be the horizontal kind (Fig. 11) or the vertical kind (Fig 9). First fasten the head strings: a wire should be pushed right through the head and the ends made into a small loop for the purpose. Next come the strings from the shoulders and lastly the hands. The legs should always be strung to a separate bar.

For a puppet that has to bow or bend, the horizontal control is best but the upright control, although more trouble to make, gives better head movement. If you cannot get screw eyes wire staples are a good substitute. If, when you have finished stringing the marionette, it does not move as well as you wish, it may be necessary to fasten a piece of sheet lead to the bottom of the body or the feet to give it the necessary weight.

Now comes the great moment. Will the puppet work? Hold the control lightly in the left hand and the leg bar in the right. Remember to keep the puppet's feet just touching the floor and when you use the leg bar, your other hand should work with it by slightly swaying the body to correspond with the leg movements. Practise working the puppets to music, make them dance to a lively tune on the gramophone or wireless, aim at lightness of touch and don't grip the controls too tightly.

Next you must think about a stage. While you can do quite well with a temporary affair made by a curtain rod stretched across two chairs, or by using the family clothes horse suitably draped, it is better to have a more elaborate stage. If you are allowed to

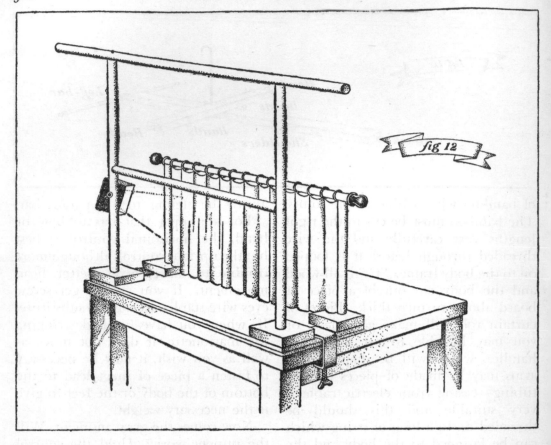

fig 12

use the kitchen table, you can make quite a good theatre with a wooden frame, broomsticks and curtain rods. Make four wooden blocks three inches square by one and a half to two inches thick and with a brace and centre bit make a hole one inch in diameter, then fasten one to each end of a piece of wood two feet long by three inches wide and half an inch thick. These can be clamped on to the sides of the table with a G cramp and into the sockets. You will need three broomsticks five feet long, two for the front sockets and the other cut in half for the back sockets. Here is a sketch (Fig. 12).

You see from this that you will also want some curtain rods, curtain blind cord and screw hooks. A strong table

is essential as two or three operators may be standing on it. If you have no table available and your audience is willing to sit on the floor, you can screw your sockets on to two battens, say four feet long, and fit your stage up on the floor.

Lighting is the next problem and it is best to have a light box fastened to each of the front parts—footlights are not necessary or desirable. They dazzle the operators and throw shadows on the backcloth. The lights at the sides can be connected by means of a bayonet or two-pin plug with either a light or wall socket.

Many plays, pantomimes and variety turns are suitable for marionettes. Here is a short play specially written for you.

KING NEPTUNE'S DAUGHTER

The whole of this little play for marionettes takes place in an under-water scene. If you can paint a back-cloth, make it blue-green in colour, and paint under-water plants on it. You will find pictures of them in books such as an *Encyclopædia*. Otherwise have curtains of bluey-green gauze or something like that. There should be a rock-like throne in the middle of the stage for Neptune to sit on.

It is a good idea to put in some music if you have a gramophone. The sailor could do a little dance when he first comes on to the stage, and after his wedding to the mermaid. The King could enter to a flourish of trumpets, and the wedding march could be played at the end.

Here is the play:

Enter Neptune.

NEPTUNE: Here come I, old Neptune,
The king below the water.
Of all my lovely treasures,
The fairest is my daughter.
To find a fitting mate for her
I've searched both far and wide,
And found a handsome sailor lad
A-drifting on the tide.

(He sits down on the throne; then the mermaid, his daughter, comes swimming in and kneels before him. Some soft music on the gramophone would sound very well.)

MERMAID: O father, dearest father
A handsome sailor boy
Has now become my dearest love.
Pray, will you wish us joy?
Bestow on us your blessing,
And give us leave to marry;
And he will not go back to earth
But here with us will tarry.

(Enter the sailor.)

SAILOR: Yo heave ho, my hearties,
And shiver my timbers too!
For here's the sweetest, neatest lass
That I could wish to woo.
So give me leave, Lord Neptune,
To search the ocean floor
For all the treasures of the deep
The glories of your store;
Then to this lovely maiden
These riches I will give,
And in some cave—domestic-like
We two will gladly live.

(He falls on one knee before Neptune, and beside the mermaid. Neptune stands up.)

NEPTUNE: Indeed, indeed, my charm-ing boy,
It shall be as you say;
Go seek your fortune in my groves;
Your bride with me shall stay
Until you come to claim her—
Then we will celebrate
Your wedding here before my throne
In all our royal state.

(Neptune and the mermaid then go off on one side of the stage and the sailor on the other. Then the octopus enters. He should crawl about the stage for a few moments before speaking.)

OCTOPUS: *I* am a fearsome octopus,
The terror of the deep.
The fishes flee in horror
As o'er the sand I creep.
With my long slimy tentacles
My wicked way I wend,
And all who dare to cross *my* path
Come to a sticky end.
This cheeky sailor upstart
Aspires to Neptune's daughter;
I'll show him who's the master here
And rules below the water.
I'll lie in wait behind a rock

Until he comes this way,
Then creeping on him unawares
My victim I will slay:
I'll clutch him tightly till he yells
And breaks in pieces fine;
For me will be the wedding bells,
The maiden shall be mine!

(The octopus then goes and hides behind the throne, and a little starfish comes in.)

STARFISH: Twinkle, twinkle, I'm the fish
That's heard this wicked fellow
Foretell the crime he will commit
Upon this sand-floor yellow.
But I will warn the sailor
And twinkle in his ear,
That he may slay the octopus
And save his pretty dear.

(The starfish goes out, and in a moment or two the sailor comes rushing in, with a sword in his hand.)

SAILOR: Now, where's the wicked monster
Who seeks to take my life?
He'll find the British Navy
Has naught to fear from strife.
I'll cut him up in pieces
And feed him to the fishes,
And serve him to the oysters
On little scalloped dishes.

(The octopus comes out from behind the rock and they fight. Be very careful not to get the strings of the sailor and the octopus entangled in each other. The sailor then kills the octopus, who dies in great convulsions.)

(Enter King Neptune, the mermaid, the starfish and as many other fishes and oysters as you can make. The fishes and oysters can be all on one control.)

MERMAID: My darling, oh my hero!
The monster you have slain
And safely now we two may live
Beneath the rolling main.
Seek not for fame or riches,
But stay here at my side,
Lest you should meet some other foe
To rob you of your bride.

NEPTUNE: Well done, my brave and handsome lad,
No fortune need you seek.
For you have slain the bad and strong,
To save the small and weak.
A dowry will I gladly give
With my one darling daughter,
And you shall be my son and heir—
The Prince Below the Water.
                    WEDDING TABLEAU.

Made and Printed by The Aberdeen University Press
Reprinted 1947.   T.148.   2R T.